EDWARD O. DODSON

ASSOCIATE PROFESSOR OF ZOOLOGY, UNIVERSITY OF NOTRE DAME

GENETICS

THE MODERN SCIENCE OF HEREDITY

WITH ILLUSTRATIONS BY FREDERICK S. BECKMAN

W. B. SAUNDERS COMPANY

PHILADELPHIA & LONDON · 1956

Made in U. S. A. Press of W. B. Saunders Company, Philadelphia

To the Memory of

Ernest Brown Babcock

For over forty years a leader among American geneticists

Inspiring teacher, humble gentleman, warm and generous friend

This book is respectfully and affectionately dedicated

Preface

"Of the writing of many books there is no end," and so far as textbooks in the experimental sciences are concerned, this is probably a good thing, for new data and new viewpoints require the constant re-evaluation of the old, which may itself be very recent as judged by the standards of other fields. This is particularly true of genetics, which, although one of the newest of the sciences, has in the short space of a half a century achieved a central place among the biological sciences, both pure and applied.

In view of the rapid development of the science of genetics, and of its great importance for medicine, for plant and animal breeding, and for the understanding of evolution and of other biological disciplines, surprisingly few new textbooks of genetics have appeared in recent years. Some of those that have been published are designed primarily for a purely cultural course, in which the students are not ordinarily expected to make use of genetics in their professional careers. Still others, while ostensibly introductions to genetics, are pitched on such a level that their greatest usefulness has actually been in the training of graduate students. In between these levels, there is a broad spectrum of courses in many institutions presented for the benefit of those many students who may later apply their genetic knowledge in medicine, in plant or animal breeding, in one or another of the specialized fields of botany or zoology, or even as professional geneticists. There are only a few good texts which fit this niche, and none is well adapted to the course as presented in many institutions. It is the aim of the present author to present the fundamentals of genetics with a degree of rigor, thoroughness, and theoretical depth which will challenge the mettle of the best students, yet with sufficient background material, detail, and clarity of exposition to help their less gifted classmates to achieve a working understanding and appreciation of genetics. This is a difficult goal, and it remains for those who use the book to decide whether it has been achieved.

The present book contains considerably more material than can be encompassed in a one semester course. In the first fourteen chapters, the principles of genetics are developed, together with some indications of current trends and theoretical implications. Probably most teachers will consider all or most of this material to be essential. Chapters 15 through 21 are concerned with more advanced aspects of genetics (such as physiological genetics), or special applications of genetics (such as plant and animal breeding), and teachers will want to select among them those chapters which best serve the needs of their own classes. Chapter 21 is devoted to human genetics, and so it will be of especial importance to those many classes which are made up predominantly of premedical students.

The final chapter is largely historical, and some teachers will want to leave its use to the initiative of the students. The author places considerable importance upon it, because it is based upon the archives of Mendel's monastery and upon other primary historical sources. This material was collected during the thirties under the direction of the Bishop of Covington, Kentucky, who entrusted the material to Sister M. Julitta, of Villa Madonna College. The latter, who was once a student of mine, gave the material to me. It is now my privilege to present a short history of the first days of genetics, based upon the archives of Mendel's monastery and of the Augustinian Order in Rome, as well as some more recent sources cited in the chapter itself. A more extensive report on this material will be published elsewhere.

I am indebted to many persons for their help in the preparation of this book. Drs. Karl Stiles, James B. Kitzmiller, and Maurice Whittinghill read the entire manuscript, while Dr. Harold O. Goodman read the chapter on statistics, and Dr. Sheldon Reed read the chapter on human genetics. Their critical suggestions have resulted in improvements throughout the book. To Mr. Frederick S. Beckman, Associate Professor of Art at the University of Notre Dame, I am indebted for the many excellent original illustrations. Dr. Charles Ehret, of the Argonne National Laboratory, gave very valuable assistance in the planning of the chapter on cytoplasmic inheritance. I am also in-debted to many publishers for permission to quote copyrighted material. These include the Academic Press, W. H. Freeman and Company, Genetics, the Journal of Heredity, the Macmillan Co., the McGraw-Hill Book Co., and the W. W. Norton Co. I am also indebted to Professor Sir Ronald A. Fisher, Cambridge, and to Messr. Oliver and Boyd Ltd., Edinburgh, for permission to reprint Table No. III (the chi-square table) from their book Statistical Methods for Research Workers. I am also indebted to those publishers who have generously granted permission to use figures from their books. Each of these is acknowledged at the appropriate place. Finally, I would like to acknowledge the generous and competent assistance of the fine staff at the W. B. Saunders Company.

This book is based upon a course which was first rehearsed at the Dominican College of San Rafael, California, in the spring of 1947, then developed at Notre Dame during the following years.

EDWARD O. DODSON

April, 1956

Contents

1	GENETICS AMONG THE BIOLOGICAL SCIENCES	I
2	ELEMENTARY MENDELISM—I	8
3	THE CYTOLOGICAL BASIS OF ELEMENTARY MENDELISM	20
4	ELEMENTARY MENDELISM—II	34
5	ELEMENTARY STATISTICS	43
6	MODIFICATIONS OF MENDELIAN INHERITANCE— I. Sex-Related Inheritance	63
7	MODIFICATIONS OF MENDELIAN INHERITANCE— II. Lethal Genes	82
8	MODIFICATIONS OF MENDELIAN INHERITANCE— III. Multiple Alleles	88
9	MODIFICATIONS OF MENDELIAN INHERITANCE— IV. Collaboration of Genes	97
10	MODIFICATIONS OF MENDELIAN INHERITANCE— V. Quantitative Inheritance	112
11	LINKAGE AND CROSSING OVER	126
12	ARCHITECTURAL CHANGES IN THE CHROMOSOMES	144
13	MUTATION	157
14	CHROMOSOMAL MUTATION	168
15	THE DETERMINATION OF SEX	179
16	THE PHYSIOLOGY OF THE GENE *Phenocopy*	193
17	THE THEORY OF THE GENE	205
18	CYTOPLASMIC INHERITANCE	215
19	GENETICS AND EVOLUTION	224
20	GENETICS IN THE SERVICE OF AGRICULTURE	242
21	HUMAN GENETICS	249
22	HISTORICAL RETROSPECT	273
Appendix A	EXPERIMENTS IN PLANT-HYBRIDIZATION by Gregor Mendel	285
Appendix B	LABORATORY SUGGESTIONS	312
	INDEX	321

To the Student

This book is a summary of the facts and concepts necessary for an understanding of heredity and variation in plant and animal forms. The knowledge presented here is the fruit of the patient investigation and deliberation of many scientists over a period of nearly a hundred years. In the brief time you must devote to your course in genetics and to the study of this textbook you can make this assembled knowledge your own if you will apply a relatively small effort purposefully.

Intelligent study of this book will illuminate and reinforce what you learn in class. What is equally important, this book will serve as a quick and useful reference in the future.

Everyone knows that we may easily forget what we learn. But we can also the more easily learn again if we have learned well to begin with. Occasional reference to this book in the future will restore and fortify your memory of the principles of genetics throughout your life. Here are some suggestions that will help you to get the most out of this book:

As you read an assignment, stop now and then to recall in your own words the important facts and ideas which you wish to remember.

Remember that many of the illustrations have been prepared especially to clarify the more difficult concepts presented in the text. Don't overlook them.

Pay attention to the headings, which by themselves serve as a systematic outline of the topics presented.

Take notes in class. Keep them and occasionally try to rewrite in your own words a topic, an idea or experimental evidence your instructor has presented.

Make notes in the margins to identify or summarize information you want to refer to again. Such notes will help you when you study the book again before class or for examinations or when you are reviewing a concept or a problem in heredity years from now.

CHAPTER 1

Genetics Among the Biological Sciences

Genetics is the science of variation and inheritance in organisms. Its objects are to determine to what extent the variable characters of plants and animals are inherited from parents to offspring, to what extent they are the results of environmental influence, and by what biological mechanisms such characters are transmitted from generation to generation. The term *genetics* was coined by William Bateson, a pioneer of genetics in England. Speaking before the Third Conference on Hybridisation and Plant-breeding in 1906, he pointed out that the rediscovery of the work of Mendel had led to a large body of related work on inheritance in plants and animals, yet there was no name for the rising new science. "To meet this difficulty," said Bateson, "I suggest for the consideration of this congress the term *Genetics*, which sufficiently indicates that our labours are devoted to the elucidation of the phenomena of heredity and variation: in other words, to the physiology of Descent, with implied bearing on the theoretical problems of the evolutionist and the systematist, and application to the practical problems of breeders, whether of animals or plants." This is still a good definition of genetics today. Babcock and Clausen define genetics simply as "the science which seeks to account for the resemblances and differences which are exhibited by organisms related by descent."*

The fact of biological inheritance has been a subject of great interest to man since remote antiquity. It has always been realized, indeed it has been almost self-evident, that the organisms of the present generation owe their characteristics to their ancestors, immediate and more remote. This conviction has been crystallized in such aphorisms as "Like begets like," and "Blood will tell." From the time that primitive men first learned to cultivate plants and to keep domestic animals, it must have been seen that those strains which had desirable traits tended to pass the same traits on to the next generation, while undesirable traits were similarly perpetuated. Hence farmers and breeders have, since the dawn of history, valued good breeding stock. As long ago as the sixth century B.C., the Greek poet Theognis wrote a few verses admiring the care with which the best livestock is selected for breeding, while deploring the lack of similar good judgment in marriage. Yet in all of the intervening centuries, the efforts of many men to understand the mechanism of inheritance and to put it to the service of man failed, until an Austrian monk, Gregor Mendel, solved the most fundamental problems of inheritance in the middle of the nineteenth century. (For the complete story of Mendel and his work, see Chapter 22.)

1. THE PLACE OF GENETICS IN THE BIOLOGICAL SCIENCES

Although genetics is among the youngest of the biological sciences, it has already achieved a central place among them. Practically all the biological sciences present problems

---

* By permission from Genetics in Relation to Agriculture, by Babcock and Clausen, 1928, McGraw-Hill Book Company, Inc.

which can be understood fully only when attacked with the tools of genetics. Some examples will be cited below.

GENETICS AND MEDICINE A large number of pathological conditions in man are based upon inherited anomalies or susceptibilities, and a working knowledge of the principles of genetics is therefore a valuable part of the armamentarium of the modern physician. This is particularly obvious in the case of preventive medicine, for knowledge of genetics may permit prediction of probable victims of specific disorders, thus making preventive measures feasible. For example, a young mother suffered from manic-depressive psychosis. An inherited factor plays an important (but not exclusive) role in the causation of this disease. Hence especial attention was given to the mental hygiene of her children, and there is good basis for the hope that none of them will become psychotic.

But diagnosis and treatment are the major factors in the daily work of most physicians. In these, too, genetics can play an important

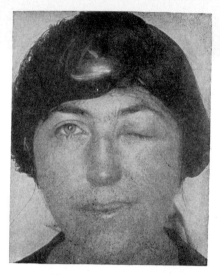

Fig. 2. *Angioneurotic edema. Note that the swelling has closed one eye. (From Andrews, Diseases of the Skin.)*

role. For example, a patient had very fine, sparse hair, few teeth, and ran a high fever without any apparent infection (fig. 1). The attending physician thought that she had a thyroid deficiency, and so treated her with this hormone, unsuccessfully. Another physician recognized some of the same symptoms, in milder form, in the patient's mother. He realized that this was an inherited syndrome, ectodermal dysplasia, in which ectodermal derivatives are generally defective. The tendency to run a fever resulted from sparsity of sweat glands, and the consequent inability to cool the body normally. Thyroid treatment aggravated this situation. The correct diagnosis was based upon genetic knowledge. While in this case no adequate treatment was then possible, at least it was possible to discontinue an irrational treatment, and to take some steps to protect the child from excessive heating.

Again, a woman whose eyelids were swollen shut was treated unsuccessfully by several physicians. Finally, the affliction was recognized as angioneurotic edema, a rare inherited condition which can cause swelling

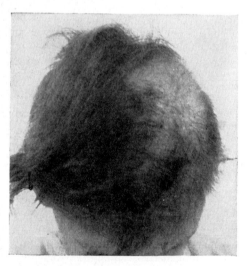

Fig. 1. *Ectodermal dysplasia. Note the sparsity of the hair and its fine texture. (Courtesy of Dr. J. V. Neel and the Heredity Clinic of the University of Michigan.*

of many tissues of the body (fig. 2), and which may cause death by suffocation if the larynx or trachea is attacked. On the basis of this knowledge, adequate treatment was begun.

Because genetics is a very young science, it has not yet established adequate contacts with the much older discipline of medicine. Only a very few medical schools offer any instruction in genetics, and not many more require a course in genetics for admission. But ever greater numbers of medical and premedical students are demanding training in this field, and it seems probable that the role of genetics in medical practice will become increasingly important.

GENETICS AND AGRICULTURE From an economic point of view, perhaps the most important aspect of genetics has been its application to the problems of improvement of agricultural plants and animals. Probably there is not a single variety of cultivated plant or domestic animal in the world today which is not very much different from its wild ancestors. And the differences, most of which are improvements from our point of view, have been produced very largely through the efforts of plant and animal breeders. This has not been entirely a result of the development of modern genetics, for breeders have always used genetic principles, although often unknowingly. But carefully planned application of genetic principles to breeding programs has very much accelerated the rate of improvement of agricultural stocks in recent years.

As an example, consider the cattle industry of Texas. This was originally based upon the Texas Longhorn (fig. 3), a very tough, semi-wild breed which thrived under the difficult conditions of the range. But it produced rather scanty beef, and that of poor quality. Very superior beef breeds, the Hereford and the Shorthorn, had been developed in England. These were imported to the United States and were very widely used to replace the older and less desirable beef breeds. They proved to be well adapted to the northern states, where they are now the most generally used beef cattle. But they did not stand up under the conditions of heat, drought, and rugged range of south Texas. Brahman cattle of East Indian origin were also imported. They thrived under sub-

Fig. 3. *Texas Longhorn cattle. Compare these rangy animals with that shown in figure 4. The color pattern on the calf in the foreground probably indicates some Hereford blood. (Courtesy of Mr. Graves Peeler.)*

3

Fig. 4. *Manchado, a Santa Gertrudis bull, a representative of a highly improved breed of beef cattle. Comparison of figures 3 and 4 provides a visual summary of the practical value of genetics. (Courtesy of Mr. R. C. Wells and the King Ranch.)*

tropical conditions, but did not forage so well and lacked the fine beef qualities of the English cattle. In 1910, Mr. Robert J. Kleberg, of the famous King Ranch, undertook a program deliberately designed to produce a new breed of beef cattle, adapted to the conditions of south Texas. At first, exploratory crosses were made, principally between Shorthorn and Brahman cattle. The most favorable progeny were selected, and a program of inbreeding was begun. This led to a distinctive type which was recognized as the Santa Gertrudis breed (fig. 4) by the United States Department of Agriculture in 1940. Thus in the short span of thirty years, a superior breed of beef cattle, well adapted to a great American range, was developed.

During World War II, man power on our farms and total acreage under cultivation were both severely reduced in order to get a maximum number of men under arms. Nonetheless, the dietary standards of large numbers of Americans were raised during the war years, and no Americans suffered any severe reduction in dietary standards. Yet we were still able to ship large quantities of food to our allies. This achievement was based in part upon mechanization of the farms and upon improved methods of cultivation, as well as upon other factors. But a very large measure of this success was based upon forty years of plant and animal breeding in accordance with the principles of genetics. There appears to be no other way so effective to keep food upon the tables of the world. An important factor in this success was the development of hybrid corn. Early in the present century, geneticists studying corn had found that inbred lines always deteriorated. A cross between two such inbred lines, however, produced superior corn, but unfortunately the yield was small because of the poor seed set of the parent varieties. Late in World War I, it was found that crossing two such hybrids to yield a double-cross hybrid gave an abundant yield of superior seed. After many years of testing such hybrid corn, it began to come on the market in 1933. By the time the U.S. entered World War II, hybrid corn was in very general use throughout the corn belt. The result was more dependable production of larger crops from smaller acreage. Because corn is not only an important food for man, but also our basic feed for livestock, the result was a general increase in farm productivity.

GENETICS AND ANATOMY But it is not only the applied sciences for which genetics is important. Genetics has also achieved a central position among the pure biological sciences. The major development of anatomy, and especially of comparative anatomy, occurred without reference to genetics. It was largely a matter of description and comparison of organ systems in the different classes of a phylum, or in the various subunits of smaller categories. But this led inevitably to questions which could only be answered in genetic terms. As an example, let us consider the concept of homology (fig. 5), so fundamental to comparative anatomy. When an anatomist says that the femurs of amphibians, reptiles, birds, and mammals are all homologous, he means that the bones are similarly formed and located, they afford attachment to similar muscles, and they have the same innervation. In short, it looks as though an identical structure has simply been varied in some details from group to group. No further insight is possible until a genetic concept is added: namely, that homology can only be based

upon descent from common ancestors. But, then, how do those differences arise which characterize the various groups? And how can an hereditary mechanism, which is so conservative that its effects show homology between different classes, still permit the wide range of variability which exists within

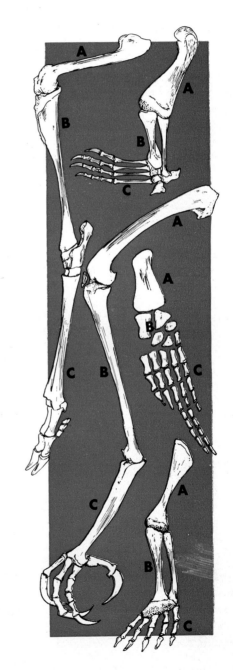

Fig. 5. *The concept of homology. In the upper left is the hind limb of a deer; in the upper right, that of an alligator; in the left center, the leg of an eagle; in the right center, the hind limb of a plesiosaur, an extinct, aquatic reptile; and in the lower right, the hind leg of a salamander. Bones labeled with the same letter are homologous throughout the series. They are modified in size, in details of shape, and by reduction, or by fusion of bones (part C) in the deer and eagle.*

and between the classes? These are all genetic questions.

Adult anatomy, however, is the end point of a long period of embryological development (developmental anatomy). Sooner or later, the comparative anatomist wants to know what are the developmental processes by which differences in homologous structures are established. He therefore turns to embryology and to physiological genetics, the study of the means by which hereditary effects are obtained.

GENETICS AND TAXONOMY   G. G. Simpson of the American Museum of Natural History, has pointed out that taxonomy is at once the most elementary and the most inclusive of the biological sciences. It is the most elementary because no progress can be made in the study of organisms until some classification has been achieved, so that generalizations can be made from typical series of organisms to the groups which they represent. But taxonomy is also the most inclusive and erudite of biological sciences because it must eventually assemble, utilize, and harmonize all of the diverse data from the numerous fields of specialization. Everything that is known about an animal enters into the final judgment on its taxonomic position.

In the immediate post-Darwinian period, taxonomists were in the front ranks of the investigators of the relationships among species. But by the end of the century, their work seemed to have degenerated into a combination of labeling specimens and wrangling over hypotheses which could not be objectively evaluated on the basis of available evidence. They were looked upon as mere biological hack workers. The advent of genetics changed all of this. It now became possible for taxonomists to analyze their data experimentally. On the subspecific level, it became possible to distinguish between inherited variations which, if favored by natural selection, could lead to the formation of new subspecies and species; and environmentally caused fluctuations which have no permanent importance for the species. Direct experimentation has not generally been possible at the higher taxonomic levels, but knowledge gained at lower levels has been fruitfully applied. As a result, the new taxonomy has become one of the most progressive of biological disciplines, and it is no longer isolated from the experimental branches of biology.

GENETICS AND BIOCHEMISTRY   A contact with biochemistry was established in the earliest days of genetics, when geneticists studied such problems as the inheritance of flower colors. They tried to relate their data to the prevailing biochemical theories on the pigments. In this, biochemistry was of great service to genetics. But recently this debt has been repaid. A new subscience, biochemical genetics, has emerged. The biochemical geneticists use the techniques of genetics to study biochemical reactions of microorganisms (and, to some extent, of larger organisms). In this way, it has been possible to establish the exact sequence of synthesis of complex compounds in the living organisms, information which had often been inaccessible to purely chemical methods.

Although extensive exploitation of biochemical genetics awaited the discovery of a suitable experimental organism (the mold *Neurospora* has been the most important one), the first example of genetic control of a biochemical reaction was found in man. Alkaptonuria is a well known constitutional defect characterized by the blackening of urine upon exposure to air. This results from the excretion of large quantities of homogentisic acid, which is readily oxidized to form a black compound. Homogentisic acid is a degradation product of the amino acid tyrosine, and it is normally formed in fairly large amounts from the excess of tyrosine above that needed for normal metabolism.

6

Normal people have an enzyme which degrades homogentisic acid to carbon dioxide and water, which are then excreted. A simple genetic factor controls the presence or absence of this enzyme, with alkaptonurics lacking it.

Tyrosine also plays a more positive role in the body metabolism, for much of it is converted to protein, or to the hormones thyroxine, epinephrine, or norepinephrine, or to melanin, the basic pigment of the human body. Another genetic factor determines the presence or absence of tyrosinase, the enzyme which controls the first step of the chain of reactions which leads from tyrosine to melanin. Hence those individuals who inherit the lack of this enzyme are albinos, possessing only the respiratory pigments.

GENETICS AND THE RELATIONSHIP BETWEEN BOTANY AND ZOOLOGY The two main branches of biology had their early development largely independently of one another, and botanists and zoologists were often antagonistic. But the advent of genetics showed that the principles of inheritance are identical in the two kingdoms. Some of the most important principles of genetics are most easily investigated with animal material, others with plant material. Major discoveries of importance to plant geneticists were made by zoologists, and vice versa. Thus geneticists, regardless of the departments in which they were trained, soon found that they had to be *biologists* first and botanists or zoologists second. Not a few were equally at home in both fields. Thus genetics became a broad connecting link between the two major divisions of biology.

This description of the interrelations of genetics with other fields could be extended indefinitely. But the present discussion is enough to show that our subject is not an isolated curiosity on the periphery of the life sciences, but rather a subject vitally necessary for the full understanding of any biological discipline. It will be the purpose of the following chapters to make this subject available to the student beginning first with elementary mendelism.

CHAPTER 2

Elementary Mendelism—I

Modern genetics is grounded upon five bases. The first of these is the Mendelian experiment, which has now been verified by a great host of investigators in all parts of the world. The second is the science of cytology, which had not yet emerged in Mendel's time, but which even before 1900 had shown that the chromosomes have properties which later proved to parallel very closely the facts of Mendelian inheritance. It is now conclusively established that the chromosomes are the physical basis of Mendelian heredity. The third is the pure line concept, which made it possible to distinguish between hereditary and environmental effects. The fourth is biometry, the science of statistics applied to biological problems. The last is the fact of mutation, the change of a gene (the unit of inheritance) to form a new, stable, inheritable unit. The first four of these will be taken up in this and the succeeding chapters, while the last will be taken up after additional genetic tools have been developed.

2. MENDEL'S MONOHYBRID EXPERIMENTS

The most elementary and the most basic of Mendel's experiments was the *monohybrid* cross, that is, a cross between two pure-breeding varieties of peas which differed from one another in only one character. The resulting hybrids were then self-fertilized in order to obtain the second generation of offspring. Mendel reported seven such monohybrid crosses in peas, as follows (fig. 6):

1. Round × wrinkled seed. These characters are self-explanatory, if dry seeds be examined, although the fresh seeds are all round.

2. Yellow × green cotyledon color. The cotyledons are the thick, leaf-like structures of the very young seedling. They are the major nutritive organs of the seedling.

3. Grey-brown × white seed coat. The seed coat is a thin, transparent coat, suggestive of an envelope of cellophane, which encloses the pea.

4. Evenly inflated × constricted seed pods. The evenly inflated pods are the familiar ones of market peas. The constricted pods pinch in between the successive peas.

5. Green × yellow unripe pods.

6. Axial × terminal flowers. This refers to the position of the flowers on the plant. Axial distribution means that the flowers are distributed along the length of the stem, while terminal distribution means that the flowers are all clustered about the top of the stem.

7. Tall × short plant height. Pure-breeding races are available which range all the way from extremely short bush-type plants to extremely tall "telephone" (in modern seed catalogues, but not in Mendel's time) peas. For his short variety, Mendel selected peas which did not exceed a foot and a half in height, while his tall variety grew to a height of not less than six feet.

Each of these seven pairs of alternative traits with which Mendel made his monohybrid crosses presents a pair of clear-cut, easily-diagnosed alternatives. He thus reduced to the simplest possible terms the problem of analyzing hereditary transmission. In contrast, his predecessors had generally crossed different species, or at least well-marked varieties, which differed in many traits, and not necessarily in easily distinguishable ones. But before going on to the actual results obtained by Mendel, it may be well to take up a somewhat simpler example which was first reported by Carl Correns many years later. This concerns the inheritance of flower color in the four-o'clock, *Mirabilis jalapa*. Incidentally, Mendel's correspondence with Nägeli indicates that he had also investigated this case, although details were not included. In re-

porting it to Nägeli, Mendel was primarily interested in an experiment by which he had proved—in the face of opposition of most of the biologists of his time—that only one pollen grain was effective in fertilization.

ELEMENTARY MENDELISM IN THE FOUR-O'CLOCK Correns had red-flowering and white-flowering varieties of four o'clocks. These were *pure-breeding* varieties, that is, if reds were crossed only with reds, they would produce only red offspring for generation after generation. The same was true of the whites. But when Correns crossed the two varieties, the resulting hybrids were all pink. Mendel's predecessors would have stopped the experiment at this point, concluding that inheritance consisted of a blending of the parental characteristics, and assuming that the pink hybrids would give rise only to pink offspring. Not so Mendel and his followers: they made the critical experiment of interbreeding the hybrids (actually, the plants were self-fertilized). But the second generation plants were not uniformly pink: about one fourth of the plants were red, one half pink, and the remaining one fourth white. Thus the parental and hybrid types had *segregated* out in the second generation in a ratio of 1 : 2 : 1. If these plants were again self-fertilized to produce a third generation, the reds and whites bred true like the original parental varieties, while the pinks again produced a segregation of one red to two pinks to one white.

SOME GENETIC TERMINOLOGY Some technical terminology makes the description of such an experiment much simpler. The original pure-breeding plants which are used for hybridization are referred to as the *parental*, or P, generation. The first hybrid generation is referred to as the first filial generation, and this is almost always abbreviated to F_1. The subsequent generations are similarly designated as F_2, F_3, or whatever may be called for. Using these designations, Cor-

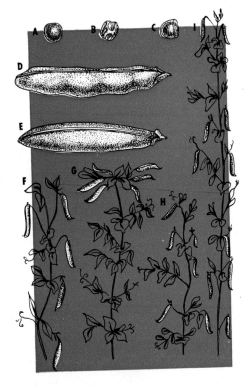

Fig. 6. *Mendel's materials. A and B, smooth and wrinkled peas; C, the seed coat, partially dissected off of the seed; D and E, constricted and smooth seed pods; F and G, axial and terminal inflorescences; and H and I, dwarf and tall growth habit.*

9

rens' example may be summarized as follows:

P	red	$\times$	white
F$_1$		pink	
F$_2$ 1 red	:	2 pink :	1 white

F$_3$ all red   1 red : 2 pink : 1 white   all white

As a matter of convention, geneticists generally write the female parent first in such a tabular summary of an experiment. Hence it is indicated above that a red–flowering plant was used as the female parent, while a white-flowering plant was used as the male parent. The question obviously arises as to what the result would be if the *reciprocal* cross were made, that is, if a white-flowering plant were used as the female parent with a red-flowering plant as the male parent. Actually, it makes no difference: the F$_1$ and subsequent generations will still be just as indicated above. However, situations will be encountered later in which the reciprocal crosses give different results.

MENDEL'S EXPLANATION OF MONOHYBRID INHERITANCE   Some of Mendel's predecessors had made similar observations, but it remained for Mendel to devise a rational explanation for the data. In brief, this was his explanation: each hereditary trait must be determined by a pair of "elements," one of which has come from each parent. In modern language, the "elements" of Mendel are called *genes*. The parental red-flowering plants develop from zygotes having a pair of genes for red flower color, that is, they are genetically *pure* for red flower color. Similarly, the white-flowering plants are genetically pure for the gene for white flower color. But each of these parental plants passes only one gene of each pair to each seed produced. Thus the F$_1$ plants have a pair of flower-color genes consisting of a gene for red color received from one parent, and a gene for white color from the other parent.

Hence the pink color of the hybrids is based upon the interaction of the two unlike genes for this color difference.

But in the F$_2$ not only pink plants, like the F$_1$'s, but also reds and whites appear in the progeny. Mendel saw that this could be possible only if the members of each pair of genes in the hybrid were separated into sister gametes at the time of gamete formation, with two types of gametes being formed in equal numbers, one type carrying the gene for red-flower color, while the other type carries the gene for white-flower color. This is, in substance, Mendel's first law, the Law of Segregation. It may be restated in more general terms as follows: *members of a pair of genes are separated into sister gametes when gametes are formed.*

It may be noted that the term *segregation* is used in two somewhat different ways. On the one hand, it refers to the separation of the two members of a pair of genes into sister gametes. On the other hand, it refers to the appearance of visibly different types in the progeny of hybrids, which are themselves uniform in appearance. But, as the second is the visible evidence of the first, they are very closely related ideas. The question may be asked whether segregation occurs in crosses between members of the same genetically pure strain, for example, the red-flowered plants. Gametic segregation still occurs, because the members of the pair of red-determining genes are separated from one another into sister gametes. But the visible segregation of characters cannot occur, because the plants are pure breeding.

THE PURITY OF GAMETES   The concept of the Law of Segregation was radically opposed to the prevailing concept of heredity of Mendel's time, which was that the hereditary elements of a hybrid were blended together to form a new unit, intermediate between those of the parents, much as an artist mixes the paints on his palette. Proponents of this idea would have thought it confirmed by the pinkness of the flowers of the F$_1$ four-o'clocks. But the parental types segregated out in the F$_2$, and they bred true for many generations subsequently. Further, the colors of these F$_2$ reds and whites were indistinguishable from those of the parental plants: the reds were not at all diluted, and the whites were not at all tinged with a pinkish cast.

Mendel realized that these results could be possible only if the two genes of a pair remained distinct in the hybrid, unchanged by their association in the heterozygote. Thus when a hybrid forms gametes, the segregating genes are identical with those of the pure-breeding strains from which the hybrid was derived. This is Mendel's second law, the Law of the Purity of Gametes. It may be stated more tersely as follows: *in a hybrid, neither gene of an unlike pair is modified by its association with the other.* Thus when the hybrid forms gametes, each must contain one gene or the other, but no intermediate gamete is possible. This does not mean that the genes cannot enter into physiological reactions. It is undoubtedly through specific physiological reactions that they obtain their effects. But, such reactions cannot result in a permanent change in the gene.

One more principle was necessary in order to explain the results obtained. The first two Mendelian laws lead to the conclusion that the F$_1$ hybrids must form two types of gametes, the parental types, in equal numbers. But it is imaginable that like gametes might have an especial affinity so that the zygotes would be mostly pure reds or pure whites. Or it is equally plausible that unlike gametes might have an especial attraction, so that most of the zygotes would be pink-flowering, with only a few of the pure types being formed. Actually, the observed ratio was one red to two pink to one white. Mendel saw that this was exactly what should be expected if either type of pollen had an equal probability of fertilizing either type of ovule. This is Mendel's principle of random fertilization, that when hybrids are crossed any type of pollen (or sperm) has an equal probability of fertilizing any type of ovule (or egg). Because the principle of random fertilization is not universally applicable, it is not designated as a law but as a generally valid principle.

MENDELIAN SYMBOLS These observations are most easily presented in terms of symbols. R may represent the gene for red-flower color, and r the gene for white-flower color. It is an important convention of genetics that *always* (when letter symbols are used) the two forms of a pair of genes are represented by different forms of the same letter rather than by different letters (for example, R and W). This makes it easy to see at a glance which genes belong together and which ones are members of unrelated pairs. Gametes will now be represented by only one letter symbol for each gene, while zygotes (and the organisms derived from them) will be represented by two. The flower color cross in four-o'clocks may now be summarized with a symbolic diagram paralleling the word diagram already presented on page 10:

P	red	×	white		RR	×	rr
				Gametes	R		r
F$_1$		pink				Rr	
				Gametes	R		r
F$_2$	1 red	: 2 pink :	1 white		1 RR	: 2 Rr :	1 rr
F$_3$	all red	1 red : 2 pink : 1 white	all white		RR	1 RR : 2 Rr : 1 rr	rr

All of the principles discussed above are at once quite transparent in such a diagram. But the principle of random fertilization can be most easily represented by the Roman square or Punnett square (for R. C. Punnett, a distinguished English geneticist who was among the first of the Mendelians). One simply draws a square with as many subdivisions along each side as there are types of gametes produced by each parent. The genic formulas of the eggs (or ovules) may be written along the left side of the square, while those of the sperm (or pollen) may be written across the top. Now, in each space in each vertical column the gene symbol at the head of the column may be entered. Similarly, in each space in each horizontal row the gene symbol to the left of the row may be entered. This automatically gives all possible zygotic combinations in the proportions required by the principle of random fertilization. Inspection of such a Punnett square for the flower color cross in four-o'clocks (fig. 7) will show one pure red

(RR), two pinks (Rr), and one pure white (rr).

DOMINANCE Mendel's own experiments were somewhat more difficult to understand than that of Correns which is discussed above. The cross between varieties of peas with yellow and with green cotyledons (fig. 8), respectively, will typify Mendel's monohybrid crosses. In the F_1 of this cross, all of the plants had yellow cotyledons. At this point, his predecessors would have concluded that yellow cotyledon color was inherited, while green was not. But in the F_2, out of 8023 plants observed, 6022 had yellow cotyledons, while 2001 had green cotyledons. When the F_2 plants were self-fertilized to produce an F_3, it turned out that the plants with green cotyledons never produced anything but offspring with green cotyledons. That is, they *bred true*. But, of the F_2 plants with yellow cotyledons, one third were true breeding, while two thirds of the plants produced yellows and greens in a ratio of about 3 : 1. The two kinds of yellows could not be

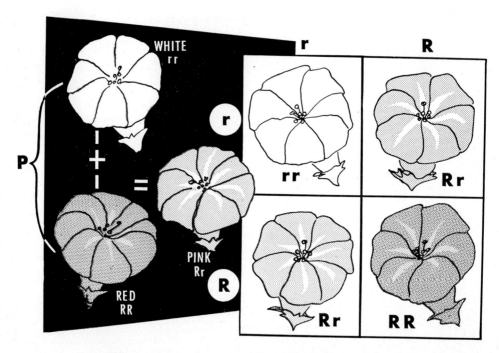

Fig. 7. *A Roman square for the flower color cross in four-o'clocks.*

Fig. 8. *Cotyledons. The cotyledons are the thick "leaves" midway on the stems. The left hand seedling shows the first true leaves just emerging between the cotyledons, while these are fully developed in the right hand seedling.*

distinguished except by a *progeny test,* that is, by breeding another generation to determine whether all yellows would breed true or whether some would segregate.

It was evident, then, that the plants with green cotyledons were always genetically pure, while those with yellow cotyledons might be pure or they might be hybrids. Thus, in the hybrids one character showed up to the exclusion of the other. But, the reappearance of both parental traits in the F_2 proved that the genes were unimpaired. Mendel found that, in his original series of crosses, one parental character always showed up to the exclusion of the other in the F_1, and he called this phenomenon *dominance.* The gene for yellow cotyledon color is thus said to be *dominant* over the one for green, while that for green is said to be *recessive* to the gene for yellow. (In the case of flower color in four-o'clocks, which was discussed above, neither gene is dominant, and so the color of the hybrids is intermediate between the two pure types.)

It must be emphasized that dominance is simply a matter of the functional relationship between the two unlike members of a pair of genes in a hybrid. It has nothing to do with the frequency of characters in populations. Thus, in man the gene for brown eyes behaves as dominant over the gene for blue eyes. If a Mediterranean population is studied, the dominant gene will also be the common one. But if a Scandinavian population is studied, the dominant gene will be rather rare and the recessive gene will be common.

In the F_2, Mendel obtained 6022 plants with yellow cotyledons and 2001 plants with green cotyledons. This amounts to 75.06 per cent yellow and 24.94 per cent green. Mendel realized that this was just a chance deviation from a ratio of three yellows to one green. Because of the phenomenon of dominance, the first two classes in the 1 : 2 : 1 F_2 ratio were added together. *Selfing* (a standard term for self-fertilizing a plant) the F_2 plants to produce an F_3 shows that there are two different types of F_2 dominant plants, one third of them being pure yellows which breed true, and two thirds of them being hybrids which again segregate. This cross can be easily visualized with the aid of parallel diagrams in words and in symbols. For the symbolic diagram, let Y stand for the gene for yellow cotyledons and y stand for the gene for green cotyledons (it is customary to use the capital letter for the dominant member of a pair of genes).

The cross now appears as follows:

P	yellow × green		YY	×	yy
		Gametes	Y		y

F₁   Yellow

$$Yy$$

Gametes Y y

F₂   3 yellow : 1 green   1 YY : 2 Yy : 1 yy

F₃   1/3 breed true   all breed   all breed   segregate   all breed
     2/3 segregate   true   true   in 3 : 1   true
     in a 3 : 1 ratio   ratio

Represented as a Roman square, the F₂ becomes:

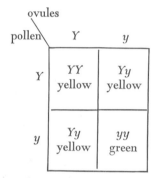

It may be seen that this cross does not differ from the flower-color cross in four-o'clocks in regard to the manner of inheritance of the genes. The general principles of segregation, purity of gametes, and random fertilization are applicable without modification. The only difference is the introduction of the principle of dominance, with the result that the F₁ resembles one of the parents, and that two genetically different F₂ classes are indistinguishable. Dominance is a very common phenomenon, but it is by no means universal.

3. SOME MENDELIAN TERMINOLOGY

The description of such phenomena is much simplified by the use of some technical terminology. At the outset, it would obviously be useful to have some term to designate the alternative members of a pair of genes. *Allele* (Greek—*allelon*, alternative) is used in this sense. Thus the genes for yellow and green cotyledons are said to be alleles or, as an adjective, allelic. An organism in which both members of a pair of genes are alike (as YY) is said to be *homozygous* (Greek—*homo-*, alike + *zygos*, yoke). But a hybrid, with unlike alleles, is said to be heterozygous (*heteros*, unlike). When used as nouns, these words become *homozygote* and *heterozygote*. A *zygote* is, of course, the cell formed by the union of egg and sperm. But, in genetics it is often convenient to extend this definition to include the individual which develops from the fertilized egg. As individuals of identical appearance may have different genetic constitutions, it is useful to have words to designate the genetic constitution on the one hand and the appearance of the organism on the other. *Genotype* is used in the former sense and *phenotype* (Greek—*phaino*, to appear) in the latter. Thus, plants with genotypes YY and Yy have an identical phenotype, yellow cotyledons.

THE BACKCROSS OR TEST CROSS   Three types of crosses involving a single pair of genes have been mentioned thus far. Two homozygous dominants may be crossed (or a single one may be self-fertilized), and only homozygous dominants may be expected among the offspring. Or a similar cross may be made with homozygous recessives. In symbols, these crosses are as follows:

$$YY \times YY \to YY$$

$$yy \times yy \to yy$$

The third type is the cross between the two different homozygous types. This gives the F_1 hybrid and leads to the $1 : 2 : 1$ genotypic ratio or to the $3 : 1$ phenotypic ratio (if dominance applies) in the F_2, as follows:

$$YY \times yy \to F_1 \; Yy \to F_2 \quad 1 \; YY : 2 \; Yy : 1 \; yy$$
$$\underbrace{}_{} $$
$$3 \quad : \quad 1$$

Two more types of crosses are possible with monohybrids, that is, the hybrid can be crossed to either of the homozygous types:

$$Yy \times YY \to 1 \; YY : 1 \; Yy$$

$$Yy \times yy \to 1 \; Yy : 1 \; yy$$

Because in each case the hybrid is crossed to a homozygous type, like those chosen for the P generation of a simple Mendelian experiment, these are referred to as *backcrosses* (symbolized by B.C., BX or RF$_2$). In the first instance, the second parent is homozygous dominant, and hence random fertilization results in a $1 : 1$ genotypic ratio, but all of the offspring are identical phenotypically. Such a *dominant backcross* has little usefulness in genetic experiments, but it has an especial importance in human heredity, as will be explained much later. The second type, the *recessive backcross*, has great importance for experimentation, *because the genotypic and phenotypic ratios are identical*. Because the homozygous parent is recessive, and all of its gametes must carry the recessive gene, the phenotype of the zygote is determined by the gamete from the heterozygous parent, that is, $y + Y \to Yy$, a plant with yellow cotyledons; while $y + y \to yy$, a plant with green cotyledons. Thus in a recessive backcross the various phenotypes produced will indicate what kinds of gametes were produced by the heterozygous parent, and in what proportions they were produced. Similarly, crossing a dominant individual to the homozygous recessive type provides a simple way of distinguishing be-

tween homozygous and heterozygous dominants, for only the latter could have any recessive progeny. Because it does yield so much information, the recessive backcross is often referred to as a *test cross*. And, for the same reason, any reference to a backcross ordinarily means a recessive backcross unless the dominant type is specified.

4. ELEMENTARY MENDELISM IN MAN

When the question is raised as to whether the principles of Mendelism can be exemplified in man as well as in other organisms, the answer is unequivocally "yes." A few examples may be cited below.

White forelock, the possession of a single lock of white hair at the front and center of an otherwise normally pigmented head of hair, has been known as a familial character for hundreds of years. It has commonly been an object of family pride. A person who has a white forelock (fig. 9) always has at least one parent with the same character, and he transmits it to about half of his children. It never skips a generation. Hence it is clear that white forelock depends upon a single dominant gene, with its recessive allele determining the more usual, evenly pigmented condition. Another hair color with a simple genetic basis is red hair. When two red-haired persons marry, all of their children are also red-haired, indicating that the parents must have been homozygous. On the other hand, parents with other hair colors do sometimes have red-haired children. These facts indicate that red hair is based upon a pair of recessive genes. Hence any red-haired person must be homozygous, but nonred-haired persons may carry the gene for red hair, unsuspected, in the heterozygous condition. Other hair colors appear to be inherited in a more complex fashion.

Many conditions of the eyes have been shown to be inherited. Nearsightedness is dominant over normalcy, and farsightedness

Fig. 9. *White forelock, a simple dominant trait in man. This group includes a mother, her son, and her daughter, all with prominent white forelocks. Another daughter lacks the white forelock. (Photo by John S. O'Brien.)*

and astigmatism have also been reported to be dominant over their respective normal alternatives. With respect to eye color, blues and grays are recessive to the darker colors.

Probably the most generally known example of Mendelian heredity in man is that of the blood groups, which will be discussed in detail in Chapter 8, and so need not be treated here. Many more examples will be introduced below, especially in Chapter 21, but those cited above may suffice to show that the same principles which apply to heredity in other organisms apply also in man.

5. THE MENDELIAN LAWS TODAY

There remains the question of the present status of Mendel's basic assumptions after nearly 100 years. The primary test of the Law of Segregation is the regularity of the production of the Mendelian ratios when appropriate crosses are made. Many independent tests have been made in laboratories throughout the world, using experimental organisms from all major groups of plants and animals, ranging from bacteria to trees, from protozoa to man. The result has been the complete vindication of the Law of Segregation: whenever sexual reproduction occurs, Mendel's first law is applicable. (Exceptions may occur when the behavior of the chromosomes is abnormal, as in nondisjunction. See Chapters 13 and 14.) In addition to this, it has been established beyond a reasonable doubt that the genes are located in the chromosomes, and the cytological study of meiosis has revealed that the behavior of the chromosomes exactly parallels the genetic phenomenon of segregation. As this will be taken up in the following chapter, it need only be mentioned here that this fact constitutes an important additional proof of the validity of the Law of Segregation.

Mendel's second law, the Law of the Purity of Gametes, is also a necessary consequence of the behavior of the chromosomes. As the chromosomes maintain their structural integrity, their constituent parts, the genes, must also. Again the regularity of the production of the Mendelian ratios is itself the primary proof of the validity of the law. For the establishment of the validity of the Law of the Purity of Gametes, the backcross has been used particularly effectively by Raymond Pearl of Johns Hopkins University. There is a recessive gene, *vg*, in the fruit fly, *Drosophila melanogaster*, which causes the wings to be vestigial. In 1920 Pearl crossed a normal female fruit fly to a male with vestigial wings (fig. 10). The offspring were all normal. Such F_1 females were now backcrossed to males from a pure breeding vestigial stock. The backcross progeny showed a one-to-one ratio of normals to vestigials. Again, the normal (but heterozygous) females were backcrossed to vestigial males, and this procedure was repeated at every generation. When Pearl reported this experiment in 1935, it had gone through 300 generations. He pointed out that this would be the biological equivalent of 9000 years of human breeding, if thirty years be taken as an average interval between human generations (perhaps this is a little long for an average). In all of this immensely long period of continuous heterozygosity, during which the two alleles had been exposed each to the influence of the other, neither allele showed any tendency whatever to blend with the other, nor to vary in the direction of the other. In the three-hundredth backcross generation, the phenotypes did not differ from those of the original parental generation! The normal wings showed no tendency toward reduction, and the vestigial wings were not at all enlarged. Thus the Law of the Purity of Gametes was most impressively proven. Countless tests upon a smaller scale have all led to the same conclusion.

The principle of random fertilization has not fared quite so well. It is generally true; every experiment which yields the predicted Mendelian ratios attests its validity. But there are many specific examples known in which fertilization is not at all random. For example, the endosperm (food material of a seed) of maize may be either starchy or sugary. This alternative depends upon a single pair of genes, with starchy (Su) being dominant over sugary (su). If pure-breeding starchy and sugary strains are crossed, the F_1 plants will all have starchy endosperms. In the F_2, one would expect a ratio of three starchy to one sugary. But actually the ratio obtained is more on the order of five to one. Some insight into this unexpected situation may be obtained by backcrossing the F_1 hy-

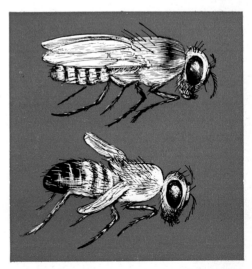

Fig. 10. *Normal and vestigial winged*
Drosophila. *Above, a normal
female, and below, a vestigial male.*

brids to both parental types. In the recessive backcross (*Su su* × *su su*), starchy and sugary progeny are obtained in a one to one ratio, just as expected on the basis of Mendelian principles. But in the dominant backcross (*Susu* × *SuSu*), an excess of plants homozygous for starchy endosperm is obtained. It has been demonstrated that such disturbances of the Mendelian ratios occur whenever the female parent is starchy, and that the reason is that pollen grains bearing the sugary gene grow more slowly than normal on the silks of starchy plants. Hence there is a failure of random fertilization because the pollen with the gene for starchy endosperm get to the ovules ahead of those with the gene for sugary endosperm. But the growth rates of the two types of pollen on the silks of sugary plants do not differ, hence random fertilization does occur in the recessive backcross.

Thus the half century of experimentation which has followed the rediscovery of Mendel's laws has resulted in the verification of the laws of segregation and of the purity of gametes. And, while some exceptions to the principle of random fertilization are known, the great majority of experimental crosses are understandable only upon the basis of the assumption that random fertilization does occur. The exceptions are far less important than the great regularity of the applicability of this fundamental principle of genetics.

As a result of the operation of these laws, a cross between two homozygous varieties differing in a single trait yields an F_1 which may be intermediate (no dominance) or which may be identical with one parental type (dominance). If the F_1 then be interbred to produce an F_2, each parent must produce two types of gametes in equal numbers, and random fertilization must then lead to an F_2 in which each of the homozygous types comprises 25 per cent of the offspring, and the hybrids comprise 50 per cent. If the hybrid phenotype is intermediate, this will give a 1 : 2 : 1 phenotypic ratio, as in the case of flower color in four-o'clocks; but if

dominance is shown, the first two classes are added together to give a 3 : 1 ratio, as in cotyledon color in peas.

Questions and Problems

1. Define
   Allele
   Backcross
   Gene
   Heterozygous
   Homozygous
   Law of Purity of Gametes
   Law of Segregation
   Random fertilization
   Zygote

2. In the cucumber, leaves are typically palmate, but a gene is known which causes the leaves to be fan-shaped. The latter are called Gingko leaves, as they resemble leaves of that tree. Each type breeds true, but when the two are crossed, the F_1 is all palmate. Which gene is dominant?

3. Assign gene symbols to the cucumber alleles of problem 2, then:
   a. Write out the P generation in symbols.
   b. Write the F_1.
   c. Write the F_2.
   d. Write the two possible backcrosses of the F_1 to the parental types.

4. In man, the second toe is sometimes longer than the great toe, and this anomaly is inherited. An affected person always has an affected parent. Is the gene for long second toe dominant or recessive?

5. Let *Ls* symbolize the gene for long second toe, and *ls* its normal allele. What will be the genotypes and phenotypes of the children from a marriage *Lsls* × *lsls*? And if each of these children also marries a person of genotype *lsls*, what will the results be?

6. In tomatoes, red fruit color (*R*) is dominant over yellow (*r*). Give the genotypes and phenotypes, and their proportions, derived from the following crosses:
   a. *RR* × *rr*
   b. *Rr* × *rr*
   c. *Rr* × *Rr*
   d. *rr* × *rr*
   e. *Rr* × *RR*

7. When oats with normal green leaves were crossed with a variety with golden leaves, the F_1 were all normal, while the F_2 included 130 green plants and 40 golden plants. Which member of this pair of genes is dominant? Assign gene symbols and diagram the cross with these symbols.

18

8. Genes for blue and brown eyes are a well known allelic pair in man. In a study of a Danish population, the following data were obtained from 337 families:

PARENTS	couples	CHILDREN blue	brown
A. Blue × blue	150	625	0
B. Blue × brown	158	317	322
C. Brown × brown	29	25	82

a. Which allele is dominant? Why?

b. Using the symbols B for brown and b for blue, diagram each type of cross to show how the results would be obtained.

c. More than one kind of cross could be included in B and C, but the data indicate that in each group one of the alternatives predominates. For each, designate the predominant cross, and state your reasons. State the results expected from each of the alternative crosses.

9. In man, albinism (a) is recessive to normal coloring (A). 34 normal couples had a total of 79 normal children and 21 albino children. What must have been the genotype of these parents? Diagram the cross in Mendelian symbols.

10. Give the phenotypes and their proportions in the following crosses in four-o'clocks:

a. RR × RR
b. RR × rr
c. Rr × rr
d. Rr × Rr

11. Phenyl-thio-carbamide (PTC) is a substance which tastes bitter to most people, but to some it is tasteless. The difference is inherited. One study of 100 families yielded the following results:

PARENTS	couples	CHILDREN tasters	non-tasters
Both tasters	40	90	16
One taster, one non-taster	51	80	37
Both non-tasters	9	0	17

a. Which allele is dominant? Why?

b. Using the symbols T for taster and t for non-taster, write these crosses in Mendelian symbols.

c. How can you account for the obvious failure to obtain a 1 : 1 ratio in the second series of families (taster × non-taster)?

References

Goldschmidt, R. B., 1952. Understanding Heredity. John Wiley and Sons, New York. Probably the simplest reliable book on heredity now in print.

Mendel, G. J., 1866. Experiments on Plant Hybridisation. Translated by Bateson and republished by the Harvard University Press, this classic of genetics is presented as Appendix A to this book.

CHAPTER 3

The Cytological Basis of Elementary Mendelism

In the interim between the publication of Mendel's paper and its discovery by the scientific world, the science of cytology emerged and developed rapidly. Thus, even before the elements of genetics were known to biologists generally, they realized that the chromosomes, the stainable bodies of the cell nucleus, must be the physical basis of heredity. Many biologists contributed to this advance in knowledge, but a few may be singled out for mention.

6. THE CHROMOSOMES, THE BEARERS OF HEREDITY

It was Wilhelm Roux who first suggested that, as the hereditary elements must necessarily behave in a regular, orderly fashion,

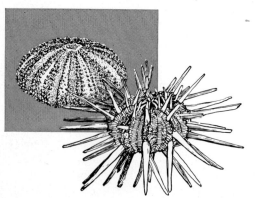

and as only the chromosomes were divided in an orderly fashion in mitotic division, the chromosomes must be responsible for heredity. August Weismann developed Roux's suggestion energetically, and through his many publications brought the chromosomal theory of heredity very much to the forefront of biological thought. As Weismann's ideas will be developed more thoroughly in Chapter 22, it need only be mentioned here that he did much to stimulate interest in the chromosomes and their role in heredity.

BOVERI'S EXPERIMENTS   More than any other one man, it was Theodore Boveri who accumulated the factual evidence of the role of the chromosomes in heredity. In 1887, he published the first of a long series of papers describing his experiments on the chromosomes of sea urchins. The papers are masterpieces of cytological and embryological experimentation and analysis, and they have secured their author's position as one of the truly great biologists. A few of his more suggestive experiments may be summarized below.

Sea urchins belong to the phylum Echinodermata, and like their better known relatives, the starfishes, they are constructed on a pentamerous plan. However, the entire body is enclosed in a rigid globular test, and from this long spines project (fig. 11). Although in most animals crosses between different species are difficult or even impossible,

Fig. 11.   *Sea urchins, with and without spines.*

among sea urchins intergeneric and even interfamilial crosses can be made. Such crosses are instructive, because, while the egg contributes both cytoplasm and nucleus to the zygote, the sperm contributes only nucleus. Hence the difference between a hybrid and the usual purebred zygote is simply the difference between the sperm nuclei of the two species. The cross between *Sphaerechinus granularis* and *Strongylocentrotus lividus* is particularly suggestive. The larvae of these two species show easily recognized differences. In the cross of a female *Sphaerechinus* to a male *Strongylocentrotus*, larvae are obtained which are generally intermediate between the two parental types. But if the reciprocal cross is made, then the resulting larvae are purely maternal in character (like *Strongylocentrotus*), that is, they are *matroclinous*. A study of the behavior of the chromosomes in these two cases shows a close parallel and offers a ready explanation of the observed facts. In the first instance (*Sph.* × *Str.*), all of the chromosomes participate in the cleavage of the egg and in its subsequent development. In the second case (*Str.* × *Sph.*), the chromosomes from the male parent are eliminated, largely or completely, during the first two cleavage divisions. Hence there is a one-to-one relationship between the phenotype of the larvae and the kinds of chromosomes they have. In some other intergeneric crosses in sea urchins, the male pronucleus may be extruded from the egg irrespective of which species is used as the female parent. In such cases, the larvae are always matroclinous.

Of similar import are Boveri's experiments on *merogony*, or the development of enucleated fragments of eggs. The eggs of sea urchins will break up into many fragments if shaken up, and only one fragment from each egg can include the nucleus. But all will round up and are capable of uniting with a normal sperm and undergoing some development. In some cases these enucleated fragments may form perfect dwarf larvae, while, in others, development is less successful. Boveri showed that such egg fragments can be fertilized by sperm of another species, and that the larvae so produced from enucleated fragments are always *patroclinous*, that is, they resemble the paternal species rather than the maternal. Thus, as in the case of interspecific crosses, the experiments with merogony show that the chromosomes determine the hereditary characters of the larva. If only one parent contributes a nucleus to the embryo, then that parent will determine the morphologic characters of the embryo irrespective of which parent contributes the cytoplasm.

A final experiment of especial interest in this connection is that of double fertilization, that is, the fertilization of one egg by two sperms. This can be accomplished easily in sea urchins by the simple expedient of adding a dense suspension of sperm to the eggs. When this is done, the double-fertilized egg forms a multipolar mitotic figure and divides at once into three or four blastomeres. Participating in the division are a total of three haploid sets of chromosomes, one from the egg and one from each of the two sperm. These chromosomes are distributed at random upon the several spindles, and the result is that only occasionally will blastomeres with a full normal set of chromosomes be formed. It had already been demonstrated that blastomeres would separate and develop independently into dwarf larvae if they were treated with calcium-free sea water. Boveri now tried this with the double-fertilized eggs. He found that some blastomeres failed to develop at all, some developed defectively, and some developed into normal, although dwarfed, larvae. But *only those with the normal chromosome complement ever developed normally*. It was clear, then, that the first cleavage division of the double-fertilized eggs had established abnormal chromosome complements in some or all of the blas-

tomeres; that subsequent mitoses had maintained the same combinations in the cell-
descendants of each blastomere; and that
normal development required a normal
chromosome complement. As the chromosome numbers of sea urchins are rather high
(18 and 36 are the most common diploid
numbers), it is very difficult to diagram the
possible divisions. However, the principles
involved are well-illustrated in figure 12,
which is modified from one of Boveri's
original figures. Here he has shown two of
the ways in which the divisions might occur
if there were only four pairs of chromosomes
(three of each kind are therefore involved in
these divisions).

These experiments, then, and many others,

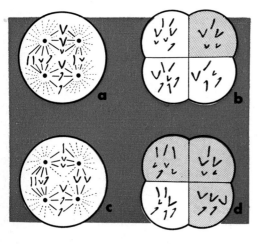

Fig. 12. *Boveri's experiment on double
fertilization in the sea urchin. Each zygote
(a and c) has three haploid sets of
chromosomes, one from the egg and one from
each sperm. For diagramming, four
chromosomes have been drawn to represent each
haploid set, a large V, a small v, a J,
and a rod. These are arranged at random on
four spindles, with a and c representing
two possible arrangements. Zygote a then divides
to form four blastomeres as in b, while
zygote c divides to form four blastomeres as in d.
Only those cells which get at least one
chromosome of each kind are viable. The stippled
cells all lack at least one kind of chromosome,
and these are inviable. (Redrawn from Boveri.)*

make it clear that the chromosomes have an
especial relationship to heredity, and it therefore becomes highly important to examine
the life cycle of the chromosomes.

7. MITOSIS

The most critical stages in the life cycle of
the chromosomes are the cell divisions, that
is, cell reproduction. In somatic tissues, the
cells ordinarily divide by a process called
mitosis, or equational division, which results in daughter cells with chromosome
complements identical to each other and to
the mother cell from which they came. In
the formation of germ cells, however, there
is a somewhat different sort of cell division
in which the number of chromosomes is
halved. This is called *meiosis,* or reductional
division.

In the process of mitosis (Greek, *mitosis,*
thread formation), stainable threads, the
chromosomes, become visible in the nucleus.
Each chromosome is duplicated lengthwise,
then the duplicates are separated and are
moved to opposite poles of the cell. The cell
now divides into two, and the group of
chromosomes in each daughter cell re-
forms a typical nucleus. Thus, each daughter
nucleus is a perfect replica of the other and
of the parent nucleus. The entire process is a
continuous, unified action in which any
subdivisions are rather artificial, but it is so
complicated that it can be adequately described only if broken up into convenient
stages for analysis. For this reason, mitosis is
conventionally described in five phases: interphase, prophase, metaphase, anaphase,
and telophase. Between prophase and metaphase, many cytologists speak of prometaphase.

INTERPHASE The ordinary, metabolic,
non-dividing cell has traditionally been
called a "resting" cell. This is a misnomer,
for actually the major metabolic functions

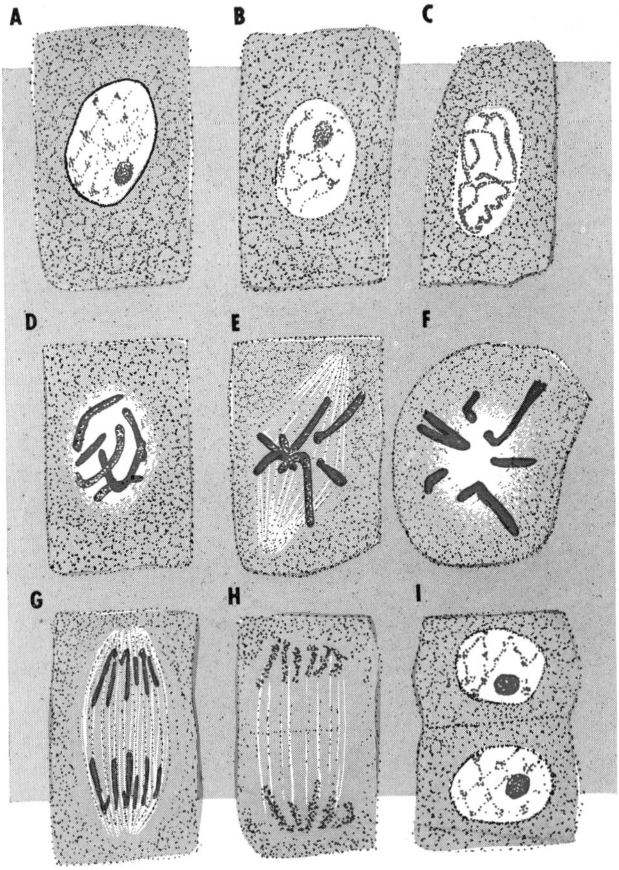

Fig. 13. *Mitosis in* Crepis capillaris. *A, interphase; B, early prophase; C, middle prophase; D, late prophase; E, metaphase in side view; F, metaphase in polar view (note that the two chromatids of one chromosome are rather widely separated); G, anaphase; H, telophase; and I, daughter cells.*

of any cell are carried out during the "resting" phase. The misnomer was applied by the early cytologists because of the lack of visible evidence of activity in the "resting" cells, in contrast to the obvious cycle of visible changes in mitotic cells. Modern physiological research has exposed the error decisively, and so cytologists now prefer the term "interphase" to "resting phase." One American physiologist has capitalized on this trend in thought by entitling his very readable book on general physiology, "Unresting Cells."[*] The cell is, of course, a body of protoplasm controlled by a nucleus (fig. 13). Near the nucleus is a prominent, deeply stainable granule, the *centriole*. The nucleus includes many small, irregular granules

[*] Gerard, R. W., 1949. Unresting Cells. Harper, New York.

which stain deeply with basic stains, like hematoxylin. These are the *chromatin* granules. They appear to be interconnected by very fine threads which are difficult to stain, or which take acid stains like eosin. This is the *achromatic network*. There may be one or more large, rounded, deeply staining bodies, the *nucleoli* (singular-*nucleolus*), in the nucleus. Finally, the entire nucleus is surrounded by a membrane.

PROPHASE The beginning of prophase is marked by changes in the centriole and the nucleus. The centriole divides into two, and the two slowly move apart toward opposite poles of the cell. As they separate, a spindle appears between them. Around the ends of the spindle, there are star-like radiations, the *asters*. As centrioles are not characteristic of the cells of higher plants, neither the

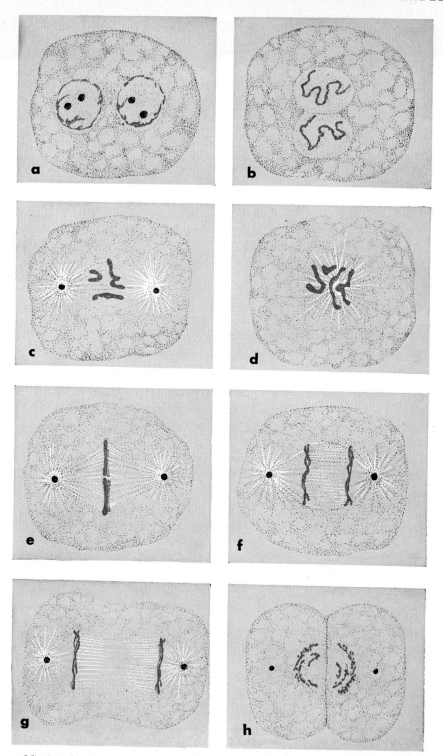

Fig. 14. *Mitosis in Ascaris. A, interphase; B, middle prophase; C, late prophase; D, metaphase in polar view; E, metaphase in side view; F, middle anaphase; G, late anaphase; and H, telophase.*

centrioles nor the associated structures appear in figure 13. However, they are well illustrated in figure 14, which is drawn from the cleaving eggs of *Ascaris*, and is representative of mitosis in typical animal cells.

The nuclear changes of the prophase are complex and of long duration, so that it is customary, for descriptive purposes, to subdivide it into early, middle, and late prophase (figures 13 and 14). During the early prophase, chromatin granules tend to appear a little more coarse and they draw closer together, so that it looks as though definite alignments occur, but no strand can be followed very far. Meanwhile, the nucleolus begins a progressive loss of its affinity for stains, and the nuclear membrane becomes somewhat less distinct than in the interphase. By middle prophase, the condensation of the chromosomes from the diffuse chromatin has progressed far enough that rather definite, though not compact, strands can be easily followed for considerable distances. They commonly present a rather tangled appearance in which no orderly arrangement is apparent. Also during the middle prophase, the nucleolus becomes still fainter and may disappear entirely. It is said to dissolve. The nuclear membrane also becomes fainter. All the while, the centrioles have continued their movement toward the opposite poles of the cell.

By late prophase, the chromosomes have condensed to a maximum degree, and they appear as short, dense bodies relative to the earlier stages. They are, however, still scattered at random. The nuclear membrane and nucleolus have by this time disappeared completely. The centrioles have now reached the opposite poles of the cell, and the true spindle of the division now is formed between them from the nuclear sap. It remains only for the chromosomes to become oriented on the plane midway between the centrioles, the equatorial plate or metaphase plate. This transitional stage is often called prometaphase. What the actual process of movement of the chromosomes to the equatorial plate may be is not known. One suggestion is that the formation of the spindle may begin at each centriole and progress toward the center, pushing the chromosomes as the two half spindles grow.

It was originally thought that the duplication of the chromosomes occurred at metaphase; however, many cases have been found in which the chromosomes are visibly double in the prophase (fig. 15), even the very early prophase. It seems probable that duplication of the chromosomes never occurs later than the prophase, while it may occur earlier. In fact, there is much evidence that the chromosomes may have latent divisions for two or three mitotic cycles ahead. Electron micrographs of chromosomes, for

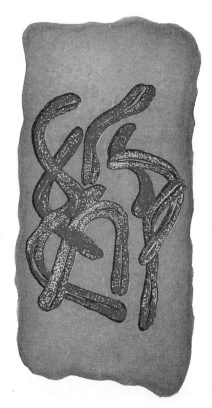

Fig. 15. *Prophase in an onion root tip cell.*
Note that the chromosomes are visibly
double in places.

Fig. 16. *Electron micrograph of a chromosome. Note that the heavy fiber separates out into smaller ones at three successive levels, so that there are a minimum of eight fibrils in each chromosome. This is a composite drawing based upon the electron micrographs of Yasuzumi.*

chromosomes of *Crepis* (a common weed resembling the dandelion) (fig. 13) do not appear to be very well aligned, although there is a greater concentration of chromatin on the equatorial plate because of the centromeres. But, although the chromosomes of *Ascaris* are also long, they appear to be almost perfectly aligned (fig. 14). This is because each chromosome has a whole series of centromeres attached to the spindles (an unusual condition). As all move actively to the metaphase plate, exact alignment of the whole chromosome results. But a very clear metaphase plate may also result when each chromosome has only a single centromere, if the chromosomes are short. This is the case in the whitefish (fig. 17), in which there are 80 chromosomes, which form a diagrammatically clear metaphase plate.

Although most of the chromosome is duplicated during the prophase or earlier, the centromeres are undivided until the metaphase, and it is the duplication of the centromeres which permits the separation of the daughter chromosomes, and thus the beginning of the anaphase. The duplication of the

example, have been found to show eight strands in chromosomes which appear single at the level of resolution of the light microscope (fig. 16). The mode of duplication of the chromosomes is by no means clear at present, but it seems probable that each chromosome acts as a contact catalyst for synthesis of a replica of itself from materials present in the nucleus.

METAPHASE The principal diagnostic character of the metaphase is the alignment of the chromosomes on the equatorial plate. This is, however, a somewhat deceptive statement, for often the chromosomes appear to be rather widely dispersed through the cell at metaphase. There is a specific chromosomal organelle, the *centromere* or *kinetochore*, by which the chromosome is attached to the spindle. The centromere is actively aligned on the metaphase plate, while the rest of the chromosome is passively pulled along after it. As a result, the long

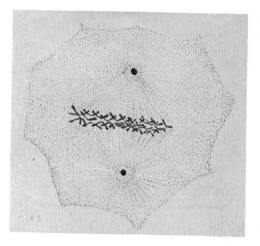

Fig. 17. *Late prometaphase in the whitefish. Note how beautifully the chromosomes are becoming aligned.*

centromeres is perhaps the most important aspect of the metaphase.

ANAPHASE The salient feature of the anaphase is the movement of the daughter chromosomes from the equatorial plate to the opposite poles of the cell. What the cause of this movement may be is one of the important unsolved problems of cytology. There appear to be fibers connecting each chromosome to the centrioles, and it was originally assumed that contraction of these spindle fibers pulled the daughter chromosomes to their respective poles. But much evidence has been marshalled against this theory, and it is now not given very much support by most cytologists. Yet neither has any generally satisfactory theory been proposed in its stead.

TELOPHASE When the anaphasic movement is completed, the telophase begins. This is more or less a reversal of the prophase changes, and, like the prophase, it is much prolonged. The chromosomes begin to vacuolate and become diffuse. At first they obviously form dense threads, but the chromatin becomes more and more dispersed, and finally chromosome strands cannot be followed with any assurance. A nuclear membrane forms again around each daughter nucleus, and the nucleoli are formed anew. Also during the telophase, the division of the cytoplasm occurs. In plants, the first indication of this is the formation of a delicate *cell plate* across the spindle. This continues to grow until it completely bisects the cell. It serves as the site of formation of a new cellulose membrane. In animal cells, the cell membrane constricts around the equator of the cell, and new membranes are formed between the daughter cells to complete the division. There are now two interphase cells where formerly there was but one.

SIGNIFICANCE OF MITOSIS Some aspects of the mitotic cycle deserve especial attention. First, because every chromosome divides into two identical daughter chromosomes which are separated into different daughter nuclei, each daughter nucleus should have a chromosome complement identical with that of the other, and both should be identical with the parent cell from which they came. Thus mitosis is a conservative factor in heredity. It tends to keep the genotype constant.

Second, reference to figures 13 and 14 will show that the chromosomes exist in pairs. In *Ascaris* there are only two pairs of chromosomes, while in *Crepis* there are three pairs. Further, each of the three pairs in *Crepis* has a different shape, so that the members of a pair are easily recognizable in favorable preparations. But it is noteworthy that the two members of a pair behave independently in mitosis: they are not located in any special relationship to one another on the metaphase plate. This pairwise existence of the chromosomes is a general characteristic of sexually-reproducing organisms, and it is called *diploidy* (Greek—*diploos*, double). It is the cytological counterpart to the pairwise existence of the genes, and constitutes a partial confirmation of the fact that the chromosomes carry the Mendelian genes.

8. MEIOSIS

The necessity for a periodic reduction of the chromosome numbers was first demonstrated by Weismann. If gametes carried the full diploid set of chromosomes, then their union would result in zygotes with twice as many chromosomes as the parents, and this doubling of chromosome numbers would occur at every generation. It was Weismann's realization of the instability of such a situation that led him to predict that reduction divisions would be found to occur in the formation of gametes. This prediction has been fulfilled: *meiotic, maturation,* or *reduction divisions* occur in the life cycles of all sexually reproducing organisms. The reduced cells, containing only one chromosome of each kind, are said to be *haploid* (Greek—*haploos*, single). In animals, the meiotic divisions lead immediately to the formation of gametes. In plants, the meiotic divisions result in the formation of spores, which then develop into gametophytes, or plants with the haploid number of chromosomes. The gametophytes (which in higher plants appear to be simply organs of the flowers) then produce the gametes by ordinary mitotic divisions.

The reduction of the chromosome numbers is accomplished by a series of two divisions. The essential feature is that the chromosomes divide *only once* while the cell divides twice. This can only result in halving the number of chromosomes per cell. It is important to note, however, that the reduced set of chromosomes so produced is not merely a numerical half of the diploid set: it is a very special half, comprising one chromosome from each pair. The chromosomes appear in the early prophase of the first divi-

sion as very slender threads in the full diploid number, six (three pairs) in the case of *Crepis*. Soon, however, the homologues, or members of each pair, become closely joined point for point. This process is called *synapsis* (Greek—*synapsis*, union). Synapsis is highly specific, for it always occurs only between the two members of a single pair, containing as they do the allelic genes derived from the two parents. Each synapsed chromosome is now duplicated, except for its centromere, the daughter strands attached to each centromere being called sister *chromatids*. Each synapsed pair now consists of four strands, and is called a *tetrad* (Greek—*tetras*, four). The number of tetrads is equal to the haploid number of chromosomes, three in the case of *Crepis*. When the chromosomes go to the metaphase plate for the first meiotic division, each tetrad has two centromeres, one from each synapsed chromosome. The homologous centromeres separate toward the opposite poles, drawing their respective *dyads*

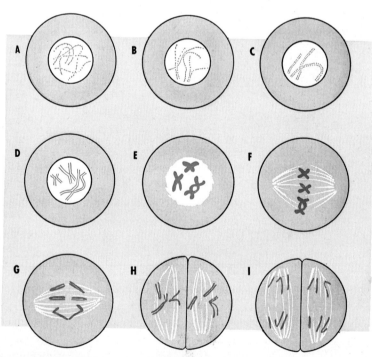

Fig. 18. *Meiosis in Crepis capillaris (male). A, leptotene; B, zygotene; C, pachytene; D, diplotene; E, diakinesis; F, metaphase I; G, anaphase I; H, metaphase II; and I, anaphase II.*

(a pair of sister chromatids) with them. Thus the chromosome number is already reduced, for there is one haploid set of chromosomes at each pole, although each chromosome is already duplicated for the next division. Some modification of this statement will be necessary below. The dyads go to the metaphase plate of the second division, and this time the centromeres divide just as in mitosis, with the result that only a single strand of each kind goes to each pole. The resulting cells become the functional gametes.

THE PROPHASE OF THE FIRST MEIOTIC DIVISION   The most critical differences between mitosis and meiosis occur in the prophase of the first meiotic division, when synapsis and tetrad formation occur; and in the metaphase of the first meiotic division, when the centromeres fail to divide. The details of the first meiotic prophase are covered in books on cytology, however, a brief outline may be given here (fig. 18).

The chromosomes first appear as exceedingly slender threads with fine granules, the *chromomeres*, along their lengths. The stage is called the *leptotene* (Greek—*leptos*, slender + *tainia*, ribbon). At first, the arrangement of the leptotene chromosomes, which are present in the diploid number, appears to be completely random, but in many species the chromosomes soon become oriented with the ends of the chromosomes gathered toward the centrosome and the central portions dispersed through the nucleus, suggesting a *bouquet* of flowers. It is thought that the bouquet arrangement facilitates synapsis. Soon the actual pairing of the homologues begins. It may begin at the ends of the chromosomes or it may begin at the centromeres, but in either case it proceeds in zipper-fashion, chromomere by chromomere, until it is complete. The stage during which synapsis is in progress is called the *zygotene* (Greek—*zygon*, yoke + *tainia*). The nature of the synaptic force is not known.

After synapsis is complete, the chromo-somes may be said to be *bivalent* for they are present only in two-by-two associations. The bivalents, of course, look thicker than the leptotene chromosomes, and they now begin a progressive shortening and thickening, hence this stage is called the *pachytene* (Greek—*pachys*, thick + *tainia*). There is some evidence that the chromosomes are duplicated to form the tetrads at this stage, but this is not usually visible until the following stage, the *diplotene* (Greek—*diploos*, double + *tainia*). In the diplotene, the synaptic attraction of the homologues seems to be lost, and the homologues tend to separate while the sister chromatids of each homologue are firmly synapsed. Yet the homologues remain rather closely associated in tetrads, bound together by cross-figures of the chromatids called *chiasmata* (singular, *chiasma*; Greek—*chiasma*, cross). It appears that the chromatids sometimes break in corresponding places in the two homologues of a pair during the pachytene. When the breaks reheal, they may join the "wrong" chromatids. This fact will be important for a later chapter. As a result, the chiasmata bind the homologues together.

The shortening and thickening which began in the pachytene continue through the diplotene and reach an extreme in the final phase, *diakinesis*, which corresponds to the prometaphase of mitosis. The chromosomes are especially easy to count at this stage, as they are very short and thick, and the tetrads are, of course, present in the haploid number. The chromosomes now move onto the metaphase plate, and the two maturation divisions proceed as described above, that is, homologous centromere separates from homologous centromere at the first division, pulling their dyads to the opposite poles; while at the metaphase of the second division, the centromeres divide and pull single strands to opposite poles.

OOGENESIS AND SPERMATOGENESIS COMPARED   The behavior of the chromosomes is the same in plants and in animals, in male and in female. But in animals, there is an important difference between the two sexes in the divisions of the cytoplasm during the maturation of the gametes (fig. 19). In each case, the primordial sex cells are multiplied by a long series of mitotic divisions. These mitotically dividing germ cells are called *oogonia* (female) or *spermatogonia* (male).

The final mitotic division leads to cells called, respectively, *primary oocytes* and *primary spermatocytes*. These primary gametocytes undergo a growth phase during prophase I (the meiotic divisions are often identified by Roman numerals). In primary spermatocytes, this growth phase is minor, but in primary oocytes it is spectacular,

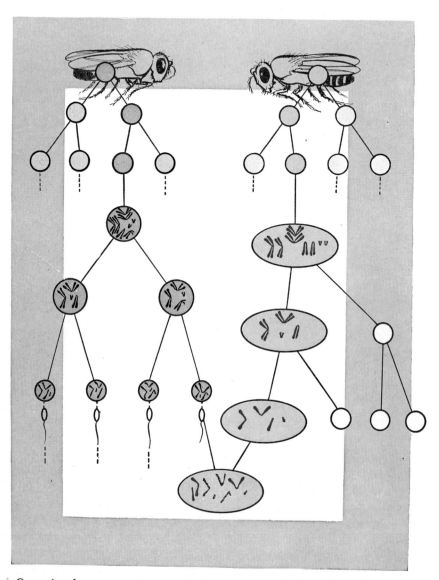

Fig. 19. *Oogenesis and spermatogenesis compared. Both oogonia and spermatogonia are multiplied by many mitotic divisions. While any of these cells may become gametes, one line on each side has been followed. Each primary spermatocyte gives rise to four functional sperm, but each primary oocyte gives rise to only one functional egg and three polar bodies. Finally, a fertilization is shown. This diagram is based upon Drosophila.*

making these the largest of cells, often truly macroscopic. While the actual mass of protoplasm is increased, deposition of yolk is the major factor in this growth.

Each primary spermatocyte undergoes the first meiotic division, giving rise to two cells of equal size, the *secondary spermatocytes*. These in turn each undergo the second meiotic division, producing four cells called *spermatids*, each of which is then transformed without further divisions into a functional sperm cell. The spermatids are, except for haploidy, typical cells. They now undergo a series of morphological changes including condensation of the nucleus, development of a long flagellate tail, and great reduction of the total amount of cytoplasm. These modified cells are the spermatozoa, and, as the transformation from spermatid to spermatozoon is accomplished without any further cell divisions, each primary spermatocyte gives rise to four grand-daughter cells, each of which becomes a functional sperm. Comparable facts relative to plants will be presented in another chapter.

In the female, the primary oocytes also undergo the first meiotic division. But the division of the cytoplasm is very unequal. The spindle is typically very near one side of the cell, and almost all of the cytoplasm remains in one daughter cell, the *secondary oocyte*, while a mere trace goes to the other daughter cell, the *first polar body*. But the nuclear contributions to the two cells are the same. Now the polar body and the secondary oocyte undergo the second meiotic division. Again the division products of the latter include a small *second polar body* and a large cell, the *ovum* or *egg* (fig. 20). Thus each primary oocyte gives rise to four grand-daughter cells, only one of which is a functional egg cell, while the other three are polar bodies, the prospective fate of which is disintegration.

The question of why the polar bodies should be formed rather than functional egg cells belongs in books on cytology rather than genetics, but the question is inevitable and so must be discussed briefly. Unlike the sperm, the egg must include sufficient nutritive material for the developing embryo, as well as adequate reserves of those formative materials which are necessary for the development of the embryo. As a result, the eggs are already the largest of cells, but the primary oocytes would have to be much larger if four functional eggs were to be derived from each one. There is then, an obvious biological economy in retaining most of the cytoplasm in a single cell, while using the polar bodies as a means of eliminating chromosomes. But why not let the reduction divisions occur before the great growth of the egg, so that the formation of four equal daughter cells need not tear down the great deposit of yolk and other materials? Inas-

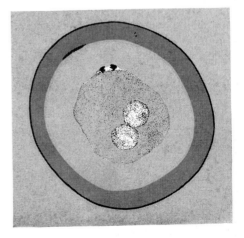

Fig. 20. *Egg and polar bodies in Ascaris. The first polar body is the black streak at 11 o'clock on the inner surface of the shell. The second polar body is adhering to the egg, and its chromosomes still appear as separate, compact bodies. Only two polar bodies appear, because the first one has not yet divided. Within the egg are the male and female pronuclei.*

much as the chromosomes are major organelles in the biosynthesis of proteins and other substances in the cell, there is some advantage to carrying out so extensive a process as the growth of an egg while the full diploid set of chromosomes is available. This explanation is reasonable, but, it should be added, unproved.

FERTILIZATION   The climax of the story of the gametes is fertilization, the union of an egg and a sperm. The details of the process of fertilization vary widely from species to species. Most commonly the sperm enters the egg when the egg is at the metaphase of the first meiotic division. The entrance of one sperm causes changes in the surface of the egg so that additional sperm cannot enter. The maturation divisions of the egg are then quickly completed, and the nuclei of egg and sperm unite and begin the first cleavage division of the new, diploid individual. Because there is no phase of the process of fertilization which is not radically modified in some species, it is very difficult to define fertilization morphologically. But, from a genetic viewpoint, two features stand out: first, fertilization does activate the egg, so that it develops through the usual embryonic processes and stages to an adult individual; and second, the inheritance of the zygote (and so of the new individual) is derived equally from the two parents, one complete set of genes coming from the mother and another complete set coming from the father.

9. MEIOSIS AND MENDELISM

It remains only to point out the parallels between the facts of meiosis and of elementary Mendelism. At the outset, the fact that the chromosomes ordinarily exist in pairs in somatic cells and singly in the gametes corresponds perfectly to the conditions of the genes. The first of Mendel's laws, the Law of Segregation, states that, when gametes are formed, the members of a pair of genes are separated from one another into sister gametes. Paralleling this is the cytological observation that, when gametes are formed, the two members of each pair of homologous chromosomes are separated into sister gametes. It is plain that, if the theory is correct that the genes are parts of the chromosomes, the segregation of the genes is a simple consequence of the behavior of the chromosomes.

Similarly, the purity of gametes appears to be a necessary result of the fact that the homologous chromosomes do not fuse at synapsis, but rather each remains distinct and they separate intact. But there is a difficulty here: it was pointed out above that in the pachytene or diplotene, segments of chromatids may be exchanged between the two members of a pair of homologous chromosomes, with chiasma formation resulting. Might this not cause an intermingling of alleles, giving rise to impure gametes? The evidence indicates decisively that this is not the case. Chiasma formation never alters a gene, hence it is generally believed that chiasmata occur only between genes.

One final point relative to the behavior of the chromosomes may be taken up in anticipation of the following chapter. Every diploid cell includes two haploid sets of chromosomes, one derived from the father (paternal) and one derived from the mother (maternal). Now it is imaginable that in meiosis all of the paternal chromosomes might go to one pole and all of the maternal chromosomes to the other. Or it might be that the different homologous pairs behave independently of one another, gametes with all possible combinations of paternal and maternal chromosomes being formed in equal numbers. The latter alternative has proved to be correct. As it applies to *Crepis*, the results of this *independent assortment* of the chromosomes have been diagrammed in figure 21. Now up to the present, only monohybrids have been discussed. But it is obvious

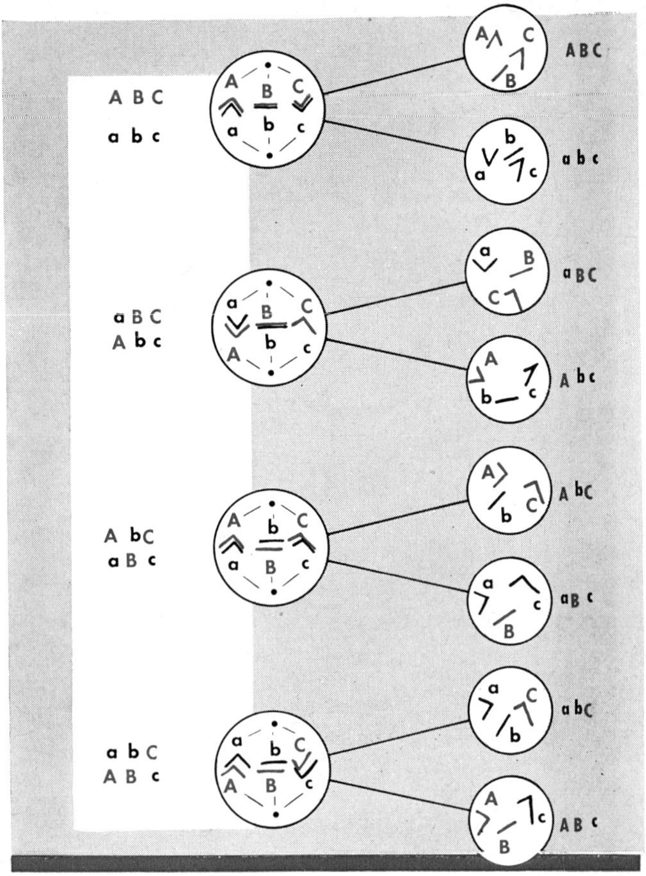

Fig. 21. *This diagram shows the eight different sorts of gametes that could be formed by an organism with three pairs of chromosomes and one factor difference in each pair. This phenomenon of independent assortment will be fully discussed in the next chapter.*

that, if an organism heterozygous for two or more pairs of genes located on as many different chromosomes were studied, the pattern of inheritance of the genes would be influenced by this independent assortment of the chromosomes. But this is the subject of the next chapter.

Questions and Problems

1. Define:

Chromatin	Merogony
Chromosome	Metaphase
Hybrid	Mitosis
Matroclinous	Patroclinous
Meiosis	Prophase

2. Explain the experiment which you believe most strongly supports the chromosomal theory of inheritance.

3. Make a series of sketches illustrating the main facts of mitosis.

4. Now make a parallel series of sketches illustrating the main differences between mitosis and and meiosis.

5. Define:

Pachytene	Synapsis
Polar body	Tetrad
Reduction	

References

DeRobertis, E. D. P., W. W. Nowinski, and F. A. Saez. Second edition, 1954. General Cytology. W. B. Saunders Co., Philadelphia.

Wilson, E. B., 1925. The Cell in Development and Heredity. The Macmillan Co., New York.

CHAPTER 4

Elementary Mendelism—II

Having seen how closely the facts of cytology parallel the most elementary facts of genetics, we may turn our attention once again to Mendel's experiments. After experimenting with the seven monohybrid crosses, Mendel tried crossing strains of peas which differed in two characters. The nature of such a *dihybrid* cross may be illustrated by the cross between a strain of peas having round seeds and yellow cotyledons with a strain having wrinkled seeds and green cotyledons. The F_1 was uniform, all of the plants having round seeds and yellow cotyledons. But the F_2 was much more complex. Out of a total of 556 plants, 315 were round-yellows, 101 wrinkled-yellows, 108 round-greens, and 32 wrinkled-greens. With his unusual mathematical insight, Mendel saw that this approximated a ratio of 9 : 3 : 3 : 1, for which the ideal figures would be 312.75 round-yellow, 104.25 wrinkled-yellow, 104.25 round-green, and 34.75 wrinkled-green. This observation was the basis for his third law, the Law of Independent Assortment.

10. THE DIHYBRID CROSS

That the F_1 from this cross should all have round seeds and yellow cotyledons is hardly surprising, for it had already been demon-

strated that these characters were dominant over their alleles, wrinkled seeds and green cotyledons, respectively. But the F_2 ratio of 9 : 3 : 3 : 1 was something new. The few plants which had wrinkled seeds and green cotyledons had to be homozygous for both pairs of genes—*rryy*—as these are the recessive alleles. However, the remaining plants, showing one or both dominant characters, could be either homozygous or heterozygous. In order to determine the exact genotypes of his F_2 plants, Mendel self-fertilized them, collected the seeds from each plant individually, and then recorded the nature of their progeny. The results of the entire experiment are tabulated in table 1.

THE DIHYBRID RATIO EXPLAINED Table 1 makes it clear not only that a dihybrid cross leads to a 9 : 3 : 3 : 1 ratio in the F_2, but that there are nine different genotypes which make up the four phenotypic classes, and that these genotypes also occur in definite, predictable ratios. What does this all mean? A clue may be obtained by considering the two character pairs one at a time. If the cross be treated as a monohybrid cross between round and wrinkled strains, then the F_2 includes 423 rounds (315 round-yellows plus 108 round-greens) and 133 wrinkleds (101 wrinkled-yellows and 32 wrinkled-greens). 423 to 133 is a fair approximation of the expected F_2 ratio of 3 : 1. Again, if the cross be treated as a monohybrid cross between yellow and green varieties, the F_2 includes 416 yellows (315 and 101) and 140 greens (108 and 32). 416 to 140 is an excellent approximation of a 3 : 1 ratio.

A further clue is obtained from Mendel's original notation of the genotypes. Today, the genotype of a diploid organism is always

Table 1. The Dihybrid Cross—Round-Yellow × Wrinkled-Green

P	round-yellow × wrinkled-green		$RRYY$ ×	$rryy$
F_1	round-yellow		$RrYy$	

		Proportions	
F_2	315 round-yellow	9/16	9 $R?Y?$
	101 wrinkled-yellow	3/16	3 $rrY?$
	108 round-green	3/16	3 $R?yy$
	32 wrinkled-green	**1/16**	1 $rryy$
	‾556 F_2 plants		

F_3

Proportion out of 16 progenies from F_2 plants			Genotype of F_2 parent was	Mendel's notation
From the 315 F_2 round-yellows:				
1	38	yielded only round-yellows	$RRYY$	RY
2	65	" round-yellow and wrinkled-yellow	$RrYY$	RrY
2	60	" round-yellow and round-green	$RRYy$	RYy
4	138	" all four F_2 types	$RrYy$	$RrYy$
	‾301★			
From the 101 F_2 wrinkled-yellows:				
1	28	yielded only wrinkled-yellows	$rrYY$	rY
2	68	" wrinkled-yellow and wrinkled-green	$rrYy$	rYy
	‾96			
From the 108 F_2 round-greens:				
1	35	yielded only round-greens	$RRyy$	Ry
2	67	" round-green and wrinkled-green	$Rryy$	Rry
	‾102			
From the 32 F_2 wrinkled-greens				
1	28	yielded only wrinkled-greens	$rryy$	ry

★ Note that the number of plants recorded is in each case less than the number of seeds planted. This is because some of the seeds fail to germinate. Actually, a germination rate of 528 out of 556 (95%) is excellent.

written in full (as $RrYy$) in order to distinguish it from the gametes. The utility of this had not become apparent in Mendel's time, and so he wrote a particular gene symbol only once when the plant proved to be pure-breeding, and twice when it was necessary to indicate that two allelic forms were present. Thus the two monohybrid crosses referred to above would be written as follows:

P	R × r	Y × y
F_1	Rr	Yy
F_2	1 R : 2 Rr : 1 r	1 Y : 2 Yy : 1 y

If the F_2 of the dihybrid cross be summarized in the same way, taking the data from the last column of table 1, we have: 1 RY + 1 rY + 1 Ry + 1 ry + 2 RrY + 2 RYy + 2 rYy + 2 Rry + 4 $RrYy$. Mendel examined

35

this series, and saw it to be the simple algebraic product of the two simpler expressions, $R + 2 Rr + r$ and $Y + 2 Yy + y$.

THE LAW OF INDEPENDENT ASSORTMENT Taking these facts together, and especially the last mentioned algebraic considerations, it becomes apparent that the two different pairs of genes in a dihybrid cross behave independently of one another, each pair of genes being distributed as though the other were not there. In other words, the proportions of their combinations are the products of their separate combinations

$$[(3/4 + 1/4) \times (3/4 + 1/4) =$$
$$9/16 + 3/16 + 3/16 + 1/16].$$

This is the substance of Mendel's third law, the *Law of Independent Assortment*, which may be concisely stated as follows: *members of different pairs of genes segregate independently of one another when gametes are formed.* Like the other Mendelian laws, this one has been thoroughly vindicated, but it is limited by the fact that each pair of chromosomes includes many pairs of genes. Clearly, if two pairs of genes under study happen to be in the same pair of chromosomes, they could not behave independently. But this is the phenomenon of linkage, and its development may be deferred to a later chapter. For the present, let it suffice to state that the Law of Independent Assortment is applicable only when the genes studied are located on different chromosomes.

Unless the gametes united at random, independent assortment would not be sufficient to account for the results of a dihybrid cross, however. The dihybrid cross is therefore subject to the same theoretical limitations that were discussed in chapter 2, as well as to the additional limitations imposed by the fact of linkage, which will be taken up much later.

DIHYBRIDISM AND THE ROMAN SQUARE Punnett's Roman square method was explained above in connection with the mono-

hybrid cross, but its usefulness is very much greater as an aid to visualizing independent assortment and random fertilization in a dihybrid cross. Thus, in Mendel's dihybrid cross, the F_1 plants have the genotype $RrYy$, and as the result of independent assortment, they will produce four types of gametes in equal numbers: RY, rY, Ry, and ry. (Note that every gamete must contain one representative of each allelic pair, and that none can possess more than one.) Because there are four types of pollen and four types of ovules, the Roman square must have four columns and four rows. Thus the completed square will appear as follows:

F_1 $RrYy$ gametes: RY, rY, Ry, ry

♀ \ ♂	RY	rY	Ry	ry
RY	$RRYY$	$RrYY$	$RRYy$	$RrYy$
rY	$RrYY$	$rrYY$	$RrYy$	$rrYy$
Ry	$RRYy$	$RrYy$	$RRyy$	$Rryy$
ry	$RrYy$	$rrYy$	$Rryy$	$rryy$

Enumeration of the various types of zygotes shown on the square will disclose the same types and proportions as were listed in Table 1. Further, it may be noted that all of the homozygous types lie on the diagonal from the upper left-hand corner to the lower right-hand corner. This will always be true if the gametes are written in the same order on both the horizontal and vertical axes. A Roman square for a dihybrid cross in an animal, specifically the guinea pig, is illustrated in figure 22.

COMBINATION BREEDING A practical application of dihybridism (and especially of more complex cases, or polyhybridism) is the art of *combination breeding*, that is, the

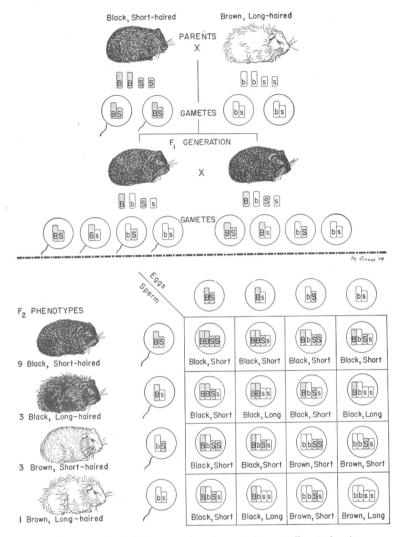

Black, Short-haired   Brown, Long-haired

PARENTS
X

B B S S   b b s s

BS   BS   GAMETES   bs   bs

F₁ GENERATION

X

B b S s   B b S s

GAMETES

BS   Bs   bS   bs   BS   Bs   bS   bs

F₂ PHENOTYPES

Eggs
Sperm   BS   Bs   bS   bs

9 Black, Short-haired

	BS	Bs	bS	bs
BS	BBSS Black, Short	BBSs Black, Short	BbSS Black, Short	BbSs Black, Short
Bs	BBSs Black, Short	BBss Black, Long	BbSs Black, Short	Bbss Black, Long
bS	BbSS Black, Short	BbSs Black, Short	bbSS Brown, Short	bbSs Brown, Short
bs	BbSs Black, Short	Bbss Black, Long	bbSs Brown, Short	bbss Brown, Long

3 Black, Long-haired

3 Brown, Short-haired

1 Brown, Long-haired

Fig. 22. *A dihybrid cross in the guinea pig.* (*From Villee, Biology.*)

crossing of different varieties of plants or animals in order to obtain new pure-breeding stocks with combinations of the characteristics of the two original varieties. This may be illustrated with the guinea pig example of figure 22. Let us suppose that a dealer has one pure-breeding stock which has long, black hair (BBss) and another which has short, brown hair (bbSS). But a customer orders guinea pigs for breeding stock, specifying that they must be pure breeding for short, black hair (*BBSS*). So the dealer makes the cross *BBss* × *bbSS*, and

gets all short, black-haired progeny in the F₁. But he cannot send these to his customer for they are known to be heterozygous for both genes. He therefore breeds an F₂. The progeny include nine-sixteenths of the desired phenotype, but these include only one-sixteenth which are pure breeding, and eight-sixteenths which will segregate for one or both genes.

How are the desired, homozygous animals to be picked out? Mendel answered this question in the case of his peas by self-fertilizing each plant, and then recording the progeny of each. Whenever a plant yielded only one type of offspring, he knew that the parent plant (and its progeny) must be homozygous. But this method is not applicable to guinea pigs, nor even to most hermaphroditic animals, for these are generally not self-fertilizable. One or the other of two methods may be followed. First, brother-sister matings of the F_2 short-blacks could be used, and any pairs that proved to be pure breeding for at least two generations could then be reserved for breeding stock. Short-black progeny of pairs which did not breed true could again be used for brother-sister matings. Such intensive inbreeding should, in the course of a few generations, produce enough pure-breeding (homozygous) pairs to establish a productive breeding stock.

The second, and much more efficient method, is to backcross the F_2 short-blacks to the double recessive type (which is also included in the F_2 progeny). The several possible crosses will be the following:

Thus the backcross progeny, because one parent can only produce gametes with both recessive genes, is a tool for determining what kinds of gametes are produced by the parent being tested (the dominant one), and in what proportions. It confirms the fact that the dihybrid produces four types of gametes in equal numbers. But of especial interest here is the fact that it makes it possible to identify the homozygous short-blacks. These are the ones which produce only short-black progeny, a result of their production of only one type of gamete, *BS*. If these animals were heterozygous for either pair of genes, they would have additional kinds of progeny. Thus these are the animals which can be used for breeding stock to fill the customer's order.

The guinea pig example is a trivial one, presented here because of its simplicity. However, combination breeding is a fundamental tool of practical plant and animal breeding. It frequently happens, for ex-

BBSS × *bbss* → all *BbSs* — black-short

BbSS × *bbss* → 1 *BbSs* : 1 *bbSs* — 1 black-short : 1 brown-short

BBSs × *bbss* → 1 *BbSs* : 1 *Bbss* — 1 black-short : 1 black-long

BbSs × *bbss* → 1 *BbSs* : 1 *bbSs* : 1 *Bbss* : 1 *bbss* — 1 black-short : 1 brown-short : 1 black-long : 1 brown-long

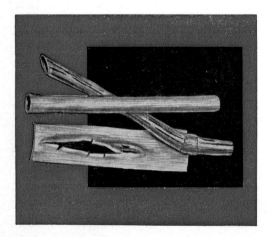

Fig. 23. *Rust infected and normal wheat stems. The upper, horizontal stem is healthy, while the other two are infected. The lowermost one shows a single lesion enlarged.*

ample, that the wheats (fig. 23) which are most resistant to rust are of no commercial value, while the most valuable wheats are quite susceptible to this destructive disease. The task of the plant breeder is to try to combine the rust resistance of the first with the useful cereal characteristics of the second by an appropriate series of crosses. It is a never-ending task, because, when a new resistant wheat is developed, it is not many years before a mutant rust capable of attacking it also occurs. The new rust then becomes increasingly common and widespread, until finally the development of yet another resistant wheat is the only alternative to crop failure. Again, a variety of excellent beef-producing cattle may nevertheless have yellow fat, a poor market character. Appropriate crosses with a white-fatted variety may achieve the desired combination of characters.

The practical use of combination breeding actually began with Mendel himself. For, when he showed Mr. Eichling through the monastery garden (see chapter 22), he showed him peas which he had reshaped in height and type of fruit. When asked how he did it, he replied, "It is just a little trick, but there is a long story connected with it which would take too long to tell." But he did say that he had imported many shelling varieties of peas, which were, however, bush peas. These he had crossed with the local tall, non-shelling variety in order to obtain the practical advantage of easy shelling along with the productiveness of tall vines. It is thus plain that he had selected the appropriate pure breeding types from the F_2 in order to get a more useful variety for the monastery garden. Thus Mendel also ranks as the first of the modern, scientific plant breeders!

11. TRIHYBRIDISM AND POLYHYBRIDISM

Mendel's final experiment was the making of a trihybrid cross. Thus he crossed a plant of genotype $AABBCC$ with one of genotype $aabbcc$. The F_1 plants showed all three dominant characters, and were, of course heterozygous for all three pairs of genes ($AaBbCc$). The characters which he used were round and wrinkled seed form; yellow and green color of cotyledons; and grey-brown or white color of the seed coat. The F_1 plants therefore showed round, green, and grey-brown. The results of the F_2 can be plotted on a Roman square, but not as simply as in the case of the dihybrid. The square must have eight columns and eight rows, because a trihybrid produces eight types of gametes (ABC, aBC, AbC, ABc, abC, aBc, Abc, and abc). One may make such a square if he wishes, but, with sixty-four units to be filled in, it must be done very carefully if it is not to become chaotic. And even if it be very carefully done, it is a chore to pick out all of those genotypes which lead to a particular phenotype. When the job is done, it will turn out that, out of 64 potential types of zygotes, 27/64 show all three dominant characters; 9/64 show recessive a but dominant B and C; 9/64 show recessive b but dominant A and C; 9/64 show recessive c but dominant A and B; 3/64 show only A dominant; 3/64 show only B dominant; 3/64 show only C dominant; and finally only 1/64 show all three recessives. Thus, there are eight phenotypic classes, corresponding to the eight types of gametes produced by the F_1, and these occur in the ratio of $27 : 9 : 9 : 9 : 3 : 3 : 3 : 1$, with those phenotypes which show the most dominants being the most abundant. This is what Mendel actually found. And he demonstrated that this series of genotypes, if written as in the last column of table 1, is the algebraic product of $(A + 2 Aa + a) \times (B + 2 Bb + b) \times (C + 2 Cc + c)$. Hence he concluded that these results are also determined by the Law of Independent Assortment, and by the other laws outlined above for simpler crosses.

Mendel did not attempt more complicated

crosses, but he assumed, in view of the mathematical regularity of the three types which he tested, that polyhybrids should follow the same mathematical laws. The experimental difficulties increase rapidly as the number of heterozygous genes increases. During the early years of genetic studies, it appeared that such crosses had more value as mathematical exercises than as practical tools of genetics. Recently, however, it has become apparent that characteristics of great practical importance—yield of wheat, for example—may be based upon many separate pairs of genes, each with a very small individual effect. The study of such characters is very important, and it can be done effectively only with the tools of statistics.

THE PROGRESSION METHOD   As pointed out above, the use of the Roman square, so effective for visualizing the results of random fertilization in simpler crosses, is decidedly awkward for trihybrid crosses, and is completely impractical for higher degrees of polyhybridism. But, fortunately, there is a much more widely applicable method, and this is the *progression* method of E. B. Babcock. Table 1 is a progression table for a dihybrid. As may be seen by reference to the table, the various genotypes are grouped together according to the phenotypes which are based upon them. There will always be as many phenotypes as there are types of gametes produced by the F_1, and therefore the gametic symbols can be used to head each series of genotypes. Thus *ABC* will head the series of genotypes which includes at least one dominant gene of each pair in a trihybrid experiment. The first member of the series will be the completely homozygous one, and the coefficient 1 may be written before it. This means, in the case of a trihybrid, that this genotype should make up 1/64 of the total progeny. For a dihybrid, it would be 1/16, and for a tetrahybrid, 1/256. In any case, the first member of a progression should always be the completely homozygous dominant, and its coefficient should be 1. Following this, all possible combinations with one heterozygous pair of genes should be written, and their coefficients will be 2. Next, all possible combinations with two heterozygous genes are written with the coefficient 4. Finally (for a trihybrid cross), the combination with all three genes heterozygous is written with the coefficient 8. Thus, every time the number of heterozygous genes is increased, the preceding coefficient is doubled. When the last member is reached, one goes to the next group of phenotypes (*aBC* for example), again starting with the coefficient 1.

The usefulness of the progression method can be increased if the series of genotypes is written as a left-hand column, with progeny expected from self-fertilization (or cross-breeding to an organism of identical type) comprising the right-hand column. But further description of the progression method would be less instructive than an actual example. A progression for a trihybrid cross is therefore give in table 2.

Some of the advantages of the progression method deserve mention. Not the least of these is the fact that it affords a mechanical way to derive the F_2 genotypes. Second, these genotypes are automatically grouped together by phenotypes. Third, the proportions of each phenotype and genotype are immediately apparent. Fourth, the breeding behavior of any F_2 type is readily apparent and can easily be included in the progression table if desired. Finally, it is quite simple to write out any part of the table without reference to the rest of it, if that should be desired.

RÉSUMÉ   Crosses between organisms differing in two or more pairs of genes follow the same laws that apply to monohybrid crosses. In addition, however, they also follow the Law of Independent Assortment, that is, members of different pairs segregate each as though the others were not present.

40

Table 2. A Trihybrid Cross Represented by the Progression Method

P *AABBCC*   *aabbcc*

F$_1$ *AaBbCc*

F$_1$ gametes: *ABC, aBC, AbC, ABc, abC, aBc, Abc, abc*

F$_2$ phenotypes and genotypes: Breeding behavior (F$_3$ produced):

ABC

1 *AABBCC*   Breeds true
2 *AaBBCC*   3 *ABC* : 1 *aBC*★
2 *AABbCC*   3 *ABC* : 1 *AbC*
2 *AABBCc*   3 *ABC* : 1 *ABc*
4 *AaBbCC*   9 *ABC* : 3 *aBC* : 3 *AbC* : 1 *abC*
4 *AaBBCc*   9 *ABC* : 3 *aBC* : 3 *ABc* : 1 *aBc*
4 *AABbCc*   9 *ABC* : 3 *AbC* : 3 *ABc* : 1 *Abc*
8 *AaBbCc*   27 : 9 : 9 : 9 : 3 : 3 : 3 : 1
—
27

aBC

1 *aaBBCC*   Breeds true
2 *aaBbCC*   3 *aBC* : 1 *abC*
2 *aaBBCc*   3 *aBC* : 1 *aBc*
4 *aaBbCc*   9 *aBC* : 3 *abC* : 3 *aBc* : 1 *abc*
—
9

AbC

1 *AAbbCC*   Breeds true
2 *AabbCC*   3 *AbC* : 1 *abC*
2 *AAbbCc*   3 *AbC* : 1 *Abc*
4 *AabbCc*   9 *AbC* : 3 *abC*: 3 *Abc* : 1 *abc*
—
9

ABc

1 *AABBcc*   Breeds true
2 *AaBBcc*   3 *ABc* : 1 *aBc*
2 *AABbcc*   3 *ABc* : 1 *Abc*
4 *AaBbcc*   9 *ABc* : 3 *aBc* : 3 *Abc* : 1 *abc*
—
9

abC

1 *aabbCC*   Breeds true
2 *aabbCc*   3 *abC* : 1 *abc*
—
3

aBc

1 *aaBBcc*   Breeds true
2 *aaBbcc*   3 *aBc* : 1 *abc*
—
3

Abc

1 *AAbbcc*   Breeds true
2 *Aabbcc*   3 *Abc* : 1 *abc*
—
3

abc

1 *aabbcc*   Breeds true

★ Notations in this column are not actually genotypes, but simply gene symbols used as phenotypic descriptions. The same is true of the headings in the left-hand column.

In a dihybrid cross with dominance, this leads to a phenotypic ratio of 9 : 3 : 3 : 1. Independent assortment applies only when the gene pairs under observation are located in different pairs of chromosomes. A dihybrid cross can be conveniently diagrammed by the Roman square method, however the progression method is much easier in more complicated crosses. Combination breeding is a highly practical application of these principles.

Questions and Problems

1. In the tomato, red fruit (R) is dominant over yellow fruit (r), and round fruit (O) is dominant over oval (o). What will be the progeny from each of the following crosses:

    a. $RROO \times rroo$
    b. $RrOo \times rroo$
    c. $RrOo \times RrOo$
    d. $RRoo \times rrOO$
    e. $Rroo \times rrOo$

In problems 2 through 5, state the genotypes of parents and offspring.

2. A red, round tomato crossed to yellow, oval produces only red, round offspring.

3. Another red, round crossed to a yellow, oval yields red, round; red, oval; yellow, round; and yellow, oval offspring.

4. A red, oval crossed to a yellow, round yields red, round and yellow, round offspring.

5. A red, oval crossed to a yellow, round yields only red, round offspring.

6. Construct a Roman square for the F₂ from the cross $RROO \times rroo$. Now color in red each square representing a genotype with both dominants; color in yellow each square representing a genotype homozygous recessive for color but dominant for shape; color in blue each square representing a genotype dominant for color but recessive for shape; and leave uncolored the square

representing the genotype with both factors homozygous recessive. Or you may mark the four classes in some other way.

7. Now write out a progression table for the F₂ of the cross in question 6.

8. In man, brown eye color (B) is dominant over blue (b), and right-handedness (R) is dominant over left-handedness (r). A right-handed, brown-eyed man marries a left-handed, blue-eyed woman. They have only one child, which is left-handed and blue-eyed. State the genotypes of all three persons.

9. Now, suppose that the child in question 8 had been right-handed and brown-eyed. Could question 8 have been answered completely? Explain your answer.

10. A brown-eyed, left-handed man whose mother was blue-eyed marries a blue-eyed, right-handed woman whose father was left-handed. What are the genotypes of this man and woman? What genotypes and phenotypes may be expected among their children?

11. Taking the possible types of children from problem 10 one at a time, suppose that each marries someone of identical genotype. What would be the expected offspring in each case?

12. Now suppose that the children of question 10 each married a person of genotype $bbrr$. What would be the expected offspring in each case?

13. What gametes are produced by the trihybrid $AaBbCc$?

14. Write the progression table for phenotypes AbC derived from the F₂ of the cross $AABBCC \times aabbcc$.

15. Now write the progression for phenotype ABC.

16. Is an individual of genotype $aaBbcc$ a trihybrid?

References

Babcock, E. B. and R. E. Clausen, 1927. Genetics in Relation to Agriculture. Second edition. McGraw-Hill Co., New York.
References for chapter 2 are also applicable here.

CHAPTER 5

Elementary Statistics

Throughout the preceding chapters, numerical concepts have been introduced repeatedly. Mendel was able to conceive the laws which bear his name only after he grasped the numerical relationships of the F_2. The various relationships which have been treated thus far are summarized in table 3, the study of which may help to clarify much that has gone before.

And thus, because every genetic principle is predicated upon numerical data and serves as a basis for numerical predictions, it becomes necessary to examine some of the elementary principles of statistics and biometry. Statistics may be defined as the science of the systematic study of the relationships of numerical data. Biometry is the application of statistics to biological problems. The science of statistics had scarcely passed its infancy when Mendel published his major paper, and biometry was as yet only in gestation. L. A. J. Quetelet (1796–1874), a Belgian astronomer, meteorologist, and statistician, seems to have had the distinction of being the first to apply statistical methods to the study of biological materials, and one of his examples will serve to introduce this field.

Table 3. Numerical Data on Hybrids and Their Progeny

Modified from "Genetics in Relation to Agriculture," by Ernest B. Babcock and Roy E. Clausen, McGraw-Hill Company.

	1	2	3	4	5	6	n
Number of heterozygous gene pairs							
Number of classes of gametes							
Number of phenotypic classes in F_2*	2	4	8	16	32	64	2^n
Number of homozygotes in F_2							
Number of phenotypes in backcross							
Number of genotypic classes in F_2	3	9	27	81	243	729	3^n
Number of possible combinations of F_1 gametes	4	16	64	256	1024	4096	4^n

* Complete dominance within each gene pair is assumed in line 3, on the number of phenotypic classes in the F_2.

12. THE FOUNDATIONS OF BIOMETRY

Quetelet measured the heights of 1000 French soldiers and obtained the results shown at the bottom of this page. Several characteristics become apparent upon inspection of this set of data, or upon the performance of simple calculations.

First, the individual measurements are not scattered evenly over the entire range of heights, but rather they cluster about a midpoint, with the frequencies falling off rapidly toward either end of the distribution. This midclass, 67 inches in the present example, is called the *modal* class (or the *mode*), and is, by definition, that class in which the greatest number of individual measurements falls. The majority of the soldiers, of course, did not fall in the modal class; with respect to the distribution of heights, those taller than 67 inches may be designated as plus individuals, and those shorter as minus individuals.

Second, if we calculate a simple arithmetic average of the heights, it turns out to be very close to the mode, but not identical with it (in this case, 67.2 inches). Statisticians usually call this the arithmetic *mean*, and it is a very important statistic. Third, if the heights be plotted against their frequencies to make a *curve*, it is approximately symmetrical, and has a bell-shape, with both the direction and degree of curvature in the central portion differing from the tails of the curve (fig. 24). This type of curve results whenever a measured trait is determined by a number of independent variables, and hence it is of very general importance. It is called the *normal probability curve*, or simply the normal curve. This type of distribution was not new to Quetelet. It was already known that

individual observations of mathematical probabilities tended to vary about a mean in this fashion. But the demonstration that the variations of measured characters of organisms were distributed about a hypothetical average in the same way was new and it is sometimes called Quetelet's law. Thus was the much belabored "average man" introduced into modern thought. The characteristics of the normal curve will be studied in greater detail in the latter part of this chapter.

BIOMETRICAL ASPECTS OF EVOLUTION One of the founders of the science of biometry was Francis Galton, a cousin of Charles Darwin, and himself a scientist of the first magnitude. Galton developed a theory of heredity which was, in the main, simply the old blending theory restated in mathematical terms. He was also very much interested in his more famous cousin's ideas on the origin of species, and he tried to prove the effectiveness of natural selection by statistical studies. But before going into this, a very brief summary of Darwinism may be appropriate.

Darwin observed that organisms tend to reproduce in geometrical rather than arithmetical series; in other words, the expansion of a population tends to run as the series 1-2-4-8-16-32-64 etc. rather than 1-2-3-4-5-6-7 etc. This prodigality of nature quickly leads to a severe overpopulation, in which the fate of most of the individuals must be early death, for the size of a population presses hard upon the means of survival. Hence there must be a struggle for existence. But these very numerous individuals are not all just alike: they vary one from another in numerous characteristics. Some of these variations may be neutral, having no in-

Height in inches:	60	61	62	63	64	65	66	67	68	69	70	71	72	73	74	75	7
Number of soldiers:	2		2	20	48	75	117	134	157	140	121	80	57	26	13	5	2

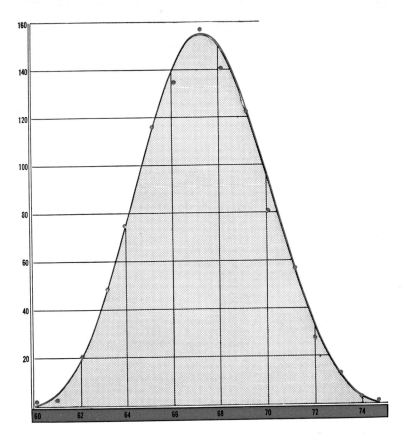

Fig. 24. *The curve of distribution of the heights of 1000 French soldiers, based upon Quetelet's data.*

fluence upon the welfare of the organism, but others may confer an advantage or disadvantage in the struggle for existence. Darwin wrote that "owing to this struggle, variations, however slight and from whatever cause proceeding, if they be in any degree profitable to the individuals of a species, in their infinitely complex relations to other organic beings and to their physical conditions of life, will tend to the preservation of such individuals, and will generally be inherited by the offspring. The offspring, also, will thus have a better chance of surviving, for, of the many individuals of any species which are periodically born, but a small number can survive. I have called this principle, by which each slight variation, if

useful, is preserved, by the term natural selection."

Thus, in the Darwinian scheme, the origin of new species depends upon overpopulation, variation among the individuals of a species, severe competition for the means of survival among these varying individuals, and the propagation of the most advantageous variants by means of heredity. Darwin and Galton thought of the tooth-and-claw type of competition as being the major factor in natural selection (this now appears to be much less important, with many other factors playing equal or greater roles), and hence large physical size was regarded as an advantage (plus) and small size as a disadvantage (minus). Galton reasoned that, if

45

Darwin were right, the size curves for successive generations should shift steadily toward the right (the "plus" end of a graph) (fig. 25).

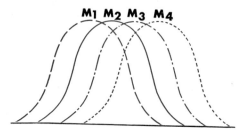

M₁ M₂ M₃ M₄

Fig. 25. Curves for four successive generations responding to selection according to Galton's conception. The mean of each generation (M_1, M_2, M_3, M_4) is shifted a little to the right of the mean of the preceding generation.

In order to test this idea, Galton made a study of the heights of London parents and their children. As expected, the heights of the parents, when graphed, formed a normal probability curve. However, it made a difference which children were studied. If the children of modal class parents were studied, then the curve for the children looked about like that for their parents, having the same mean. But, if the children of the tallest parents were studied, the mean of their curve was shifted far to the right of that of the parental generation, although still to the left of their own parents' mean. Just the opposite was the case if children of the shortest parents were studied. Galton regarded this as proof of his contention, that selection could cause the curve of a population to shift indefinitely in one direction or the other. This study is summarized in figure 26.

THE PURE LINE CONCEPT An obvious defect in Galton's work was the failure (unavoidable) to continue such selection for several generations to determine whether, in fact, the mode would continue to shift in the direction of selection. This, of course,

could not have been done in man, as it would have required controlled matings. The critical experiment was not performed until shortly after the turn of the twentieth century, when Wilhelm Johannsen, a Danish geneticist and plant breeder who was also an excellent statistician, took up this problem.

Johannsen studied the inheritance of seed size in the Princess variety of the common garden bean, *Phaseolus vulgaris*. Because beans are ordinarily self-fertilized, they are more likely than not to be homozygous for all or most of their genes, a fact already demonstrated by Mendel. This results from the fact that half of the progeny of a hybrid *Aa* will be the homozygous types, *AA* and *aa*. As the progeny of these must also have the same genotypes under a system of self-fertilization, the homozygous condition is maintained indefinitely in their descendants. And, at each succeeding generation, half of the progeny of the remaining heterozygotes are added to the swelling population of homozygotes. After ten generations of such self-fertilization, having started with heterozygous stock, less than one tenth of 1 per cent of the population would be heterozygous. This does not mean, however, that the beans must all be uniform. If the original stock were the dihybrid, AaBb, four different homozygous lines could be formed: *AABB, AAbb, aaBB* and *aabb*. The possibilities become practically unlimited when the large numbers of genes which are undoubtedly present in natural species are considered.

The field-grown beans with which Johannsen started were a mixture of many such homozygous strains. The weights of the individual beans varied from 20 centigrams to 70 centigrams. Johannsen selected nineteen mother plants, from all parts of this size range, and followed their progeny for many generations, keeping a careful record of each line, and taking pre-

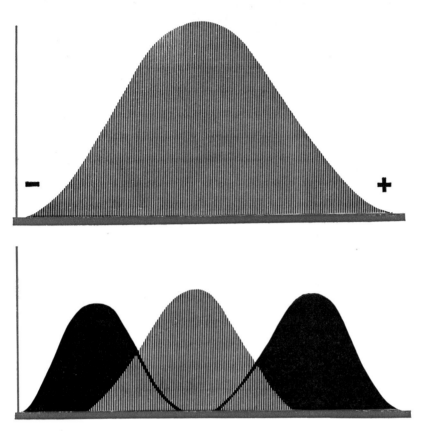

Fig. 26. *Galton's study of heights of London parents and their children. The upper curve represents the parental generation. The center curve in the lower series represents the children of modal class parents, while the left hand curve represents children of very short parents, and the right hand curve represents children of very tall parents. Note the broad areas of overlap.*

cautions to insure against cross-fertilization.

Actually, the progeny of each of these nineteen plants showed a fairly wide range of seed size, but each line was characterized by a distinct mean. It was now easy to determine whether selection would be effective within such a homozygous line. The largest and the smallest seeds from each line were selected and were grown under similar conditions. Had selection been effective, the two groups of seed should have yielded progenies with markedly different means. In fact, however, *the two means were never significantly different in such experiments,* that is, they never differed as much as either differed

from the means of other pure lines. The only possible conclusion, then, was that the variations which occur in a completely homozygous stock are effects of the environment, and are not inheritable. Johannsen called such strains "pure lines," and defined a pure line as the progeny of a single, genetically pure (homozygous), self-fertilized individual. The establishment of the pure line concept made it possible for the first time to distinguish between the effects of the genotype and the effects of the environment.

Let us examine some of Johannsen's data. Pure line number 1 showed a mean seed weight of 64.2 centigrams. When minus

47

variants weighing only 60 centigrams were selected for seed stock, they yielded progeny with a mean weight of 63.1 centigrams; while plus variants weighing 70 centigrams yielded progeny with a mean weight of 64.9 centigrams. Pure line number 7 showed a mean seed weight of 49.2 centigrams. Seeds of weights 20, 40, and 60 were selected for growing the next generation. The weight curves of their progeny had means at 45.9, 49.5, and 48.2 centigrams, respectively. In table 4, these data are summarized for several of the nineteen pure lines. In all of these, it is clear that selection had no effect upon the succeeding generation, simply because selection was acting upon non-inheritable, environmentally caused modifications of the plant, while a single, homozygous, unvaried genotype was inherited by all of the plants of a particular pure line.

The environmental factors which cause the fluctuations within a pure line are, of course, not constant from year to year, and so the mean of one year may be shifted to the right or to the left in the following year But the means of different pure lines maintained their differences, showing that only the environmental factors changed, while the genotypes remained constant. Johannsen demonstrated this by following particular lines for several consecutive years. The

annual means for pure lines 1 and 19 over a period of six years are shown in table 5.

This discussion of pure lines began with the question of whether selection could in fact, as Galton believed, effect a progressive shift in the mode of a population. Johannsen concluded that selection could only be effective in a heterozygous population. The effect of selection would then be to drive the population toward a homozygous condition. But once homozygosity was achieved, selection could have no further effects. Genetic variability is the necessary substrate for the effective action of selection. In summarizing, Johannsen coined an aphorism which might very well be a motto for biometricians: "Biology must be handled with mathematics but not as mathematics." Or, to paraphrase, the best calculations cannot lead to correct results if they are based upon biological premises which are incorrect. Galton had failed to distinguish between genetic variability (based upon gene differences) and environmentally produced modifications, hence his excellent calculations led him to a false conclusion.

WHY PURE LINES ARE NOT UNIFORM One final question, before leaving the pure lines, is, why do members of a pure line vary at all? As they are all homozygous for the same genes, why are they not all identi-

Table 4. Results of Selection for Size in Pure Lines of Beans

PURE LINE NUMBER	MEAN WEIGHT IN PURE LINE	WEIGHT IN CENTIGRAMS OF SELECTED PARENT (TOP ROW) AND MEAN WEIGHTS OF PROGENY (ALL SUBSEQUENT ROWS)					
		20	30	40	50	60	70
1	64.2	....	....	....	....	63.1	64.9
2	55.8	....	....	57.2	54.9	56.5	55.5
7	49.2	45.9	....	49.5	....	48.2	....
9	48.2	....	48.5	....	47.9	....	....
18	40.8	41.0	40.7	40.8	....	....	....
19	35.1	....	35.8	34.8	....	....	....

Table 5. Annual Means for Weight of Beans in Pure Lines 1 and 19 During the Years 1902–1907

| HARVEST YEAR | MEAN WEIGHTS | |
	Line 1	Line 19
1902	64.0	35.3
1903	73.1	40.6
1904	55.6	32.0
1905	63.6	38.7
1906	73.7	38.9
1907	68.4	37.2

cal? Galton's famous pinball machine presents a very suggestive analogy for the visualization of the answer to this question. The machine is illustrated in figure 27. A quantity of shot is first placed in the uppermost chamber. The shot is then released through a small hole at the center and permitted to fall the length of the board into spaces at the bottom which are separated into columns by a series of dividers. The unmodified action of gravity would direct all of the shot into the center column, the overflow going into the adjacent columns only after the center one was full. However, the action of gravity is not unmodified: the shot must fall through a gridwork of nails. In the course of the fall, the shot bounces off the nails and off each other many times, sometimes bouncing to the left, sometimes to the right. On the average, any particular ball is likely to make about the same number of bounces in each direction, and hence more

balls fall into the center column than into any other. However, some take more bounces in one direction than the other, and so land in a side column. And a few take all of their bounces in one direction, and so land in the outermost columns. If the experiment be tried, it turns out that the pattern of shot describes a normal probability curve just as do the weights of the beans in a pure line.

But what has the pattern of shot in a pinball machine to do with beans in a pure line? Like the force of gravity which tends to drive all of the shot into the center column, the common genotype tends toward the production of uniform beans. But the nails which disrupt the action of gravity also have analogues in the case of the beans. And these are the many variable conditions under which the beans grow. Even within a single garden plot there are differences in fertility and texture of the soil, availability and drainage of water, incidence of sunlight and

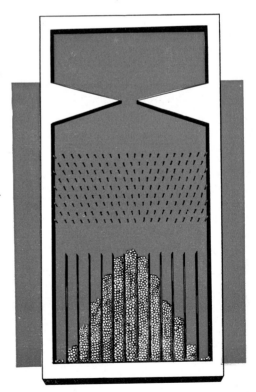

Fig. 27. *Galton's pinball machine. Note how beautifully the shots describe a normal probability curve.*

shadow, attack by insects or fungi, and other factors which influence the growth of the plant. Generally, any particular plant is likely to be affected by approximately equal numbers of these in a plus and in a minus way. Exceptional plants may get "all the breaks," good or bad, but the population measurements will describe a normal probability curve. Much the same is true for any organism: the specific conditions of development may be different, but in any case, the mature organism is a product of its genotype reacting with the environmental conditions. The old argument of heredity versus environment has become largely meaningless, for both are absolutely essential to the organism. Their relative importance, however, varies according to the specific character studied. Some characteristics, like the blood groups of man, appear to be so rigidly determined by the genotype that they cannot be modified by environmental factors short of destruction of the organism. Others, such as crop yield in plants, may be very strongly influenced by environmental factors such as cultivation, use of fertilizers, and other standard agricultural practices. All possible intermediate situations occur.

It should finally be added that, while Johannsen's definition of a pure line is not strictly applicable to animals except in rare cases (because it depends upon self-fertilization), substantially the same result (homozygosity) can be obtained by close inbreeding (such as brother-sister matings), and this is a standard practice in animal breeding.

13. THE MAJOR PROBLEMS OF STATISTICS

Several of the major problems of statistics will be discussed below. These are: the problem of *central tendency*, or the selection of a single figure to represent a whole array of data; the measurement of *typical dispersion*, or the selection of a figure to represent the tendency of the series of data to vary from the mean; the problem of *probability*; and, finally, the *testing of the reliability* of statistical data. But before taking up these problems, it may be well to discuss a few very fundamental statistical concepts.

SOME FUNDAMENTAL CONCEPTS Perhaps the most basic concepts in statistics are the *population* and the *sample*. A population, from the statistical viewpoint, is somewhat different from the population of common experience, and it can perhaps be best understood in contrast to the sample. The actual material of an experiment is a sample. Thus the 8023 plants which Mendel studied in his yellow-green cross comprised a sample. However, no sample is valued for its own sake. The experiment was considered worth while because the experimenter had confidence that it indicated what would happen in *any* cross of varieties of peas with yellow and green cotyledons. The population then, consists of all possible crosses of peas with yellow and green cotyledons. A statistical population need not even be made up of living things, or even of things: there can be a population of events. Thus a statistician may speak of a population of tosses of a coin.

From the foregoing, it should be evident that it would rarely, if ever, be possible to measure a population, or any of its attributes, directly. It would be patently impossible to make all potential crosses of a particular kind or all possible tosses of a coin, because a statistical population is generally infinite. Yet, in studying any sample, what we are really interested in is getting some ideas about the population, some basis for generalization. These inaccessible characteristics of the population are called *parameters,* while the calculated characteristics of the sample are called *statistics*. The importance of a statistic is that it is the best estimate available of the corresponding parameter. Accordingly, it is clear that great care must be used to assure that the sample is a good one, not biased so as to misrepre-

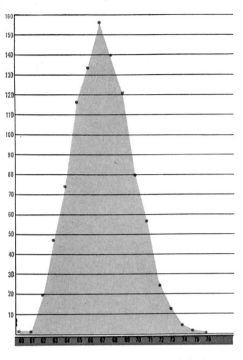

Fig. 28. *A frequency polygon of Quetelet's data. The several points are simply plotted and then connected by straight lines.*

sent the population from which it is drawn. Each separate unit in a sample is called a *variate*.

Some of the basic problems of *frequency distribution* should be already understood from elementary mathematics; however, they may be reviewed here in part. In this connection, one thinks first of graphic presentation of the data by the frequency polygon (fig. 28), the histogram (fig. 29) and other types of graph used to represent the number of units in each of the several classes of a variable. Any such distribution is characterized by a *range*, which is described by the smallest and largest numbers. Thus the range of heights in Quetelet's study was from 60 inches to 76 inches. If such a range is divided into a series of equal intervals, and the number of variates in each interval is recorded, then one has a frequency distribution.

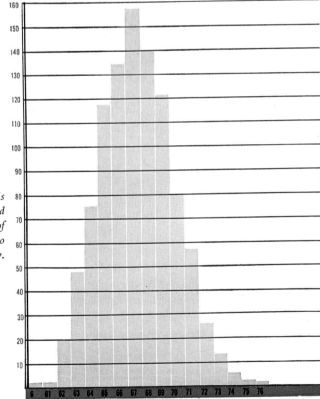

Fig. 29. *Histogram of Quetelet's data. Each class is represented by a column, the height of which is proportional to the class frequency.*

One of the most important concepts associated with frequency distribution is that of the *class interval*. The various measurements in a series are not ordinarily used just as originally recorded: they are grouped into classes for convenience in study, and *all of the members of a class are treated as though they had the value of the midpoint of the class*. Thus, Quetelet may not have measured any soldiers who were exactly 62 inches tall, but every one of the twenty soldiers who measured between 61.5 and 62.4 inches was treated as though his height were exactly 62 inches. This introduces some inaccuracy into any subsequent calculations using these figures, but it greatly increases the comprehensibility of the data. It makes it possible to present the data on heights of French soldiers with only seventeen figures instead of 1000 figures. But this can give a valid result only if the class interval be small enough that really unlike measurements are not lumped together—confounded, in the language of statisticians. Thus there is a conflict between the need for a small number of classes (for comprehensibility) and the need for many small classes (for accuracy). There is no simple guide to the selection of an appropriate class interval, but in general there should be not less than six to eight nor more than sixteen to twenty classes in a series. The selection of an appropriate class interval is plainly one of the most important decisions to be made in any statistical study.

MEASUREMENT OF CENTRAL TENDENCY We may now return to the problem of measurement of central tendency—the selection of a single figure to represent the whole array of data. Three measures of central tendency are in common use: the *median*, the *mode*, and the *mean*. If one arranges all of the measurements in order from the smallest to largest, then the middle member of the series is the median. Or, if there is an even number of variates, then the median is taken as the average of the two variates at the middle. Its symbol is m_d. The median in Quetelet's example is 67. The median is useful when only a rough idea of the point about which the variates cluster is needed; however, it is not adapted to further statistical treatment because it is not influenced by the magnitudes of any other variates.

The *mode* is by definition the class most frequently represented, and it forms the peak of a frequency polygon (fig. 28). It is numerically equal to the median in symmetrical distributions, as it is in Quetelet's example, 67. And like the median, it is not adapted to further statistical manipulation because its value is not influenced at all by the variates in non-modal classes.

Much the most useful measure of central tendency is the *mean*, or arithmetic average. There are other kinds of means, but the simple arithmetic mean is the most widely applicable of them. To calculate it, one simply adds up all of the variates and then divides by the number of variates. In Quetelet's example that would mean adding the heights of all of the soldiers and then dividing by 1000. It turns out to be very close to the median and mode, 67.2. The symbol for the mean is $\overline{m}$ (read m bar), and its general formula is $\overline{m} = \Sigma x / N$. In this formula, x stands for each individual variate. Σ (the Greek letter sigma) is the summation sign, and the expression "Σx" means, add up all values of x. N is simply the total number of variates. Thus the formula is simply a generalized statement of a simple process which everyone learns in grade school.

When the data are arranged in a frequency table, a more wieldy formula may be used: $\overline{m} = \Sigma fx / N$. In this formula, all symbols have the same meanings as in the general formula, but x now stands for each class value and f for the frequency, that is, number of items, in each class. Thus in Quetelet's example Σfx means $(2 \times 60) + (2 \times 61) + (20 \times 62) + (48 \times 63) \ldots \ldots$ While this may, on first acquaintance, appear more complicated than the original formula, still it makes it possible to calculate the average from seventeen simple products rather than from the 1000 original measurements. Thus, the whole calculation becomes:

x	f	fx
60	2	120
61	2	122
62	20	1240
63	48	3024
64	75	4800
65	117	7605
66	134	8844
67	157	10519
68	140	9520
69	121	8349
70	80	5600
71	57	4047
72	26	1872
73	13	949
74	5	370
75	2	150
76	1	76

$$\overline{m} = \Sigma fx/1000$$
$$= 67207/1000$$
$$= 67.2$$

$$\overline{67207} = \Sigma fx$$

Another type of average which is sometimes useful in the statistical study of genetic problems is the *geometric mean*. This is calculated by multiplying the variates, then extracting the square root. This is particularly useful in problems involving growth, and will be used below in chapter 10.

All of these measures of central tendency give numerical expression to the observed fact that the variates tend to cluster about a single point, like the shot in Galton's pinball machine. They are, then, all intended to give one sort or another of an average impression of the sample under study. Indeed, statistics is often referred to as the science of averages.

MEASUREMENT OF DISPERSION But, quite as important as the tendency of the variates to cluster about a central point is their tendency to deviate from the mean. The problem of the measurement of typical dispersion is to select a single figure which best represents this tendency. The most obvious estimate of the tendency to dispersion is the average deviation, which is given by the expression $\Sigma(x-\overline{m})/N$. These symbols mean much the same as before. The expression $x-\overline{m}$ is the difference between the mean and any particular variate. The summation sign means that all such differences are to be added together. In making this calculation it is, of course, necessary to neglect the sign of these deviations, because, by definition, the sum of the deviations from the mean is zero. By treating all deviations as positive, a positive sum is obtained and is then divided by N, the total number of variates. In Quetelet's example, the average deviation is 2.03 inches.

By far the most useful measure of typical deviation is the *standard deviation*, symbolized by s. [This is sometimes given as σ (lower case sigma), but it is generally preferable to reserve the Greek letters for parameters, while using Latin letters for statistics]. The formula for the standard deviation is $s = \sqrt{\Sigma d^2/N}$, where d stands for each deviation from the mean. Thus it may be seen that the standard deviation is simply the square root of the average squared deviation. For small samples, this formula is generally modified to $s = \sqrt{\Sigma d^2/(N-1)}$. The reason is that a small sample is unlikely to include a proportional representation of the population extremes, and hence dividing by N leads to an underestimate of the actual variability of the population. Such an error, which is inherent in the nature of the sample or in the manner of its treatment, is called a *bias*. A compensating factor, in this case N-1, must be used if misleading conclusions are to be avoided. This is an important correction factor with samples of 20 or fewer variates, but it becomes progressively less important with larger samples, and serves no useful purpose with a sample so large as Quetelet's.

As usual, this formula can be modified for use with tabulated data, and it then becomes, $s = \sqrt{\Sigma fd^2/N}$. This means that the deviation of each class from the mean is squared and the square multiplied by the class frequency; these summed squares for the several classes are added, and the total is divided by N, the number of variates, thus giving the average squared deviation; finally the square root is taken, and this is the standard deviation. The calculation of the standard deviation in Quetelet's example is given at the bottom of the page.

It may be asked, what would one have if he failed to extract the square root? Actually, this quantity, $\Sigma d^2/N$, is an important measure of variability, and it is called the *variance*. It is, by definition, the average of the squared deviations from the mean. But it may be noted that the variance, being a squared number, is not directly comparable to the original data. By extracting the square root of the variance (thus getting the standard deviation), the original units are restored, and the various figures are now directly comparable. While the analysis of variance forms a very important chapter in books on statistics, it need not be treated in an introductory course in genetics. For present purposes, the standard deviation is a much more important statistic.

THE STANDARD ERROR   The value of the mean of a sample is that it is the best available estimate of the population mean. But how good an estimate is it? Had Quetelet measured several samples of French soldiers, as many means would have been obtained. It is important to have some estimate of how closely a particular sample mean approximates the population mean. Because a series of sample means themselves form a normal probability curve, it is possible to calculate a standard deviation of the mean. As about 68 per cent of the variates in a normal distribution differ from the mean by no more than one standard deviation, the chances are then better than two to one that a particular sample means does not differ from the popu-

Class	d	f	d2	fd2
60	7.2	2	51.84	103.68
61	6.2	2	38.44	76.88
62	5.2	20	27.04	540.80
63	4.2	48	17.64	846.72
64	3.2	75	10.24	768.00
65	2.2	117	4.84	566.28
66	1.2	134	1.44	192.96
67	0.2	157	0.04	6.28
68	0.8	140	0.64	89.60
69	1.8	121	3.24	392.04
70	2.8	80	7.84	627.20
71	3.8	57	14.44	823.08
72	4.8	26	23.04	599.04
73	5.8	13	33.64	437.32
74	6.8	5	46.24	231.20
75	7.8	2	60.84	121.68
76	8.8	1	77.44	77.44

$$s = \sqrt{\Sigma fd^2/N}$$
$$= \sqrt{6500.2/1000}$$
$$= \sqrt{6.500}$$
$$= 2.55$$

$$6500.20 = \Sigma fd^2$$

lation mean by more than its standard deviation, which, because of its importance, is called by a special name, the *standard error*. The standard error is thus simply the standard deviation of the mean. It may be calculated by a special formula, $s_{\bar{m}} = s/\sqrt{N}$, where $s_{\bar{m}}$ is the standard error, and other symbols have their usual meanings. Thus in Quetelet's example, the calculation is:

$$s_{\bar{m}} = s/\sqrt{N}$$
$$= 2.55/\sqrt{1000}$$
$$= 2.55/31.6$$
$$= 0.08$$

Hence it is probable that the sample mean is a good estimate of the population mean.

Frequently, it is desirable to compare the variability of two distributions whose means are not the same, as, for example, the number of bushels per acre yielded by a particular variety of open-pollinated corn and by a modern hybrid corn (to be discussed in chapter 10). For such a comparision, even the standard deviation is not always satisfactory, but there is an appropriate statistic, the *coefficient of variability*, V. This is calculated by multiplying the standard deviation by 100 and dividing by the mean. Thus the general formula is $V = 100s/m$, and it evidently leads to a percentage. In Quetelet's example, the coefficient of variability is 3.8 per cent. A word of caution is appropriate: because the units of measurement cancel out, some biologists have been led to compare the coefficients of variability of totally unrelated things. This is not justified. Only genuinely *related* distributions should be compared by this or other statistical methods; otherwise, results may be obtained which are mathematically impressive (to the uninitiated) but logically meaningless and misleading. Further, there is no statistical test to determine whether the difference between two coefficients of variation is significant or random.

CHARACTERISTICS OF THE NORMAL PROBABILITY CURVE Sufficient statistical tools have now been developed to permit a more accurate characterization of the normal probability curve than was presented above. In an ideal normal probability curve, the mean, the mode, and the median all coincide. Now if one measures off on the horizontal axis a distance equal to one standard deviation on each side of the mean and erects perpendicular lines to the curve, several more characteristics become apparent. First, the perpendiculars intersect the curve at the points of inflection, at which the direction of the curve changes from concave to convex. Second, the area between these perpendiculars under the curve includes about 68 per cent of the entire area under the curve. As the area under the curve is proportional to N, this means that 68 per cent of the individuals in the sample deviate from the mean

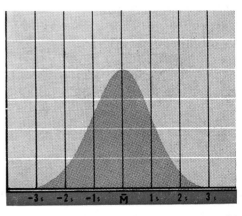

Fig. 30. *An ideal normal probability curve. Positive and negative deviations from the mean of one, two, and three times the standard deviation are marked. The area under the curve is proportional to* N.

by no more than one standard deviation, plus or minus. The tails of the curve fall off rapidly from the points of inflection, with the result that about 95.5 per cent of all of the variates fall within two standard deviations of the mean. As the rest of the curve slopes very gently, about 99.7 per cent of the variates are included within three standard deviations of the mean (fig. 30). As a result of these facts, it may be said that the curve is completely described by only three statistics (or actually parameters, since the *ideal* curve is under discussion), the mean, the standard deviation, and the number of variates, N. Since this is true, any description of a sample in terms of these statistics carries with it the inference that the sample is drawn from a population which is adequately described by a normal probability curve, and hence that an ideal curve based upon the sample mean and standard deviation describes the population *better than the original data.* Thus, if a sample approximates a normal probability distribution, much is gained in comprehensibility by reducing the data to this simple curve, fully described by three simple statistics.

THE LAWS OF PROBABILITY Another fundamental problem of statistics which is also important for genetics is that of *probability*. Probability may be defined as *the ratio of successful events to all possible events*. A few examples should make this clear. If a coin is tossed, it may be either "heads" or "tails," so that there are two possible events, but only one of these, let us say "heads," can be considered as a success in any given toss. Thus the probability of getting "heads" is

$$0.5 \left(\frac{\text{successes}}{\text{successes} + \text{failures}} = \frac{0.5}{0.5 + 0.5} = 0.5 \right).$$

Similarly, if prospective parents have a supply of blue-trimmed baby clothes, the birth of a boy will be a considered success, and the probability is thus one-half. But if a die is tossed, any number from one to six might turn up. If three be taken as a success, then,

the probability of success will be $1/6$. Or if a single seed from a self-fertilized hybrid *Aa* plant is grown, it might be the product of any one of four possible fertilizations, *AA*, *Aa*, *aA*, or *aa*. Since three of the four fertilizations lead to the dominant phenotype, the probability of getting a dominant will be $3/4$, while the probability of getting a recessive will be $1/4$. Thus probability is always expressed on a scale from 0 to 1, with 0 corresponding to impossibility, 1 to certainty, and the intervening fractions to intermediate levels of probability.

However, problems of probability are more commonly concerned with the joint probabilities of two or more events, each of which separately follows the law discussed in the preceding paragraph. How is the joint probability to be determined? The answer to this question depends upon the relationship between the events under study. If they are mutually exclusive, or in some other way mutually dependent, then they follow the *addition theorem*, which states that *the probability of the occurrence of one or the other of two (or more) mutually exclusive events is the sum of their separate probabilities*. Returning to a previous example, in the tossing of a coin, "heads" and "tails" are mutually exclusive, hence the probability that one or the other will be obtained on a particular toss is the sum of the separate probabilities, or $1/2 + 1/2 = 1$, or certainty. Again, if a die is tossed, and if either a three or a four may be regarded as a success, then the probability will be $1/6 + 1/6 = 1/3$. If two, three, and four could all be regarded as successes, then the probability of getting any one of these would be $1/6 + 1/6 + 1/6 = 1/2$. Again, if any number from one to six is considered as a success, the probability would be $1/6 + 1/6 + 1/6 + 1/6 + 1/6 + 1/6 = 1$, or certainty, which is obviously true.

Let us apply the addition theorem to a genetic example. In man, curly hair is dependent upon a gene *C*, which must be homozygous (CC) in order to cause curly hair. The heterozygous genotype (Cc) leads to more limited expression of the character, waviness, while the other homozygous type, cc, leads to straight hair. (This theory is not universally accepted.) Thus, if two wavy-haired people marry, it is known that they are both heterozygous. And so four types of fertilization are all equally probable: CC, Cc, cC, and cc. Because a particular zygote could not have more than one of these genotypes, they are mutually exclusive. The probability of a particular child being curly-haired is thus 1/4, while the probability of his being wavy-haired is 1/2. Now, if the parents wish to regard either of these phenotypes as a success (and the straight-haired phenotype as a failure), the probability of success will be $1/4 + 1/2 = 3/4$. Some traits discussed in chapter 2 lend themselves to similar analysis.

On the other hand, a series of events may be independent of one another, in which case they follow the *multiplication theorem*. The multiplication theorem states that *the probability of the occurrence of two or more independent events is the product of their separate probabilities*. If two coins are tossed simultaneously, for example, the way one falls is independent of the way the other falls. Possible combinations are HH, HT, TH, TT (HT and TH are both written to indicate that either coin might be "heads." Thus there are two ways to get the combination, and it could be written 2 HT). The probability of "heads" on either coin is 1/2, hence the probability of getting two "heads" is $1/2 \times 1/2 = 1/4$. Similarly, the probability of getting a head and a tail will be given by the same calculation. But there are two ways to get this combination, and as they are mutually exclusive, their combined probabilities must be added. Thus the whole calculation is $(1/2 \times 1/2) + (1/2 \times 1/2) = 1/2$.

APPLICATIONS The probability theorems apply in the same way to throws of two dice. Thus, if a three and a four are wanted, the probability of each is 1/6, and their combined probability is 1/36. But there are two different combinations of three and four as either number may turn up on either die, and so the complete calculation is $(1/6 \times 1/6) + (1/6 \times 1/6) = 1/18$. But if a double three is wanted, there is only one way to get it, and so the probability is simply $1/6 \times 1/6 = 1/36$.★

One of the most obvious applications of the multiplication theorem to genetic problems is in the calculation of F_2 ratios. Returning to Mendel's dihybrid cross, for example, the ratios can be easily calculated from data on the monohybrid components. The probability of any F_2 plant having round seeds is 3/4, and that of having wrinkled seeds is 1/4. Similar probabilities apply to yellow or green cotyledons, respectively. Hence the probabilities of the combinations may be calculated as follows:

Round-yellow	$3/4 \times 3/4 = 9/16$
Round-green	$3/4 \times 1/4 = 3/16$
Wrinkled-yellow	$1/4 \times 3/4 = 3/16$
Wrinkled-green	$1/4 \times 1/4 = 1/16$

★ It may be noted in passing that these calculations show why the patron of a gambling house is always a sucker. Suppose that the customer has bet that a seven will turn up when a pair of dice is thrown. Three combinations of numbers will give this: one and six, two and five, or three and four. Each may be obtained in two different ways, and so their combined probabilities amount to 1/6. Thus the customer's probability of winning is only 1/6. But the house does not suffer such a liability: it has not bet on a particular combination, but only that the customer loses. Hence the probability of the house winning is 5/6, for every combination that would mean failure for the customer means success for the house. All of this is based upon the frequently unwarranted assumption that the game is honestly run. If the house is dishonest, the odds against the sucker may be truly staggering.

Similarly, in a trihybrid, the probability of any particular dominant is 3/4 and that of the corresponding recessive is 1/4. Thus the range of probabilities will be:

Phenotype	Probability equation
ABC	$3/4 \times 3/4 \times 3/4 = 27/64$
aBC	$1/4 \times 3/4 \times 3/4 = 9/64$
AbC	$3/4 \times 1/4 \times 3/4 = 9/64$
ABc	$3/4 \times 3/4 \times 1/4 = 9/64$
Abc	$3/4 \times 1/4 \times 1/4 = 3/64$
aBc	$1/4 \times 3/4 \times 1/4 = 3/64$
abC	$1/4 \times 1/4 \times 3/4 = 3/64$
abc	$1/4 \times 1/4 \times 1/4 = 1/64$

These results are the same as those obtained by experiment, by the Roman square, or by the expansion of a binomial, and the concurrence of so many different approaches to the same problem lends very strong support to the validity of the laws of Mendel, as well as attesting the usefulness of the multiplication theorem for genetic studies.

TESTS OF RELIABILITY The final major problem of statistics to be discussed here is that of the *testing of reliability*. Before the reliability of a set of data can be tested, it is necessary to have a standard against which the data can be checked. This is done by first setting up what seems to be a reasonable hypothesis for the explanation of the phenomenon under study. Then one calculates the ideal result, as required by the hypothesis, and this calculated or "expected" set of values serves as a standard to which observed values are compared. Examples will serve to clarify this. Mendel's hypothesis for the cross between varieties of peas with yellow and with green cotyledons (as well as for the other monohybrid crosses) was that these phenotypes were based upon a single pair of genes with one (for yellow) completely dominant over its allele and that the observed numbers did not differ significantly, but only by chance, from the calculated numbers. Prior assumptions, which are

as important as an expressed hypothesis, include segregation of genes in the formation of gametes, random fertilization, and equal viability of all types of zygotes. As demonstrated in chapter 2, this leads to an expectation of three yellows to one green in the F_2 of such a cross. As Mendel raised 8023 plants in this F_2, an exact 3 : 1 ratio would be given by 6017.25 yellows and 2005.75 greens. This, then, is the standard value to which the results of the experiment must be compared. Similarly, in the case of the dihybrid cross between round-yellow and wrinkled-green varieties, the same assumptions and a hypothesis of two pairs of alleles with complete dominance leads to an expectation of a 9 : 3 : 3 : 1 ratio. As Mendel raised 556 F_2 plants in the experiment, this would lead to an expectation of 312.75 round-yellow, 104.25 round-green, 104.25 wrinkled-yellow, and 34.75 wrinkled-green. This, again, is a series of standard values against which the observed results must be checked.

For purposes of comparison of calculated and observed values, they may be tabulated as shown at the top of page 59. Inspection shows that none of these deviations is very large, and probably anyone would agree that a total deviation of only 10 in 8000 in the monohybrid cross is quite consistent with the hypothesis being tested. Probably much the same could be said of a deviation of 10 in 1000. But what of 10 in 500? or 10 in 100? or 10 in 50? or 10 in 30? Where is one to draw the line? In order to provide a quantitative answer to this question, the English statistician Karl Pearson (and some other statisticians) devised the chi-square method.

The chi-square of a set of data is obtained by squaring the deviation of each class, dividing by the expected class value, and then adding all such quotients together. The general formula is $\chi^2 = \Sigma d^2/c$, in which χ is the Greek letter chi; Σ is, as usual, the sum-

Monohybrid cross

	yellow	green
Calculated	6017.25	2005.75
Observed	6022	2001
Difference	4.75	−4.75

Dihybrid cross

	RY	rY	Ry	ry
Calculated	312.75	104.25	104.25	34.75
Observed	315	101	108	32
Difference	2.25	−3.25	3.75	−2.75

mation sign; d^2 represents the squared class deviations; and c represents the corresponding calculated or expected values (sometimes e is used instead of c). The calculation is easily made in tabular form, and the examples presented above will be carried through in that fashion. First the monohybrid example as shown by (A) below. Note that the fractions of the expected numbers and the differences were rounded off. This introduces a small inaccuracy, but where such large numbers are concerned, the inaccuracy is vanishingly small, and the gain in convenience is great. The tabulation for the dihybrid cross is somewhat more complex, but no different in principle as shown by (B) below.

INTERPRETING THE CHI-SQUARE So chi-squares have been calculated. But what bearing have chi-squares on testing of reliability or of the goodness-of-fit of the observed data to the hypothesis? Note that perfect agreement between the observed and calculated values for an experiment would lead to a chi-square of zero, and that the value of chi-square increases as the deviations become greater, or as the data give less and less support to the hypothesis. A low chi-square, then, means that the observed data are consistent with the hypothesis under question. If a quantitative experiment be repeated many times, different numerical results will be obtained each time, with the various results falling on the normal probability curve. Over two thirds of these (68 per cent) will fall within one standard deviation of the mean value, and these will have low chi-squares. Another 27 per cent of the trials will fall within two standard deviations of the mean value. These will

(A)

	Observed	Expected	Deviation	d^2	d^2/c
Yellow	6022	6017	5	25	0.0042
Green	2001	2006	−5	25	0.0125
					0.0167 = χ^2

(B)

	Observed	Expected	Deviation	d^2	d^2/c
RY	315	313	2	4	0.0125
rY	101	104	−3	9	0.0865
Ry	108	104	4	16	0.1538
ry	32	35	−3	9	0.2647
					0.5127 = χ^2

have moderate chi-square values. Finally, the remaining 5 per cent of the repetitions of the experiment will deviate from the mean value by more than two standard deviations, and will have large chi-square values. Thus, a low chi-square indicates that the data are not inconsistent with the hypothesis which is being tested. A large chi-square, however, indicates a significant deviation, which may have been caused by an error in the hypothesis. Restated, a large chi-square indicates that the data do not support the hypothesis. As the chi-square is a ratio, it is independent of the numbers of a particular experiment. That is, experiments involving very different numbers may lead to identical chi-squares, and this means that in each case there is an equal probability or P value. But the chi-square method is not applicable to very small samples, in which the expected frequency for any class is under 5. Also, the chi-square method cannot be used with percentages, because these infer a sample size of 100, which will usually be quite misleading. Tables of chi-squares and corresponding P values have been calculated and Fisher's table is reproduced here, in part, as table 6.

DEGREES OF FREEDOM   In a dihybrid experiment, there are twice as many phenotypic classes as in a monohybrid experiment.

Even with comparable deviations, one would expect a larger chi-square in dihybrid and more complicated experiments. It is clearly necessary to compensate for this in interpreting the chi-square, and one does it by tabulating the chi-squares according to *degrees of freedom.* Ordinarily, the number of degrees of freedom is one less than the number of classes. Thus there is one degree of freedom in the monohybrid example and three degrees of freedom in the dihybrid example. The meaning of this can be clarified with a simple example. Suppose that there are ten beans in a jar, and that they are to be withdrawn in not more than two tries. On the first try, there is complete freedom to withdraw anywhere from zero to ten beans. But once the first group has been withdrawn, the second is determined: it must be the remaining number. If four beans were taken the first time, six will have to be taken the second time. Thus, with two classes, there can be only one degree of freedom.

USE OF THE CHI-SQUARE TABLE   Sufficient tools have now been developed to permit the use of the chi-square table and the interpretation of the information so obtained. The degrees of freedom are listed in the left-hand column, and on the same horizontal row with each is a series of chi-square values. For the monohybrid experiment dis-

Table 6.   Values of P (top line) for Various Values of Chi-Square (vertical columns) and for Various Degrees of Freedom (N')

The degrees of freedom are one less than the number of classes.

(Table 6 is abridged from Table III of Fisher: Statistical Methods for Research Workers, published by Oliver and Boyd Ltd., Edinburgh, by permission of the author and publishers.)

N'	P=0.99	0.98	0.95	0.90	0.80	0.70	0.50	0.30	0.20	0.10	0.05	0.02	0.01
1	0.00016	0.00063	0.0039	0.016	0.064	0.148	0.455	1.074	1.642	2.706	3.841	5.412	8.635
2	0.0201	0.0404	0.103	0.211	0.446	0.713	1.386	2.408	3.219	4.605	5.991	7.824	9.210
3	0.115	0.185	0.352	0.584	1.005	1.424	2.366	3.665	4.642	6.251	7.815	9.837	11.341
4	0.297	0.429	0.711	1.064	1.649	2.195	3.357	4.878	5.989	7.779	9.488	11.608	13.277
5	0.554	0.752	1.145	1.610	2.343	3.000	4.351	6.064	7.289	9.236	11.070	13.388	15.086
6	0.872	1.134	1.635	2.204	3.070	3.828	5.348	7.231	8.558	10.645	12.592	15.033	16.812
7	1.239	1.564	2.167	2.833	3.822	4.671	6.346	8.383	9.803	12.017	14.067	16.622	18.475
8	1.646	2.032	2.733	3.490	4.594	5.527	7.344	9.524	11.030	13.362	15.507	18.168	20.090
9	2.088	2.532	3.325	4.168	5.380	6.393	8.343	10.656	12.242	14.684	16.919	19.679	21.666
10	2.558	3.059	3.940	4.865	6.179	7.267	9.342	11.781	13.442	15.987	18.307	21.161	23.209

cussed above, a chi-square value of 0.0167 was obtained. As there is only one degree of freedom, we look it up in the first horizontal line of the table. It falls between two values, 0.016 and 0.064. At the head of each vertical column is a decimal fraction, the P value for the chi-squares in its column. These are, respectively, 0.90 and 0.80. The probability that these data are actually random deviations from a population based on the monohybrid hypothesis being tested is, therefore, quite high. One could easily interpolate to get the exact P value, but it is usually considered sufficient to denote it as a P value greater than 0.8. Similarly, a chi-square of 0.5127 was obtained from the dihybrid experiment. Looking this up under three degrees of freedom, we find that the P value is greater than 0.90.

The final question is, how low a P value can be accepted as being not inconsistent with the hypothesis. Because repetitions of an experiment lead to a family of values which describe a normal probability curve, an occasional result will have a very low P value even when the hypothesis is correct. But if the hypothesis is correct, about two thirds of the experiments should vary from the mean value by no more than one standard deviation, and should have high P values, while 95 per cent of the experiments should deviate from the mean value by no more than two standard deviations, and should have P values of 0.05 or higher. For this reason, statisticians generally consider that a P value of 0.05—the 5 per cent level of probability—or higher indicates that the data are not inconsistent with the hypothesis being tested. A lower P value does not prove that the hypothesis is wrong: it merely shows that the data do not support the hypothesis, and that the experiment ought to be repeated. But if several repetitions all lead to a low P value, one looks for defects in the hypothesis. A deviation which fails to support the hypothesis tested is said to be *significant,* that is, it signifies that there

is reason to doubt the validity of the hypothesis upon which the calculation was based, and it is necessary to look for causes not considered in the original hypothesis, nor in the calculations based upon it.

Let us re-state this. If the P value is 85 per cent, it means that numerous repetitions of the experiment should lead to deviations as large as that observed in 85 per cent of the trials, due to chance deviations alone, if the hypothesis is correct. Similarly, with any P value, the probability of as great or greater deviation in further repetitions of the experiment is equal to P. And if chance alone can produce so large a chi-square, there is no need to look for other causes of deviation.

Questions and Problems

The following 9 questions deal with Mendel's data. For each, calculate the chi square, state the number of degrees of freedom, then look up the P value and write it, together with a statement of whether the data support Mendel's hypothesis. In each instance, the F_2 data will be given.

1. 5474 round, 1850 wrinkled peas.
2. 6022 yellow, 2001 green cotyledons.
3. 705 grey-brown, 224 white seed coats.
4. 882 evenly inflated pods, 299 constricted seed pods.
5. 428 green, 152 yellow unripe pods.
6. 651 plants with axial inflorescences, 207 with terminal inflorescences.
7. 787 tall plants, 277 dwarf plants.
8. 315 round, yellow; 101 wrinkled, yellow; 108 round, green; and 32 wrinkled, green.
9. Finally, in the trihybrid cross, the F_2 consisted of 269 ABC, 88 aBC, 86 AbC, 98 ABc, 27 Abc, 24 aBc, 30 abC, and 7 abc.
10. Now state the appropriate hypotheses for the preceding 9 problems.
11. Define:

Addition theorem	Normal probability
Biometry	curve
Chi-square	Parameter
Coefficient of	Population
variability	Probability
Degrees of freedom	Pure line
Mean	Sample
Median	Standard deviation
Mode	Statistic
Multiplication	Variance
theorem	

The following data will be used in problems 12 through 14. A sample of 100 beans were weighed, giving the following results:

WEIGHT IN CENTIGRAMS	NUMBER OF BEANS
38	1
39	1
40	0
41	5
42	9
43	21
44	25
45	19
46	10
47	6
48	1
49	0
50	2

12. Calculate the mean weight of the beans.

13. Diagram the data with a frequency polygon and with a histogram.

14. Calculate the standard deviation and the standard error.

The following data will be used in questions 15–19. The lengths of tobacco flowers were measured and classified in 5 millimeter intervals. Four groups were measured, a short and a long parental group, an F_1, and an F_2. The following data were obtained:

NUMBER OF PLANTS

CLASS VALUE	SHORT PARENT	LONG PARENT	F_1	F_2
20	9			
25	133			5
30	28			27
35			3	79
40			30	136
45			58	125
50			20	132
55				102
60				105
65		1		64
70		19		30
75		50		15
80		56		6
85		32		2
90		9		

15. Calculate the mean, standard deviation, and standard error for the short parental group.

16. Now make the same calculations for the long parental group.

17. Make the same calculations for the F_1.

18. Make the same calculations for the F_2.

19. Finally, draw a series of frequency polygons summarizing these data.

20. A couple are expecting their first baby. What is the probability that the baby will be a boy?

21. A couple have a boy and they are expecting another child. What is the probability that the second child will also be a boy?

22. What is the probability that the next two children (not identical twins) will be boys? And what is the probability if the next two are identical twins?

23. Persons heterozygous for a gene T show a mild blood disorder called thalassemia minor. Persons homozygous for the same gene have a serious disease, thalassemia major, which is usually fatal early in life. Only homozygous recessives are completely normal. Two heterozygous persons marry. What is the probability that their first child will have thalassemia major?

24. What is the probability that the first child of the couple in question 23 will have the disease in either form?

25. Red hair is recessive to darker colors. Suppose that each of the parents in question 3 is dark-haired, but that each had a red-haired parent. What is the probability that their first child will have red hair and thalassemia minor? dark hair and thalassemia minor? dark hair and thalassemia major? red hair and thalassemia major? dark hair and thalassemia in either form? or red hair and thalassemia in either form?

References

Fisher, R. A., 1948. Statistical Methods for Research Workers. Tenth edition. Oliver and Boyd, London.

Johannsen, W., 1926. Elemente der exacten Erblichkeitslehre. Third edition. Gustav Fischer, Jena. The last edition of a classic of mathematical genetics which was originally published in 1909.

Mainland, Donald, 1952. Medical Statistics. W. B. Saunders Co., Philadelphia. A modern introduction to biometry.

Mather, Kenneth, 1947. Statistical Analysis in Biology. Second Edition. Interscience Publishers, New York.

Quenouille, M. H., 1950. Introductory Statistics. Butterworth-Springer, London.

Quetelet, L. A. J., 1871. L'Anthropométrie. Brussels. One of the founders of biometry summarizes his work.

Simpson, G. G., and Anne Roe, 1939. Quantitative Zoology. McGraw-Hill Book Co., New York.

Snedecor, G. W., 1946. Statistical Methods. Fourth edition. Iowa State College Press, Ames.

CHAPTER 6

Modifications of Mendelian Inheritance

I: Sex-Related Inheritance

Almost before the facts of elementary Mendelism were securely established, evidence began to accumulate that many types of genetic action existed which could modify the Mendelian ratios. A whole series of these are associated with sex in one way or another, and these will be the subject of the present chapter. But first, a review of the elementary facts of sex determination is in order.

14. THE CHROMOSOMES AND THE DETERMINATION OF SEX

The first step toward the understanding of the inheritance of sex was taken in 1891 by a German zoologist, H. Henking. In a cytological study of the bug *Pyrrhocoris* (fig. 31), he noted that the number of chromosomes was always uneven in males, although it was even in females. But he was unable to relate this fact to the determination of sex. Eleven years later, the American cytologist, C. E. McClung made similar observations in grasshoppers. At first, he misinterpreted the unpaired chromosome of the males, regarding it as an "accessory" chromosome, not

represented in the females. But he boldly postulated that the accessory chromosome might form the basis of sex determination. His researches during the following years played a major role in establishing the chromosomal mechanism of sex determination, which constitutes an important part of every textbook of elementary botany or zoology. Equally important in the development of this theory were E. B. Wilson and his associates. Concerning Wilson, late professor of zoology at Columbia University, Muller has said that "we geneticists (and) all . . . . who have acquired what we are pleased to regard as 'the modern genetic point of view,' see the phenomena of life through the eyes of Wilson."*

The main facts of the chromosomes in relation to sex determination can be summarized briefly. Henking and McClung both found, in their respective materials, that the males had 23 chromosomes and the

* By permission from Genetics, vol. 34, p. 1.

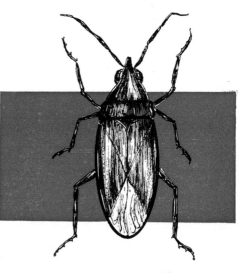

Fig. 31. *A pyrrhocorid bug.*

females 24. These existed in the cells not just as so many unrelated bodies, but as pairs of like chromosomes, or *homologues* (see chapter 3); twelve pairs in the females, eleven pairs plus an unpaired chromosome in the males. The eleven pairs of the male are homologous with the corresponding eleven pairs of the female. These chromosomes, with respect to which the sexes do not differ, are called *autosomes*. But the other one, paired in the female and unpaired in the male, was called the *X* chromosome by McClung. It is now commonly called the *sex chromosome*, or better yet, the *sex-differential chromosome*. When gametes are formed, the females can form only one type (with respect to kinds of chromosomes included), $11A + X$, if A stands for one autosome. But the males will form two types of gametes: all will contain 11 autosomes, but half will also have an X chromosome ($11A + X$), while the other half will get no representative of the X pair ($11A + O$). Mating can only lead to the parental types, with $22A + 2X$ giving the female and $22A + 1X$ giving the male phenotype. Thus sex determination

has the nature of a Mendelian backcross, with the female parent being homozygous and the male parent heterozygous. This simple *XX—XO* type of sex determination is diagrammed, with simple numbers, in figure 32.

Although the type of sex determination described above is widely distributed in the animal kingdom, there is a more common type. This is the *XX—XY* mechanism of sex determination, in which the X chromosome has an unlike mate, the Y chromosome, in the male. This is well exemplified by the common fruit fly, *Drosophila melanogaster*. As this species has eight chromosomes, the formula for a female is $6A + 2X$, while that for a male is $6A + X + Y$. Sex determination in *Drosophila* is diagrammed in figure 33. Man, with 48 chromosomes, is also a good example, in which the formula for a female is $46A + 2X$, and that for a male $46A + X + Y$. Comparison of figures 32 and 33 will show that there is no essential difference between the two. Each represents a Mendelian backcross, with *XX* being the homozygous parent in both, while *XO* is the

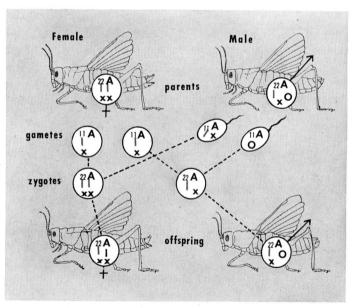

Fig. 32. *Sex determination of the XX—XO type, exemplified by the grasshopper. Note that in this figure and in figure 34, sex determination follows the pattern of a backcross.*

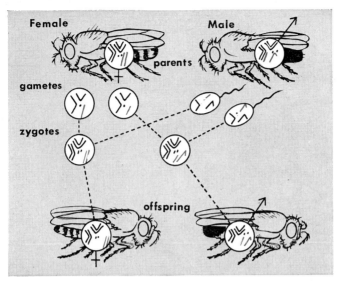

Fig. 33. *Sex determination of the XX—XY type, exemplified by* Drosophila. *The X and Y chromosomes are in color.*

heterozygous parent in the first case and *XY* in the second case. The demonstration that sex depended upon the segregation of such sex-differential chromosomes was the first successful proof of a relationship between a specific chromosome and a phenotypic character, although Weismann's ideas on this subject had been under discussion for many years.

15. SEX LINKAGE

The pattern of transmission of the *X* chromosomes from generation to generation is thus somewhat different from that of the autosomes. Hence one would expect that genes carried in the *X* chromosomes would also show a modified pattern of inheritance, parallel to that of the *X* chromosomes. Such a pattern was first reported in 1910 by T. H. Morgan of Columbia University, who was to become one of the most distinguished of American geneticists.

Morgan introduced the use of the fruit fly, *Drosophila melanogaster*, for genetic experiments. It was a very fortunate choice, for this fly with its rapid breeding (ten days to two weeks for a generation), with its numerous progeny, with its many inheritable variations, and its small chromosome number (2n = 8) has contributed a very large measure to our knowledge of heredity. In general, as discussed in chapter 2, reciprocal crosses give identical results in the F_1 and F_2. However, when Morgan made crosses between red-eyed and white-eyed flies, the reciprocal crosses gave strikingly different results, as shown at the bottom of the page. Morgan, with his remarkable insight, saw that these results would exactly parallel the distribution of the sex chromosomes, if it be assumed that the *Y* chromosome does not carry an allele for eye color. In figure 34, the transmission of *X* and *Y* chromosomes is indicated, with gene symbols inscribed in

P	red ♀ × white ♂	white ♀ × red ♂
F_1	red	red ♀ ♀ white ♂ ♂
F_2	2 red ♀ ♀ : 1 red ♂ : 1 white ♂	1 red ♀ : 1 white ♀ : 1 red ♂ : 1 white ♂

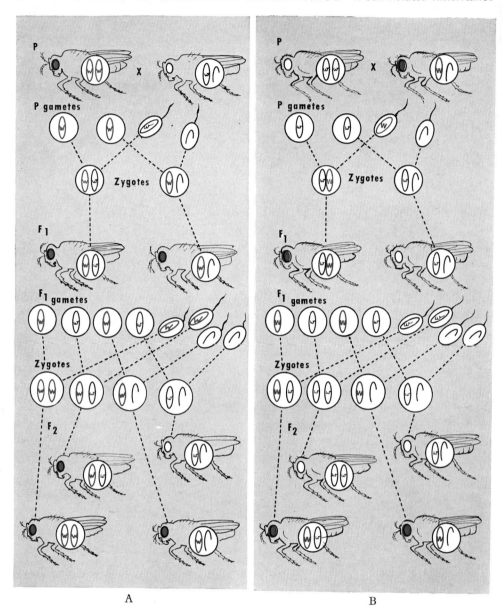

A

B

the X chromosomes in order to make this parallel as graphic as possible. The gene for red eye, the normal or *wild type* is symbolized by W, and the gene for white eye by w. The same thing may be done less graphically with gene symbols alone, as below. Here, o symbolizes the fact that the Y chromosome does not carry an allele for eye color:

P $\quad WW$ ♀ $\times$ wo ♂

F_1 $\quad Ww$ ♀ ♀ $\quad Wo$ ♂ ♂

F_2 $\quad$ 1 WW ♀ : 1 Ww ♀ : 1 Wo ♂ : 1 wo ♂

Fig. 34. *Sex-linked inheritance, exemplified by eye color in* Drosophila. *In 34 A, the female parent is red-eyed and the male parent white-eyed. In 34 B, the reciprocal cross is presented. In each instance, a chromosome with the gene for red is colored red, while a chromosome with the gene for white is black and white. Eye color corresponds to the actual phenotype.*

ww ♀ $\times$ Wo ♂

Ww ♀ ♀ $\quad wo$ ♂ ♂

1 Ww ♀ : 1 ww ♀ : 1 Wo ♂ : 1 wo ♂

Following Morgan's lead, the parallel between the inheritance of eye color and of the sex chromosomes should now be quite clear. He called this phenomenon *sex linkage*. Several secondary points should also be mentioned. First, note that eye color has nothing to do with sex. The sole criterion of sex linkage is that the gene is on the *X* chromosome. While there is no theoretical reason why a sex-linked character should not be associated with primary or secondary sex characters, actually no known sex-linked gene has any phenotypic connection with sex. Second, note that in the second cross, *ww* ♀ × *Wo* ♂ the sons all have the phenotype of their mother and the daughters all have that of their father. This phenomenon of criss-cross inheritance has given rise to the false idea that sons inherit principally from their mothers and daughters principally from their fathers. Actually, there is no difference between the sexes with respect to autosomal inheritance, and sex-linked genes show the criss-cross pattern only when the mother is homozygous recessive and the father dominant.

THE *Y* CHROMOSOME AND HETEROCHROMATIN Some change in terminology is necessary also. Up to this point it has been possible to classify any genotype as either homozygous or heterozygous. But how is one to classify the males which have only one allele for eye color? A third term, *hemizygous* or *simplex*, is used for this purpose. The phenotype is determined by a simplex gene even though the gene would behave as a recessive in a heterozygote. No normal allele is present to mask its effect. Finally, it may be asked whether it is typical that alleles are missing from the *Y* chromosome. For *Drosophila*, the answer is generally yes. There is only one known instance in which a *X*-borne gene has an allele in the *Y* chromosome. This is the gene *bobbed*, a recessive gene which causes shortening of the bristles of the fly (fig. 35). When this gene was first studied, it was thought to be sex-limited (capable of expression only in one sex—see below) because only females showed the trait. Male offspring of *bobbed* females, all of which ought to be simplex and so show the trait, were phenotypically normal. But it turned out that they were normal because the *Y* chromosome carries the normal allele of *bobbed*. Races which have the bobbed mutant on the *Y* chromosome have since been found, and these show the expected phenotype when a *bobbed X* chromosome is also received from the mother. There are also a few genes for male fertility on the *Y* chromosome. In contrast to this paucity of genes, nearly 150 genes are known in the *X* chromosome of *Drosophila*. It is clear, then,

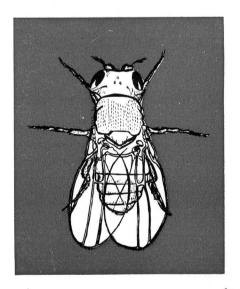

Fig. 35. *Bobbed bristles. The bristles are much reduced and the abdomen is rather deformed.*

that the Y chromosome is relatively inert, as judged by the frequency of identifiable genes. It has been shown that there are other differences in chemical constitution and in biological behavior between the Y chromosome and the others. The Y chromosome is said to be *heterochromatic*, in contrast to the *euchromatic* X and autosomes. It should be added that heterochromatin is distributed to some degree among all of the chromosomes, and that it may be quite active if judged by some other criterion than frequency of mutant genes in it.

Nor is the "inertness" of the Y chromosome equal in all species. It seems, in general, to contain a higher proportion of heterochromatin than do the autosomes or the X chromosome; yet it may be much more "active" in some species than in *Drosophila*. In man, for example, an organism far less well known genetically than *Drosophila*, around 20 Y-linked genes are known.

THE HETEROGAMETIC SEX   In the examples discussed above, the females can produce only a single type of egg with respect to sex-determining capacity. They are therefore said to be *homogametic* (Greek—similar gametes). The males, however, all produce two types of gametes, and so are said to be *heterogametic* (unlike gametes). It may be asked whether this is a necessary relationship, or whether this relationship between the sexes could be reversed. Actually, the latter is the case, although male heterogamety is much the most usual thing. But female heterogamety is found in the Lepidoptera, some fishes, the Urodela, Reptilia, and Aves. In all of these, the male has a perfectly matched pair of sex-differential chromosomes, while the female has either an odd chromosome or an imperfectly matched pair. Sometimes the XX-XO or XY terminology is applied to these cases, with XX meaning a male and XO or XY meaning a female. But often a different set of symbols is used, with WW meaning a male and WZ meaning a female. But, with either set of symbols, the essential meaning is the same: males produce a single type of gamete with respect to sex determination, while the heterogametic females hold the balance of sex determination.

The question of heterogamety does not arise with respect to most of the higher plants, as the sexes are not separate (they are monoecious). Hence sex-differential chromosomes are not possible. But there are a good many species in which the sexes are

Fig. 36.   *The currant moth,* Abraxas grossulariata. *On the left, normal; on the right, lacticolor. (Redrawn from Punnett.)*

Fig. 37. *Slow and rapid feathering, a sex-linked trait in the chicken. These are ten-day-old chicks, but the one on the left has the genotype for rapid feathering and the one on the left that for slow feathering. The effect is principally on the wing and tail feathers, which are shown in color. (Redrawn from Hutt.)*

separate (dioecious), and in these there are sex-differential chromosomes. Just as in animals, male heterogamety is the rule, but female heterogamety also occurs, as in the strawberry.

FEMALE HETEROGAMETY AND SEX LINKAGE Inheritance of sex-linked characters does not differ in principle if the organism studied shows female heterogamety. The patterns of inheritance are just as given above for eye color in *Drosophila*, but the sexes are reversed. Examples will make this clear. In the currant moth, *Abraxas grossulariata* (fig. 36) normal dark wing color, *L*, is dominant over lacticolor, *l*, a pale, milky-colored variety. The reciprocal crosses may be described in Mendelian symbols, with the sex symbols added for clarity, thus:

A second example may be taken from the domestic chicken. In Leghorns and some other breeds, the chicks feather out much more rapidly than is characteristic of most breeds. The difference is most striking from eight to ten days after hatching. At this age, a typical slow-feathering chick will have no tail feathers and only very small wing feathers. Yet a rapid-feathering chick of the same age may have tail feathers as much as an inch long, and wing feathers extending to the tail or even beyond it (fig. 37). It has been shown that the difference depends upon a single pair of sex-linked genes, with slow-feathering, *K*, being dominant over rapid-feathering, *k*. Thus the reciprocal crosses will show the pattern given at the top of page 70.

P   *Lo* ♀ × *ll* ♂
    dark   lacticolor

F₁   *lo* ♀ ♀ *Ll* ♂ ♂

F₂   1 *Ll* : 1 *ll* : 1 *Lo* : 1 *lo*
    dark   lacticolor   dark   lacticolor
        ♂ ♂   ♀ ♀

lo ♀ × *LL* ♂
lacticolor   dark

Ll ♂ ♂   *Lo* ♀ ♀

3 dark   : 1 lacticolor
1 *LL* : 1 *Ll* : 1 *Lo* : 1 *lo*
  1 ♂ ♂   1 ♀ ♀

P KO ♀ $\times$ kk ♂ kO ♀ $\times$ KK ♂
   slow   rapid   rapid   slow

F_1 kO ♀♀ Kh ♂♂ KO ♀♀ $\check{K}h$ ♂♂
   rapid   slow   slow   slow

F_2 1 Kh : 1 kk : 1 KO : 1 kO 3 slow   : 1 rapid
   slow   rapid   slow   rapid   1 KK : 1 Kh : 1 KO : 1 kO
       ♂♂   ♀♀   1 ♂♂   :   1 ♀♀

SEX LINKAGE IN MAN Sex linkage is a well-known phenomenon in man. R. R. Gates, in his comprehensive treatment of human genetics, lists no less than forty-five sex-linked genes in man, including such diverse things as color blindness, hemophilia, toothlessness, deafness, and white forelock. Not all of these are backed up by equally good evidence, but red-green color blindness will serve as a good example. Normal vision, C, is dominant over color blindness, c. (Actually, there are several types of color blindness, and the hereditary basis for the differences will be discussed in chapter 8.) Using these symbols, reciprocal crosses could be diagrammed just as for the animal crosses discussed above. But this would not be very meaningful, for experimental crosses cannot be set up in man: the student of human heredity must depend upon the study of family histories, which are called *pedigrees*. Rarely indeed will the investigator know the genotypes of the persons in a pedigree (at the outset of a study), and so it is necessary to use pedigree symbols which describe the phenotypes of the members of the family. By studying such pedigrees individually, and by the use of special methods to be discussed in the final chapter of this book, the geneticist hopes to gain an insight into the mode of inheritance of human characteristics.

The method may be introduced with an actual pedigree for color blindness in man (fig. 38). In this pedigree, each circle represents a female and each square a male. These symbols are preferred to the usual symbols, ♀ and ♂, because the latter become confusing in complicated pedigrees in which many supplementary symbols must be used.

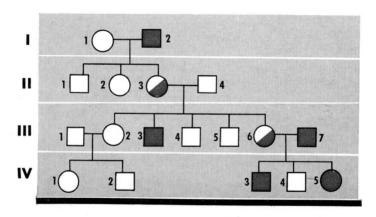

Fig. 38. *This is a pedigree for color blindness, a typical sex-linked trait in man. Circles represent females, squares males. The colored symbols represent affected persons.*

Roman numerals identify the successive generations, while Arabic numerals identify the individuals in each generation. Married persons are connected by a horizontal line, as in the case of I—1 and 2, II—3 and 4, III—1 and 2, and III—6 and 7. The children are attached to this marriage line in a definite way. Thus II—1, 2, and 3 are the children of I—1 and 2; and III—2, 3, 4, 5, and 6 are the children of II—3 and 4. Finally, persons showing the phenotype under study are indicated by a blackened symbol. When analysis of a pedigree shows that a particular person must be a heterozygous carrier of a recessive gene, the appropriate symbol may be half filled in. Thus, we know, from the facts of sex-linked inheritance, that the women designated as II—3 and III—6 must have been heterozygous, or else they could not have had color-blind sons. But we do not presume to make such a judgment on incomplete information: III—2 has a 50 per cent probability of carrying the gene (because her mother was heterozygous), yet the data do not prove that she carries it, and so her circle is left blank.

Note that the girl indicated as IV—5 is color-blind. It has often been said that color blindness (and other sex-linked traits) are limited to men. This is not true. But a woman must be homozygous in order to show a sex-linked recessive, while a man need only be simplex. It is clear that the latter is much the more probable situation, especially for a rare gene, but both are possible and have been observed many times.

Another sex-linked trait in man which has received a great deal of attention is hemophilia, the bleeder's disease. As is well known, this disease is characterized by a very slow clotting time, so that affected boys may bleed to death even from very minor wounds. Because it has played an important role in modern European history through its effect on the Bourbon and Romanoff families, it is often called the royal disease. But the disease is not so selective: it strikes at all levels of society, but usually without great publicity. If a hemophilic man is fortunate enough to live long enough to leave children, all of his daughters will be carriers but all of his sons will be normal, for they get their only X chromosome from their mother. But when a carrier daughter marries, half of her sons will get the normal X chromosome and the other half will be bleeders (fig. 39).

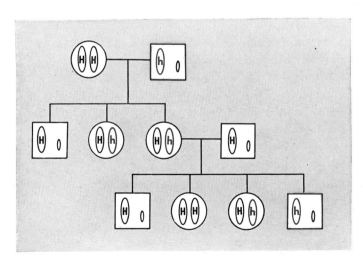

Fig. 39. *A pedigree for hemophilia in man. Chromosomes carrying the defective gene are colored red, and symbols for diseased persons are also red.*

71

Or, more exactly, each son has a fifty-fifty chance of being normal or a bleeder. Half of the daughters will again be carriers. Note that a hemophilic girl could be born only if a carrier woman should marry a hemophilic man. Actually, few hemophilics survive to marriageable age, and so one would expect such marriages to be exceedingly rare. But a few have been reported, and yet no certain cases of hemophilic girls are known. The usual interpretation of this has been that the homozygous condition, *hh*, is even more severe than the simplex condition, so that it causes the death and resorption of the embryo in the uterus. This has been supported by studies showing that hemophilic men tend to have fewer daughters than expected, and from evidence of interrupted pregnancies in such marriages. But the evidence is incomplete, and at least some of the reported cases of hemophilic girls may be genuine.

Recently, a type of hemophilia has been studied in dogs, the clinical manifestations of which appear to be identical with those of human hemophilia. This canine hemophilia is also inherited as a sex-linked recessive. It has been demonstrated that, in these dogs, homozygous hemophilic females are no more severely diseased than are their hemizygous brothers. It has been inferred from these facts that the same must be true of man, and that the rarity of hemophilic girls is a simple consequence of the rarity of marriages of genotype *Hh* × *ho*. This may be correct, but analogies between different species can be misleading, and it would appear that additional evidence from *human* families is still needed to settle the question.

16. SEX-INFLUENCED INHERITANCE

Sex-influenced inheritance should be contrasted with sex linkage, for they have nothing in common beyond their similar names. All genes which are carried by the *X* chromosome are said to be sex-linked because their inheritance parallels that of the sex-differential chromosomes themselves. Actually, all known sex-linked genes lead to phenotypes which have nothing to do with sex, although there is no theoretical reason why this should be so. Sex-influenced characters, on the other hand, are characters which may be expressed differently in the two sexes, even when their genotypes are identical. Secondary sex characters in general are examples. The most common expression of sex influence is that dominance is reversed between the sexes. Again, all known examples are autosomal, although there is no theoretical reason why there should not be some sex-linked genes for sex-influenced characters.

SOME EXAMPLES OF SEX INFLUENCE Ayrshire cattle (fig. 40) show a pattern of spotting on a white background, and the spots are always either red or mahogany. This difference is based upon a single pair of genes, cattle of genotype *MM* being mahogany and white, while those of genotype *mm* are red and white. But what of the heterozygotes, *Mm*? Males of this constitution are mahogany and white, while the females are red and white. This will lead to some modification of the ordinary Mendelian ratios, as may be seen by diagramming a standard monohybrid cross:

$$P \quad \underset{\text{mahogany}}{MM} \quad \times \quad \underset{\text{red}}{mm}$$

$$F_1 \quad Mm$$

♂♂ mahogany

♀♀ red

$$F_2 \quad \text{1 } MM \quad \text{2 } Mm \quad \text{1 } mm$$

♂♂ 3 mahogany : 1 red

♀♀ 1 mahogany : 3 red

In the above diagram, phenotypic descriptions have been abbreviated by omitting

Fig. 40. *A group of Ayrshire cattle, showing much of the range of spotting pattern which characterizes this dairy breed. (Courtesy of C. Chris Bridges, Editor, The Ayrshire Digest.)*

"white," which is part of each phenotype. The reciprocal crosses are identical in the F_1 and F_2, because the gene is autosomal. If one looks at only one sex, then the usual Mendelian ratios appear unmodified. *But the dominance relationships are reversed between the sexes.*

Another typical example of sex-influenced inheritance is afforded by the inheritance of horns in sheep. Dorset sheep are always horned in both sexes, while neither sex bears horns in Suffolk sheep. If Dorsets and Suffolks are crossed, the male offspring are horned and the females are hornless. On interbreeding the F_1 sheep, an F_2 is obtained in which the males show a ratio of three horned to one hornless, while the females show a ratio of three hornless to one horned (fig. 41). Here again, it is clear that a perfectly typical transmission of the genes has occurred, but the gene for horns is dominant in males, while its allele is dominant in

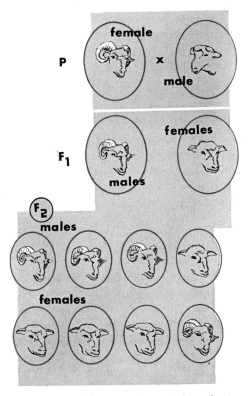

Fig. 41. *Inheritance of horns in sheep, showing sex-influenced dominance.*

females. If the gene for horns be H and its allele h, then the cross becomes:

P HH × hh
   Dorset   Suffolk
   horned   hornless

F_1 Hh

   ♂ ♂   horned

   ♀ ♀   hornless

F_2 1 HH 2 Hh 1 hh

♂ ♂   3 horned : 1 hornless

♀ ♀   1 horned : 3 hornless

Pattern baldness in man should probably also be included in this category. There are many types of baldness with different causes, some hereditary, others not. Pattern baldness is the type in which the hair first recedes around the temples, then thins and disappears from the top of the head, and finally leaves a fringe of hair low on the head (fig. 42). Analysis of many pedigrees has shown that the genotype BB leads to baldness in either sex; bb leads to normal hair in either sex, but Bb leads to baldness in men and to normal hair in women. Some authorities consider this to be a *sex-limited* gene, *sex limitation* being an extreme type of sex influence in which a particular phenotype can be expressed only in one sex. In the example at hand, it has been shown that the gene B gets its effect in collaboration with the male sex hormone. Yet numerous published pedigrees include bald women (see R. R. Gates, Human Heredity), and it may be that the small quantity of male sex hormone normally present in the blood of women is sufficient to cause baldness in women of genotype BB, but insufficient to cause it in women of genotype Bb. In support of this, there is an often-cited case of a woman who, after developing a tumor of the adrenal cortex, became bald, developed a beard, and a deep voice. The adrenal cortex normally produces a small amount of male sex hormone. After surgical removal of the tumor, her voice again became feminine, her beard disappeared, and she grew a normal head of hair. Assuming that she had the genotype Bb, the case fits the theory beautifully.

SEX-LIMITED INHERITANCE   Sex-limited inheritance is, as mentioned above, an extreme type of sex influence in which a particular phenotype can be expressed only in one sex. As the genes are autosomal (in all known cases, though it is difficult to see why this should be so), all genotypes should occur with identical frequencies in both sexes, yet the physiological differences between the sexes (probably in regard to sex hormones) are such that certain genotypes can be expressed only in one sex. Thus in the sulfur butterflies (genus *Colias*—fig. 43) males are always yellow, but females may be either yellow or white. White color in the females depends upon a dominant gene, W, so that females of genotypes WW or Ww are white, while those of genotype ww are yellow. But males of all three genotypes are yellow. Thus, white is a sex-limited color. The genotype of a male can be determined by crossing him to a yellow female. The results may be tabulated as follows:

Female Parent		Male Parent	Female Offspring
ww	×	WW	Ww all white
ww	×	Ww	1 Ww : 1 ww
			1 white : 1 yellow
ww	×	ww	ww all yellow

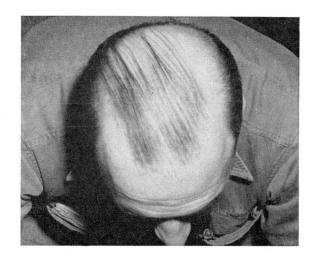

Fig. 42. *Pattern baldness.*
(Courtesy of Dr. John J. Reedy.)

Fig. 43. Colias philodice, *a*
sulfur wing. This specimen is a
gynander, with the right side being
female and white, while the
left side is male and yellow. The
white patches on the left side
may be physiologically female
also. (From Remington, in
Advances in Genetics, vol. 6.)

Fig. 44. *Polymorphism in Papilio polytes. Upper left, male; upper right, cyrus type female,*
which resembles the male; lower left, romulus type female; and lower right,
polytes type female.

Only the female offspring are taken into account, as only they can show the color difference.

A similar, but more complex, case occurs in the swallow-tail butterfly, *Papilio polytes*. All of the males and some of the females show a color pattern called the cyrus type. But females may also show two additional patterns, the romulus and polytes types, which mimic the patterns of species of the related genus *Pharmacophagus*. The species is thus said to be *polymorphic*, a fairly common thing in the Lepidoptera. This polymorphism has been shown to depend upon two pairs of genes, *A* and *B*. If a question mark be used to indicate that the second gene of a pair might be either dominant or recessive, then females of genotype *A?B?* are the romulus type; those of genotype *A?bb* are the polytes type; and those of genotypes *aaB?* or *aabb* are cyrus type. But the males are always cyrus irrespective of genotype (fig. 44).

THE PHYSIOLOGICAL BASIS OF SEX LIMITATION A well-known feature of the plumage of chickens throws much light on problems of the type discussed above. In most breeds of chickens, the males have long, pointed, fringed feathers on the neck, tail, and some other parts, while the females

have shorter, rounded feathers which lack a fringe (fig. 45). However, there are some exceptional breeds. Sebright bantams are always hen-feathered, irrespective of sex, while the males may be either cock-feathered or hen-feathered in Campine, Hamburg, Silver-laced Wyandotte, or Game breeds. It has been demonstrated that hen-feathered cocks carry a dominant gene, *Hf*. Thus chickens of either sex will be hen-feathered in the presence of genotype *HfHf* or *Hfhf*. But the homozygous recessive, *hfhf*, will be hen-feathered if female and cock-feathered if male. Thus it is clear that typical breeds of chickens are always homozygous recessive; Campines and other breeds in which the cocks may show either type of feathering include both alleles in the breeding population; while Sebrights are homozygous dominant.

Up to this point, no data on feathering have been introduced which are not comparable to data of the previous examples. But suppose that one castrates a homozygous *HfHf* chicken. Irrespective of the original sex of the chicken, cock feathering develops after the next molt. It appears, then, that the gene for type of feathering collaborates with the sex hormones in the production of the phenotype. Either sex hormone, in combi-

Fig. 45. *Hen feathering and cock feathering. The hen is on the right, the cock on the left. Note the long, pointed neck and tail feathers of the cock, also the larger comb and wattles.*

nation with the gene *Hf* produces hen feathering; but in the absence of any sex hormones, the same gene leads to cock feathering (or, rather, to an intermediate condition which is similar to cock feathering). Similarly, the genotype *hfhf*, which ordinarily leads to cock-feathered males and hen-feathered females, leads to cock feathering in all castrated chickens, regardless of sex. If such a castrated chicken is treated with male sex hormone, the cock feathering is more perfectly developed; if treated with female sex hormones, hen feathering is developed. Thus it is clear that cock feathering is a developmental norm, deviations from which may be achieved by an appropriate combination of genotype and sex hormones. The genotype *hfhf* leads to cock feathering in the presence of the male sex hormone, and to hen feathering with the female sex hormone. This is characteristic of most breeds of chickens. But the gene *Hf* prevents cock feathering in the presence of either sex hormone and so causes hen feathering.

These are secondary sex characters *par excellence*, and it seems probable that secondary sex characters in general are inherited in a comparable way, with sex hormones playing a major role in the expression of the characters. In man, the secondary sex characters (those traits which are associated with sex but which do not play a direct role in reproduction) include such things as high voice, well-developed breasts, and broad hips and pelvis in women; while in men they include deep voice, rudimentary breasts, development of beard, and narrower hips and pelvis. The involvement of the sex hormones in the development of these characters is indicated by the fact that the secondary sex characters do not develop until time of puberty. Furthermore, tumors of the adrenal gland, the cortex of which ordinarily produces some male sex hormone, may result in the development of male secondary sex characters in women.

EMBRYONIC DIFFERENTIATION OF SEX   In view of the mode of embryonic development of the sex organs, the above facts are not unexpected. For the details, reference should be made to embryology texts such as that of Arey, but it may be mentioned that the gonads and some accessory organs develop from an embryonic rudiment called the genital ridge. In its earliest stages, this is morphologically identical in both sexes, and embryologists have long referred to it as the *indifferent stage*, meaning a stage in which sex of the embryo cannot be diagnosed, and from which it might conceivably develop in either direction.

Numerous facts are available which indicate that the embryo actually is "indifferent" at this stage, and that the genetic system (*XX* or *XY* chromosomes) determines the actual course of development through the agency of the sex hormones. The oldest line of evidence is supplied by the phenomenon of freemartins in cattle. Twins of like sex in cattle are perfectly normal. Of twins of unlike sex, the male is always normal, but the female usually shows many male characteristics, especially internally, and is sterile. Such a "female" is called a *freemartin*. F. R. Lillie of the University of Chicago has investigated this, and he has found that freemartins result when the two placentas fuse, thus permitting exchange of blood between the two embryos. As the male hormone is secreted somewhat earlier than the female hormone, it causes the genetically female embryo to develop along male lines. The placentas do not always fuse, however, and in these cases the female calves are perfectly normal. In salamanders, it has been possible to achieve complete sex reversal by hormone treatments of developing larvae, and similar results have been obtained with opossums. Thus it seems clear that in vertebrates, at least, the differentiation of both primary and secondary sex characters is mediated by the sex hormones.

INVERTEBRATES AND THE DEVELOPMENT OF SEX-LIMITED CHARACTERS The discussion of sex limitation began with examples from the invertebrates, yet data for the explanation of the phenomenon have been drawn entirely from the vertebrates. To what extent can this explanation be applied to butterflies and other invertebrates? Actually, it is difficult to imagine any mechanism other than sex hormones through which sex influence and sex limitation might operate. The existence of secondary sex characters in many invertebrates has often been interpreted as evidence that they must have sex hormones. But, although other hormones of invertebrates have been successfully studied, no convincing demonstration of sex hormones among invertebrates has yet been made. The question is thus in a most unsatisfactory state.

17. MATERNAL INHERITANCE

One final sex-related modification of the Mendelian ratios is provided by the phenomenon of *maternal inheritance*. In examples of this phenomenon, the phenotype of offspring is determined by the genotype of their mother. As a result, all Mendelian ratios are perfectly normal, but they are delayed by one generation. This rather rare situation is to be contrasted with *maternal impressions*, so common in folklore, but never substantiated by scientific analysis. Maternal impressions are the supposed phenotypic effects upon children resulting from experiences of the mother, especially from emotionally charged experiences. Unlike the fictitious maternal impressions, maternal inheritance is a well-established phenomenon, though not a common one.

COILING IN SNAILS The best worked-out example of maternal inheritance is the inheritance of direction of coiling in snails. If a snail shell is held with the base toward the observer, the direction of coiling must be either counterclockwise (dextral) or clock-

wise (sinistral). Boycott has investigated this in the genus *Limnaea*. Starting with pure-breeding strains, a dextral snail may be used as female parent and a sinistral as male parent. The F_1 will all be dextral, so that the gene for dextrality appears to be dominant, and we would expect a 3 : 1 ratio in the F_2. In fact, however, if the F_1 snails are self-fertilized, the F_2 is also entirely dextral, and the expected three to one segregation occurs in the F_3. Now what of the reciprocal cross? If a sinistral snail be used as the P generation female and a dextral as the male, the F_1 will all be sinistral. But again, the F_2 is all dextral and the F_3 shows the three to one segregation.

It was Sturtevant who first pointed out that this situation would be perfectly understandable if it be assumed that the character has already been determined in the egg *before fertilization*, and hence that *the phenotype of the offspring corresponds to the genotype of the mother*. That the asymmetry of the snail is determined extremely early is quite probable, for the mitotic spindle of the cleavage divisions is already asymmetrical. If the gene for dextrality be S and that for sinistrality s, then all of the F_1 must be Ss. Those from the first cross were dextral because their mother was SS while those from the second cross were sinistral because their mother was ss. In either case the F_2 will be dextral because of dominance in the heterozygous mothers. But, although all of the F_2 are dextral, their genotypes are SS, Ss, and ss in a 1 : 2 : 1 ratio. The F_3 from the first two classes will be dextral, while those from the last class will be sinistral. Thus all expected ratios are obtained, but one generation later than expected because the character is determined in the unfertilized egg, and hence by the genotype of the mother. The entire series of crosses is illustrated in figure 46.

GYNANDRISM A more complex case of maternal inheritance has been studied in the

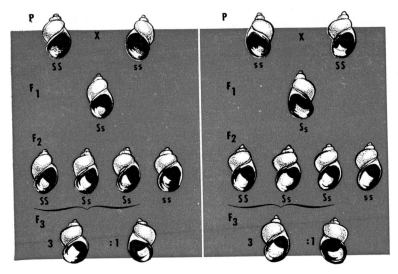

Fig. 46. *Inheritance of direction of coiling in snails. Note that the expected 3:1 ratio occurs in the F₃.*

silkworm, *Bombyx mori*, by R. B. Gold-schmidt and K. Katsuki, and will be discussed here principally to show how a really complex genetic problem can be solved. In the silkworm, the sexes are ordinarily separate, but occasional specimens are found which present a mosaic of male and female parts. These mosaic organisms, called *gynanders* (originally gynandromorphs), are *not* hermaphrodites. An hermaphrodite has no sex-differential chromosomes, and has complete, functional sets of reproductive organs of each sex. But the gynanders do not have two complete reproductive systems. Rather there is a mosaic of parts. The commonest situation in these moths is a bilateral mosaic, one side being male, the other female. Gynanders (see fig. 43) are known also in other insects and crustaceans. They have been reported also in birds and mammals, but because of the sex hormones it is more probable that these are intersexes, another kind of sex anomaly which will be discussed in chapter 15.

Gynanders in *Drosophila* have been particularly instructive. If a zygote has two X chromosomes, it should develop into a female fly. But a chromosome may sometimes fail to participate in the anaphasic movement so that it is not included in a daughter nucleus. If this should happen to an X chromosome, anomalies of sex would be expected. If one of the first two blastomeres gets the normal chromosome complement, and the other loses an X chromosome, then the first cell and its descendants will have the female genotype while the XO cell and its descendants will have the male genotype. If one cell loses a chromosome at the second division, then one fourth of the resulting fly should show male characteristics. The later in embryonic life such an accident of mitosis happens, the smaller will be the resulting sector of male tissue. That this is the basis for formation of gynanders in *Drosophila* can easily be shown by setting up a stock of females heterozygous for a sex-linked mutant, such as white eyes, *Ww*. All such flies should have red eyes, but occasionally such a fly will show male characteristics on one side, and about half of these sex mosaics have a white eye on the male side. As there is an equal probability of losing either chromosome of the pair, this is just what should be expected if the theory is correct.

79

But in *Bombyx* gynandrism is not a result of an occasional mitotic accident: it is hereditary in certain strains. The critical crosses may be tabulated as follows:

A. normal $\female$ × mosaic $\male$ → F_1 normal
B. mosaic $\female$ × normal $\male$ → F_1 mosaic
   F_1 normal × normal ⟶ F_2 normal
   F_1 mosaic × mosaic ⟶ F_2 normal
   F_1 mosaic × normal ⟶ F_2 normal
   F_3 from any F_2 → 3 normal : 1 mosaic

Inspection will show that these data are strictly comparable to the data on coiling of snails. The F_1 moths show a phenotype corresponding to the mother's genotype; dominance shows up in the F_2; and in the F_3, a typical monohybrid segregation is obtained. And so this example of gynandrism must be based upon a single recessive gene, with maternal determination of the phenotype.

But how does the gene work? Male tissue should have two X chromosomes and female tissue should have an XY pair (moths have female heterogamety). How is this possible? To investigate this, Goldschmidt and Katsuki crossed a mosaic strain with a non-mosaic strain carrying the autosomal recessive gene, *oily*. They found that *oily* (which gives the skin a translucent, oily appearance) also formed mosaics, and that the two were independent. That is, a silk worm could be a gynander but not oily; or a gynander and oily throughout; or a gynander with one half *oily* and the other half (in two different combinations) normal-skinned; or finally the worm could be normal with respect to sex (male or female) while a mosaic for the skin character. Thus the two conditions showed independent segregation, not only between different members of a brood, but also between the right and left halves of the same individual! The only possible basis for independent segregation is found in independent fertilizations, and so a cytological

study was made to determine whether the egg of the silkworm could possibly be a double zygote. In the Lepidoptera, the polar bodies are not actually extruded from the egg, but rather the polar nuclei become reduced in size and degenerate in the cytoplasm of the egg, leaving only one fertilizable nucleus in the egg. But, in the eggs of mosaic strains, it was found that the nucleus of the second polar body remained full-sized, so that the egg contains two fertilizable nuclei. If these differ in genetic content, a mosaic will result. If one contains an X chromosome and the other a Y chromosome, a sex mosaic will result. And because this retention of an extra nucleus occurs in the ovary of the mother, the mosaic character must show maternal inheritance.

In this chapter, many very diverse phenomena have been treated. The element common to all of them is dependence upon sex, but it may be well to conclude by emphasizing the differences between them. Sex linkage is concerned with the transmission and expression of genes which are carried on the sex-differential chromosomes. These need not be sexual characters. Sex influence, on the other hand, is concerned with autosomal genes which are expressed differently in the two sexes. These are commonly secondary sex characters, as are the sex-limited characters, which can be expressed in only one sex. Finally, maternal inheritance (or, better, maternal determination of the phenotype) is concerned with those characters which are already embryologically determined in the unfertilized egg. As the subsequent development of such characters is already determined before sperm entrance, the phenotype of the offspring must correspond to the genotype of the mother. All of these diverse phenomena show deviations from the ordinary pattern of Mendelian inheritance, deviations which are correlated in different ways with sex.

Questions and Problems

1. Define:

Autosome	Maternal impression
Criss-cross inherit-	Maternal inheritance
ance	Monoecious
Dioecious	Polymorphism
Euchromatin	Sex influence
Freemartin	Sex limitation
Gynander	Sex-differential
Hemophilia	chromosome
Heterochromatin	Simplex
Homologue	

2. In cats, the gene B subserves yellow coat color, while its allele b subserves black. The heterozygote, Bb, leads to a tortoise shell pattern. This pair of genes is sex-linked. If a tortoise shell female is crossed to a black male, what types of offspring should be expected, and in what proportions?

3. In the above cross, a tortoise shell kitten was included in the first litter. What was its sex? Why?

4. In the same cross, what is the probability of producing a black male? a black female?

5. A yellow female *Drosophila* is mated with a gray male. All of the female offspring are gray, while all of the males are yellow. What is the pattern of inheritance here? Draw chromosomal diagrams to illustrate.

6. What would be expected in the F_2 of the cross in question 5?

7. What would be expected if the F_1 females of question 5 were backcrossed to gray males?

8. A bald man marries a normal woman whose father was bald. What is the probability that their first son will be bald? What is the probability that their first daughter will be bald?

9. A woman whose father was hemophilic marries a normal man. What is the probability that their first son will be hemophilic? What is the probability that her first daughter will later have a hemophilic son?

Problems 10 through 12 deal with Ayrshire cattle.

10. A red and white cow whose father was mahogany and white is backcrossed to a red and white bull. Only red and white offspring result, regardless of sex. Give the genotypes of all of these cattle.

11. A mahogany and white cow gives birth to a red and white calf. What is the sex of this calf? How do you know?

12. A red and white cow gives birth to a mahogany and white calf. Can you specify the sex of this calf? Justify your answer.

13. If a horned female sheep is crossed to a hornless male, the male offspring are horned and the females are hornless. How could you prove experimentally that this is not based upon sex linkage?

14. How could you prove a male *Colias* to be heterozygous for color?

References

Ford, E. B., 1953. The genetics of polymorphism in Lepidoptera. Advances in Genetics, 5:43–88. A good, general review.

Goldschmidt, R. B., 1938. Intersexuality and development. American Naturalist, 72:228–242. A concise review.

Hutt, F. B., 1949. Genetics of the Fowl. McGraw-Hill, New York. Excellent treatment of sex linkage.

Komai, T. and A. S. Ae, 1953. Genetic studies of the pierid butterfly *Colias hyale poliographus*. Genetics, 38:65–72. Sex-limited dimorphism.

Lillie, F. R., 1916. The theory of the freemartin. Science, 43:611–613. This brief paper established the hormonal determination of freemartins.

McClung, C. E., 1914. A comparative study of the chromosomes in orthopteran spermatogenesis. Journal of Morphology, 25:651–749. A general review by one of the men who started it all.

Morgan, T. H., 1924. Heredity of embryonic characters. Scientific Monthly, 18:5–17. Summarizes most known cases of maternal inheritance.

Osborn, Dorothy, 1916. Inheritance of baldness. Journal of Heredity, 7:347–355. The first paper on a famous case of sex limitation in man. Now generally regarded as sex-influenced dominance.

CHAPTER 7

Modifications of Mendelian Inheritance

II: Lethal Genes

Fanciers of plants and animals always want to obtain pure-breeding varieties of exotic organisms, but this is not always possible. In pregenetic times, certain varieties were referred to as "ever-sporting," because they could not be made to breed true. A good example is afforded by yellow mice. The wild type coat color in mice is a salt and pepper pattern called *agouti*, after a South American rodent. This pattern is based upon hairs which are generally black, but which have a yellow band near the tip, giving a gray impression. In the yellow mice, the black pigment is missing, leaving the coat bright yellow. These mice have long been prized by breeders, but unfortunately they could not be made to breed true: yellows always had litters consisting of yellows and agoutis in a ratio of about two to one.

18. GENETIC LETHALITY

The problem of yellow mice was attacked genetically by L. Cuénot, a French geneticist, early in the present century. He demonstrated that the yellow mice do not breed true because they are always heterozygous, and the gene for yellow, A^Y, is dominant to

the gene for agouti, A (the capital letter is used because this gene is in turn dominant over certain other alleles). That this was true was shown by the fact that crosses of yellow mice to mice of other colors gave a one to one ratio. (Adding the results of eight large-scale experiments gave actual figures of 2378 yellow to 2398 non-yellow. Calculate the chi-square, and see how good this is!) But why should only heterozygous yellows occur? Where are the homozygotes which should make up 25 per cent of the F_2 of a simple monohybrid experiment? Cuénot first suggested that random fertilization did not apply here, sperm with the gene A^Y actually avoiding eggs with the same gene, but this was erroneous. It turned out that $A^Y A^Y$ zygotes actually do occur, but they do not survive long enough to be born. A clue was given by the fact that a cross of $A^Y A \times A^Y A$ gave progeny in a ratio of two yellows to one gray. When daily autopsies were performed upon a group of pregnant mice from this cross, it was found that about one fourth of the progeny were visibly abnormal and underdeveloped as early as the morula stage, and these all died and were resorbed by the eighth day. These were assumed to be the $A^Y A^Y$ embryos. Thus the cross may be symbolized as follows:

$$A^Y A \times A^Y A \rightarrow 1\ A^Y A^Y : 2\ A^Y A : 1\ A A$$
$$\text{dies} \qquad \text{yellow} \qquad \text{gray}$$

A gene capable of killing its possessor is appropriately called a *lethal* gene.

FREQUENCY OF LETHAL GENES   One might expect genetic lethality to be a rare thing, but study of the problem has revealed that it is surprisingly common. In a recent review of lethal genes in *Drosophila*, E. Hadorn listed about fifty such genes with respect to which some specific knowledge as to mode of gene action is available. It would be difficult to estimate how many others have been studied in this species, but it must run into the hundreds. F. B. Hutt lists twenty-one lethal genes in the fowl. Gates lists almost as many in man. Lethal genes may take their effect at any part of the life cycle, from the gamete to the adult. Gamete lethals are very common in plants, although they are unknown in animals. In the Jimson weed, *Datura stramonium*, for example, A. F. Blakeslee and his collaborators have found more than thirty gamete lethals. These obtain their effects in different ways: one prevents synapsis, thus leading to unbalanced chromosome complements; several cause the pollen tubes to burst (probably because of increased osmotic pressure); two cause premature germination of the pollen; several others prevent germination of the pollen altogether; and several cause slow growth of the pollen tubes, so that normal pollen has already fertilized the ovules before the defective pollen reach the ovules. Thus these data indicate specific physiologic channels through which the genetic effect is obtained.

In Hadorn's review, there are cited lethal genes of *Drosophila* which cause death in the embryo, larva, pupa, adult, or at the dividing time between two phases in the life cycle. A very common type of lethal genes in plants is albinism, in which the seedling develops without chlorophyll, and so starves to death. By culturing seedlings on artificial nutrient media, it has been possible to distinguish between two types of albinism: an absolute type in which no chlorophyll is ever developed, and a relative type in which chlorophyll is developed, but at a much later time than normal. The latter type is fully viable under the conditions of the experiment, but would be lethal in nature.

In man, lethals are known which strike in childhood, like retinoblastoma, a cancer of the retina which kills the victim by the age of five or six years. Others may strike much later in life, like inherited cancer or Huntington's chorea, which usually kills in middle life. The latter are usually not regarded as genetic lethals, for they obtain their effect sufficiently late in life that the victim is quite likely to die earlier from other causes. But there is no intrinsic difference between these genes and those that strike earlier. It may be said, then, that lethal genes are surprisingly common, and that they work through specific physiological channels which may be effective at any point in the life cycle.

TYPES OF LETHAL GENES   Up to the present, only recessive lethal effects have been mentioned, and this is the most common situation. However, there are two kinds of recessive lethals: some, like the gene for yellow color in mice, have a dominant phenotypic effect which is visible in heterozygotes. These have some times been called "dominant lethals," but they are better called recessive lethals with dominant effects in the heterozygote. Other recessive lethals have no visible effects in the heterozygous condition. These are very common in *Drosophila*. If sex-linked, they are also usually lethal when simplex, a fact which will be discussed more fully below.

Finally, there are some genuinely dominant lethal genes—genes which kill the bearer even in the heterozygous condition. These presumably must always arise by new mutation in the germ cells of a parent of the affected individual, and should not be passed on for more than one generation. How, then, can such a phenomenon be studied, and how can one establish the role of a gene? Lethality operates through specific physiological channels, and these are, at least potentially, subject to treatment. Heredity is not a magical curse (or blessing). The gene for retinoblastoma behaves as a dominant lethal in man, causing cancer of the retina in early childhood. It can be successfully treated by surgery (removal of the eyeball) if the operation is done before the tumor metastasizes to the brain. Some such operated children have grown up and raised families of their own, and their children show a one to one ratio of normals to affected children, as would be expected if the disease were caused by a dominant gene.

A distinction may also be drawn between lethal genes and *sublethal* or *semilethal* genes. Generally, genes which kill the bearer in embryonic or infantile stages are called lethals, while those which result in death later in life are called sublethals or semilethals. The names infer a distinction in severity rather than in timing, and the inference is frequently, though not always, justified. For the earlier a gene takes its effect, the more nearly 100 per cent of its bearers does it kill; and the later it takes its effect, the milder and more readily subject to treatment is it. In this connection, it should be mentioned that although susceptibility to infectious diseases is often inherited in man, these genes are not usually classed as lethals or sublethals, because an extrinsic factor (the infectious organism) is necessary for the development of symptoms.

Sex-Linked Lethals in *Drosophila* The sex-linked lethals of *Drosophila* are numerous, and they have been studied intensively because of their ease of recognition. They are lethal to males in the simplex condition, and hence the females act as carriers, but they do not become homozygous. If the symbol *l* be used for a sex-linked lethal gene and *L* for its normal allele, then the pattern of inheritance is the following:

$$Ll \times Lo \longrightarrow \underbrace{LL, \ Ll, \ Lo,}_{\text{normal}} \quad \underset{\text{dies}}{lo}$$

Thus it may be seen that a cross involving a sex-linked lethal results in a sex ratio of two females to one male. Of the females half are homozygous normal and half are heterozygous.

It may be well to introduce here a convention of notation which *Drosophila* workers have found useful, and which has also found favor with many other geneticists. The earliest geneticists used gene symbols which were based upon the name of the dominant member of each pair of characters. Later, it became apparent that most recessives are deviations from normalcy. In any organism, there are more gene pairs than there are convenient ways of describing normalcy, and so it became customary to use the initial of the name of the recessive character as a gene symbol. Finally, the *Drosophila* geneticists have agreed to designate the normal or "wild-type" alleles by a plus sign, while mutants, whether dominant or recessive, are designated by the usual letters. If confusion between different "plusses" is probable, then the corresponding symbols may be written with "plusses" as superscripts. Thus the cross diagrammed above becomes:

$$+ \, l \times + \, o \rightarrow + \, +, \ + \, l, \ + \, o, \ \underset{\text{dies}}{lo}$$

OR,

$$l^+ \, l \times l^+ \, o \rightarrow l^+ \, l^+, \ l^+ \, l, \ l^+ \, o, \ \underset{\text{dies}}{lo}$$

19. CAUSES OF LETHALITY

Lethal genes with dominant somatic effects are of especial interest because of the possibility that the somatic effects may be indicative of the mechanism of lethality. This hope is not always justified. In the case of the yellow mice, it is very difficult to see a connection between viability and so superficial a character as coat color. Yet it is probable that the disturbed pigment metabolism is symptomatic of a fundamental metabolic disorder, and only a proper experimental approach to its study is still lacking.

LETHAL GENES WITH DOMINANT EFFECTS IN THE HETEROZYGOTE Other examples have, however, been studied with more success. Dexter cattle afford a good example. Dexters are characterized by abnormally short legs and a somewhat shortened muzzle. If Dexters are crossed, one fourth of the progeny are Kerry cattle, a different breed which has normal skeletal structure; one half are Dexters, like the parents; and the remaining one fourth of the calves are stillborn, and are characterized by an extreme bull-dog like appearance. It is clear that lethality results from an extreme manifestation of the same developmental abnormalities which characterize the viable Dexter cattle. If D be used to symbolize the Dexter gene, then the cross becomes:

$$D+ \times D+ \rightarrow 1\ DD : 2\ D+ : 1+ +$$
$$ \text{dies} \quad \text{Dexter} \quad \text{Kerry}$$

The Kerry cattle are, of course, fully viable.

A comparable case in a plant was analyzed in the early days of genetics. A variety of snapdragons was available which had golden-colored leaves rather than the usual green. When these were self-fertilized, they gave a ratio of two golden to one green. By examining the early seedlings it was found that actually three phenotypes germinated in a ratio of one *yellow* to two golden to one green. Taking G as the symbol for the gene for Golden color, the cross is:

$$G+ \times G+ \rightarrow GG : 2\ G+ : 1+ +$$
$$ \text{yellow} \quad \text{golden} \quad \text{green}$$
$$ \text{dies}$$

The gene evidently causes an abnormality of the chlorophyll which is not sufficiently serious to prevent adequate nutrition in the heterozygous state, but which is lethal when homozygous.

A famous example in an animal is that of the creeper fowl. Creepers are chickens with abnormally short legs (fig. 47), and with other skeletal defects. They are always heterozygous. Embryological study of the chicks from the creeper × creeper cross shows that about 25 per cent of the chicks are grossly abnormal even in very early stages. Although the membranous bones are formed normally, cartilaginous replacement bone is formed extremely defectively or not at all. There are also abnormalities of circulatory development. Thus again, the cause of lethality in the homozygotes is indicated by the phenotype of the heterozygote.

The study of lethal genes with dominant effects has made it clear, then, that lethal genes operate by the disruption of specific developmental or physiological processes. Detailed embryological study of recessive lethals which have no effects in the heterozygote have led to similar conclusions. Hadorn lists numerous examples in *Drosophila* in which specific embryological defects are associated with specific genes. There is every reason to believe that adequate study would prove this to be true in all such cases.

Fig. 47. *Creeper fowl. Compare with figure 45, and note the extreme shortness of the legs.* (*Courtesy of A. M. Winchester.*)

20. LETHAL GENES IN MAN

The known lethal genes of man generally are effective late in fetal life or after birth. They range from such devastating lethals as amaurotic idiocy through sublethals like hemophilia to conditions such as cancer which strike so late in life that they usually are not classified as lethal genes. In addition to these well-known lethals of man, it is probable that many spontaneous abortions are caused by lethal genes, but these have not been studied adequately.

Fig. 48. *Brachydactyly in man. (From Komai, Journal of Heredity, vol. 44.)*

Two examples—retinoblastoma and hemophilia—have been discussed above in other connections. Additional examples may be added now. Amaurotic idiocy is characterized by progressive blindness and mental

deterioration, with death usually resulting within the first five years of life. This disease, for which no treatment is known, is inherited as a simple recessive. Not only is there no known effect of the gene in the heterozygous condition, but the parents of an affected child may actually be superior in intelligence and sound in general health.

Brachydactyly, the foreshortening of the fingers (fig. 48), is well-known dominant in man. It is fairly rare, and very few marriages between two brachydactylic persons have been recorded, but the indications are that the homozygous babies have grossly abnormal skeletal development and die *in utero*. Another interesting case of a lethal gene in man with a dominant effect in the heterozygote is afforded by a type of anemia called *thalassemia*, which is characterized by extremely defective red blood cells. Heterozygous persons show a mild form of the disease, thalassemia minor; while homozygous persons have the disease in its sublethal form, thalassemia major (fig. 49).

A lethal gene, then, is one which results in developmental or physiological reactions which cause the death of the organism. Such genes may be completely recessive, like many of the lethals of *Drosophila*. Or they may be dominant, like the gene for retinoblastoma in man. Still others are recessive with respect to lethality, but they have dominant phenotypic effects in the heterozy-

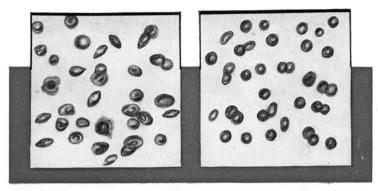

Fig. 49. *Thalassemia major (left) and minor (right). Note the different degrees of deformity of the red blood cells. (Based on photographs by Neel and by Neel and Schull.)*

gous condition. These include such examples as yellow coat color in mice, creeper fowl, and thalassemia in man. They are especially important, because their study may lead to an understanding of the causes of genetic lethality. Lethal genes may take their effect at any time during the life cycle from gamete to adult. The term "lethal," however, is generally reserved for those which kill early in the life cycle, with those which result in death at later stages being called "sublethal" or "semilethal." The whole array of types of genetic lethality has been found in man.

Questions and Problems

1. Define:

Agouti pattern	Seedling lethal
Dominant lethal	Sublethal gene
Gamete lethal	Zygote lethal
Lethal gene	

2. An anencephalic child (lacking a brain) was born, but died on the day of birth. The attending physician advised the parents that such a freak of nature would be unlikely to occur twice in the same family. Yet a second such child was born to the same couple. They also had a normal son, who was later married and also fathered an anencephalic child. How could you explain these facts? And do you think that the physician was adequately informed?

3. A female *Drosophila* has epithelial tumors. She is mated to a normal male, and the F_1 includes 35 females with tumors, 37 normal females, and 39 males, all of which are normal. Explain these results.

4. Albinism is a common recessive mutation in corn and many other plants. Yet the harvesters never see an albino plant in the corn fields. Why?

5. In crosses between Dexter cattle ($Dd \times Dd$), one fourth of the progeny are always stillborn. Why?

6. What is the genotype of the stillborn Dexters?

7. Suppose that death occurred in the stillborn Dexters at a much earlier stage—perhaps in the blastocyst stage. What would be the apparent segregation ratio? How could it be interpreted? Can you cite an analogous case that has been successfully analyzed?

8. What would be the outcome of the cross between Dexter and Kerry cattle? Write this cross in genetic symbols.

9. Discuss the economic aspects of the crosses in problems 5 and 8.

10. How could you prove the existence of a gamete lethal?

References

Blakeslee, A. F., 1928. The Genetics of *Datura*. Zeitschrift für inductive Abstammungs- und Vererbungslehre, Suppl. 1:117–130. This little paper is a classic of genetics.

Cuénot, L. 1902. La loi de Mendel et l'hérédité de la pigmentation chez les souris. Comptes Rendus de l'Academie des Sciences, 134:779–781. The original account of the inheritance of yellow coat color in mice.

Hadorn, Ernst, 1951. Developmental action of lethal factors in Drosophila. In Advances in Genetics, 4:53–85.

Hutt, F. B., 1949. Genetics of the Fowl. McGraw-Hill Book Co., New York. This book includes an excellent chapter on lethal genes.

CHAPTER 8

Modifications of Mendelian Inheritance

III: Multiple Alleles

If one has two varieties of the same species showing alternative characters of, for example, flower color or coat color, and if upon crossing they yield a three to one ratio in the F_2, it is no surprise. It simply means that the two colors are based upon a pair of allelic genes, with one being dominant over the other. But suppose that a third race, with still another color, is crossed first with one and then with the second, and these crosses also lead to monohybrid ratios in the F_2? This situation has been found repeatedly in genetic studies. The interpretation is simple: the wild type gene has mutated in more than one way so that a series of three alleles has been formed. Such series are common, and

are called *multiple alleles*. There is no reason why such a series should be restricted to three members, and in fact much larger series are known.

21. BEHAVIOR OF MULTIPLE ALLELES

The principles of inheritance in a series of multiple alleles are well illustrated by the *vestigial* series in *Drosophila*. Vestigial wings —*vg*—is a well known character in which the wings are reduced to useless rudiments. It is inherited as a simple, autosomal recessive. But there is also a series of around a dozen other genes which cause some degree of reduction in the wing size, and which are recessive to normal, long wings. These range from *nicked*, in which only a small nick is missing from the end of the wing, through *strap* in which the wings are reduced to long, narrow organs, to *no wing* (fig. 50). These alleles are symbolized by *vg* to indicate that they are all mutants of the same gene, and they are differentiated by superscripts, as vg^{ni}, vg^{str}, and vg^{Nw}. All members of this series affect the same character in varying degrees quantitatively, and this is usual for series of multiple alleles.

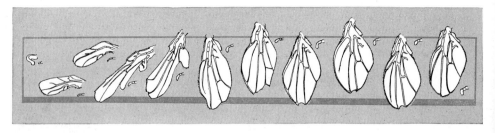

Fig. 50. *Some members of the vestigial series in* Drosophila, *together with their compounds. At the extreme left is the most extreme mutant, while at the extreme right is a normal wing. In-between is a graded series. The small structure to the right of each wing is the corresponding halter, or balancer. (Redrawn from Mohr.)*

Normal wing behaves as a dominant over all of the other members of the series. But what of heterozygotes between the lower members of the series, $vg^{ni}vg^{str}$, for example? Such heterozygotes show a phenotype intermediate between the two types represented, and they are called *compounds*. Formation of such intermediate compounds is usual in a series of multiple alleles, but it is not universal. There are cases in which members of a series form a sort of hierarchy, with each dominant over those below it in the series.

Finally, it should be mentioned that it cannot be assumed that a gene is allelic to a particular series simply because it affects the same character. Thus another gene, *m*, causes symmetrical reduction in wing size in *Drosophila*. If the cross $vg\ vg \times mo$ (*m* is sex-linked) is made, the F_1 will be all normal, because each gamete brings in the normal allele of the mutant carried by the other. In the F_2, a modified dihybrid ratio is obtained. Similarly, there is a large series of multiple alleles for eye color in *Drosophila*, and the phenotypes are a dilution series running from the wild type red through such colors as cherry, eosin, and apricot to white. But other genes cause qualitatively different eye colors, like cinnabar and vermilion, and these are not alleles of the white series. Thus only a breeding test can determine whether particular genes are alleles.

MULTIPLE ALLELES AND CHROMOSOMES It is important to note that, although a series of multiple alleles may include many members, no more than two can ever be present in a single zygote. This is a simple consequence of the facts that the genes are parts of the chromosomes, and that the chromosomes exist in pairs. A population may include, let us say, three alleles of a particular gene, but no individual in that population can carry more than two of the alleles. Thus if a population included the alleles *vg*, vg^a (antlered), and vg^{ni}, zygotic types would include $vgvg$, vg^avg^a, $vg^{ni}vg^{ni}$, $vg\ vg^a$, $vg\ vg^{ni}$, and vg^avg^{ni}. Thus the same rule applies as in other types of inheritance: each kind of gene is represented twice, and no more, in a zygote, because the genes are parts of the chromosomes, and each kind of chromosome is represented twice in the zygote.

These facts had considerable theoretical importance at the time of their discovery because of their bearing upon the theory of the nature of the gene. Bateson and Punnett had proposed the "presence or absence" theory, according to which a dominant gene was a real thing which played a definite role in the physiology of development, while a recessive gene was simply the absence of its dominant allele. Many of the facts of elementary genetics are conducive to this theory, but the facts of multiple alleles proved the theory to be wrong. For there are more than a dozen alleles in the white eye series of *Drosophila*, all of which are recessive to red. Yet it is clear that the dominant gene could not be absent in a variety of different ways. The recessive genes must be real entities just as are the dominants.

DIVERSE EXAMPLES Multiple allelism is as common in other organisms as it is in *Drosophila*. A few examples will suffice. In maize, there is a gene called *sun-red* (fig. 51) which causes the usually green plant to turn

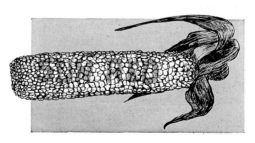

Fig. 51. *Sun red. If the husks be peeled back and replaced by a black paper cover in which the words SUN RED have been cut, sunlight will cause the development of pigment in the exposed parts of plants of genotype* srsr.

red upon exposure to sunlight. But there is a third allele, *weak sun-red,* which causes a weaker red color; and a fourth, *dilute sun-red,* which causes a very weak red color. Normal green is dominant over all of the others, but each of the recessives is dominant over those below it in the series.

The agouti series in mice has already been introduced. The gene for yellow coat, A^y is dominant over the gene for agouti coat, A. But this in turn is dominant over the gene for black, a. A similar but more extensive series has been found in rabbits (fig. 52). Full color, based upon the gene, C, is an agouti pattern with a yellow band near the tip of each black hair. The gene c^{ch}, Chinchilla, causes the yellow band to be replaced by a white one. A third gene, c^h, Himalayan, causes the rabbit to be white except for the feet, tail, ears, and nose, which are the coolest parts of the body. That temperature actually has something to do with the development of color is shown by the facts that rabbits of genotype $c^h c^h$ are all black if raised in a cold environment and all white if raised in a hot, humid room. It appears that the Himalayan gene determines a threshold temperature above which pigment cannot be formed. Under normal conditions, only the extremities fail to reach this critical temperature. The color pattern of Siamese cats is similarly determined. Finally the gene for albinism, c, is recessive to all of the other members of the series. Each gene in the series is dominant over those following it, if they be arranged in the order: C, c^{ch}, c^h, c.

22. MULTIPLE ALLELES IN MAN: THE BLOOD GROUPS

Multiple alleles are also well known in man. It has been much publicized that color blindness is inherited as a sex-linked recessive. But there are several different forms of color blindness, differing in the degree of the disability and in the specific wave lengths to which the person is blind. There is some evidence that these differences are based upon a series of multiple alleles. There is also another possibility, not readily understandable until chapter 11, and that is that the several types of color blindness may be based upon different non-allelic genes which are so close together in the chromosome (closely *linked*) that it is difficult to distinguish them from one another. But much the best known and most important series of multiple alleles in man are afforded by the blood groups. Before taking up this subject, however, a digression on the subject of immune reactions is appropriate.

IMMUNE REACTIONS If a protein-containing material, such as in a bacterial infection, invades the blood stream, it ordinarily causes the production in the blood serum of *antibodies,* proteins which have the

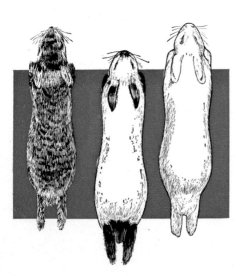

Fig. 52. *Rabbit coats. At the left is a rabbit of the agouti, or wild-type, pattern. In the center is a Himalayan rabbit, and at the right, an albino.*

specific effect of destroying the foreign protein. The foreign protein which causes production of antibodies and which may be destroyed by them is called an *antigen*. Thus if a young child is infected with the measles organism, the organism multiplies in his body and he develops typical disease symptoms. But meanwhile antibodies capable of destroying the measles organism are being developed. When the patient gets well, his blood contains a high titer of antibodies. If he is reinfected, the antibodies kill the invading organism promptly, and no disease symptoms follow. Thus the antigen-antibody reaction is a protective mechanism, and so is called an immune reaction.

It should be added that immune reactions are highly specific. Anti-measles antibodies give excellent protection against measles but no protection whatever against scarlet fever, and so on. Further, sometimes a person has antibodies against a specific infection even when he has not previously contacted the organism. One then speaks of *natural immunity* in contrast to the *acquired immunity* discussed above.

LANDSTEINER AND THE BLOOD GROUPS

Since the early 1800's blood transfusions have been attempted occasionally. But the results were, for many years, unpredictable. Sometimes the patient received the benefits for which the physician hoped, while in other cases transfusion was followed by alarming symptoms and even death. The solution was found in 1900 by Karl Landsteiner, then a Viennese serologist, but for most of his later life a member of the staff of the Rockefeller Institute of New York. Landsteiner found that a suspension of red blood cells from any person would be agglutinated—clumped together in large masses—in the sera of some persons, but not in the sera of others (fig. 53). By testing cells and sera from many people, he found that the results indicated that the red cells might carry both, either, or neither of two antigens, called A and B, in any combination, that is, A, B, AB or O. But whatever antigens a person might have on his red blood cells, his serum would contain *natural antibodies* capable of reacting with those antigens not present in his own red blood

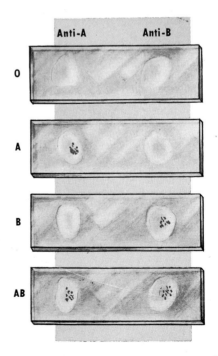

Fig. 53. *Blood group reactions. At the left end of each slide was a drop of anti–A serum, and at the right end, a drop of anti–B serum. To the anti-sera on a slide drops of blood cell suspension from the person being tested are added. No agglutination in either drop indicates that the person belongs to group O; agglutination in anti–A serum but not in anti–B indicates group A; agglutination in anti–B but not in anti–A indicates group B; while agglutination in both anti–sera indicates group AB.*

cells. These antibodies he named by the Greek letters corresponding to their antigens, α and β. The blood groups are named according to the antigens present and they may be tabulated as follows:

Blood group	A	B	AB	O
Antigens on R B C	A	B	AB	O
Antibodies in serum	β	α	O	$\alpha\beta$

When in a transfusion or in a test tube cells with A are added to serum with α or cells with B to serum with β, the cells are first agglutinated and then later destroyed (hemolysis). Thus Landsteiner's work solved the problem of why transfusion was sometimes beneficial and sometimes a disaster. He made transfusion safe by showing the need for donor and recipient to belong to the same blood group. But the Red Cross blood donor program of recent years has emphasized the importance of group O persons as universal donors. How is this possible? Obviously, the red cells of the group O donor cannot be agglutinated in the serum of any recipient, because they carry neither antigen. But why don't the α and β antibodies of the donor's serum agglutinate the recipient's cells if the recipient is of another blood type? Several points are involved here. First, a transfusion consists predominantly of cells, so that, in a one-pint transfusion, less than a half pint of serum is given. Second, this small quantity of serum is rapidly diluted at the point of entry by the much greater volume of the recipient's serum. Finally, a transfusion from a group O donor to an unmatched recipient is not *perfectly* safe: pathological transfusion reactions do occur rarely. However, if a transfusion is really needed, and if a properly matched donor is not readily available, the risk of transfusion with group O blood is far less than the risk of delay while procuring a properly matched donor.

INHERITANCE OF THE A-B-O BLOOD GROUPS It was soon realized that the blood groups which Landsteiner had discovered must be inherited, but a successful genetic analysis of the problem awaited the work of a mathematician, Bernstein. He saw that the facts of the blood groups were understandable on the basis of a series of three multiple alleles. These are designated by the letter L (honoring Landsteiner). L^A causes the presence of antigen A; L^B causes the presence of antigen B; and l prevents the formation of either of these antigens. As both L^A and L^B are dominant over l, group A and group B persons can be either homozygous or heterozygous. Group O persons must be homozygous ll, while group AB persons have the genotype $L^A L^B$. In the later type, each gene

Table 7. Inheritance of A B O Blood Groups

BLOOD TYPE	GENOTYPES
A	$L^A L^A$, $L^A l$
B	$L^B L^B$, $L^B l$
AB	$L^A L^B$
O	ll

causes the production of the antigen typical for it, a phenomenon sometimes called codominance. The possible genotypes and phenotypes are summarized in table 7.

MEDICOLEGAL SIGNIFICANCE Every person must belong to one or another of the A–B–O blood groups. Individual differences are common, and their inheritance is well understood. Hence it is practical to use this knowledge as an aid in determining relationships of persons when this is under dispute. Two general types of cases have been attacked by this method. First, although modern hospitals take great precautions to assure that parents take home their own babies, yet occasionally there is some doubt, and two sets of parents claim the same child. Blood tests may give decisive information. Let us say that a disputed child proves to be type O. His genotype must be *ll*. Mr. and Mrs. X are both type A, and so could be either L^AL^A or L^Al genotypically. Mr. and Mrs. Y are types O and AB respectively and so are of genotypes *ll* and L^AL^B. The child must have gotten the gene *l* from *each* parent, and therefore Mr. and Mrs. Y are ruled out, as her genotype does not include this gene. Hence the child must belong to Mr. and Mrs. X. If, on the other hand, both sets of parents had genotypes which could have produced the child, the test would have been of no help.

The second type of case is that in which a mother, usually unwed, sues to establish responsibility for paternity. Let us say now that the child belongs to group AB and the mother to group A. The child must therefore have received the gene L^B from its father. If the putative father belongs either to group B or to group AB, then he could potentially have fathered the child. But if he belongs to group A or to group O, he could not have fathered the child as his genotype could not include the necessary gene, L^B.

Note that blood group evidence can exclude parenthood with certainty, but it cannot establish the fact of parenthood. It can only establish the possibility. This is important, because Anglo-Saxon law has always assumed that a mother knows who has fathered her child, and that she could have no motive for naming the wrong man. Not all states will admit blood group evidence into court, but in those which do, a significant proportion of the putative fathers are excluded by the evidence. Presumably, then, as large a proportion of those not excluded are also not guilty, and as large a proportion of the accused fathers in other states are not guilty. Why is this important evidence not admitted in court in all states? Undoubtedly the traditional conservatism of

the law tends to slow down the acceptance of a new type of evidence. But more important is a constitutional question: it involves the giving of testimony against one's self. While this cannot be forced under the Constitution, it can be permitted, and it seems reasonable that courts should be required to admit this evidence whenever the accused person wants it done.

SUBGROUPS OF A   It has been shown that not all cells of group A react equally strongly with anti-A sera. Most group A persons belong to the strongly reacting subgroup A_1, but some belong to the more weakly reacting subgroup A_2. These are determined by different alleles of the same gene, with A_1 being dominant over A_2. These are the only A alleles which have clinical importance, but all of them have forensic importance in testing for parenthood. Still more weakly reacting types A_3 and A_4 have been discovered, and there is even a report of a type A_5, so weak that the antigen is not detectable except by the absence of antibody α in the sera of such persons! The reasoning is impeccable, but most serologists are understandably unconvinced.

MINOR BLOOD TYPES   After the discovery of the A-B-O series, no additional blood types were discovered until 1927, when Landsteiner and Levine reported the M—N types. These were identified by immunizing rabbits to human blood cells. A complex of antibodies was formed, and by the serological technique of antibody absorption, it was possible to demonstrate certain specific antigens (M and N) and the corresponding antibodies (anti-M and anti-N). It turned out that every human blood had one or both of these antigens, there being no negative types. The genes are *M* for antigen M and *m* for antigen N, and they show codominance, so that genotype *Mm* leads to blood type MN. The antibodies are rarely, if ever, formed in human serum, and hence they have little or no clinical importance.

Because these antigens are effective only when the bloods of different species are mixed, they are called *heteroantigens* in contrast to the isoantigens, A and B. It must be emphasized that the *M* gene is not allelic with the *L* gene; it is an independent gene concerned with a different group of antigenic proteins.

In recent years a large number of minor human antigens, usually rare, have been discovered. None has any clinical importance. For some, a clear cut pattern of inheritance has been demonstrated, and these make possible a further refinement in testing for parenthood.

THE RH BLOOD TYPES   During the course of investigations of heteroagglutination in the late 1930's, Landsteiner and A. S. Wiener found that, if a rabbit were first immunized by injection of blood from the Rhesus monkey, the resulting antibodies would agglutinate the red blood cells of about 85 per cent of the white New York population. This figure has proved to be generally valid for the white American population. Evidently, then, man and the Rhesus monkey must share the antigen concerned and hence they named it Rh. Persons whose blood cells contain Rh antigen are called Rh-positive, while the remaining 15 per cent are said to be Rh-negative. Soon afterward they found that transfusion reactions (fig. 54) sometimes occurred in man when negative persons were transfused with positive blood, even though they were matched for the A-B-O groups.

Unlike the A-B-O groups, however, Rh-negative persons do not have anti-Rh antibodies in their sera unless they have been previously immunized by Rh antigen. Immunization may occur either by previous transfusion or, in women, by pregnancy with an Rh positive fetus. In 1941, Philip Levine and his collaborators published data showing that Rh transfusion reactions occurred most frequently in women who had had babies with *erythroblastosis fetalis*. This is a hemolytic disease of newborn babies which affects about one baby in 250 and which is often fatal. Investigation showed that mothers of affected babies were Rh negative, while the fathers and the surviving babies were Rh positive. Levine postulated

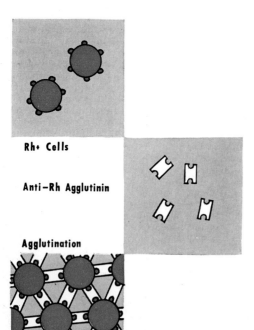

Rh+ Cells

Anti-Rh Agglutinin

Agglutination

Fig. 54.   *Diagram of a transfusion reaction. In the uppermost figure, the antigens are represented as knobs on the red blood cells. In the center figure, the antibodies are represented as macromolecules with concavities of size and shape corresponding to the knobs on the red blood cells. In the bottom figure, the two reacting parts are shown fitted together to form a lattice of cells and antibody molecules. If one substitutes reactive chemical radicals for gross structural features, then the diagram becomes quite accurate.* (*After Wiener.*)

that the Rh antigens from the positive baby must cross the placental barrier to enter the mother's blood stream. There they cause production of anti-Rh antibodies which then return to the fetus and agglutinate its cells. There are some serious difficulties with this hypothesis, not the least of which is the fact that neither red cells nor proteins (the antigens and antibodies) should be able to cross the placental barrier. But no better theory has yet been proposed, and it is backed by an immense amount of evidence. The most successful treatment is to transfuse the baby with a suspension of washed Rh-negative red blood cells in saline solution.

Actually, only about one in six of the Rh-positive babies carried by Rh-negative mothers develops the disease. This may mean that the antigens and antibodies can cross the placental barrier only if the placenta is defective, a hopeful lead for research on treatment of the condition. First born babies are rarely affected. It appears that the mother's antibody titer does not rise to a dangerous level during a single pregnancy. But some Rh-negative women have borne large series of positive children without complications. The author knows of one Rh-negative woman who has borne fourteen positive children, none of whom had erythroblastotic symptoms!

INHERITANCE OF THE Rh FACTOR Wiener showed that the gene for presence of the Rh antigen (positive) is dominant over that for ability to form anti-Rh antibody (negative). Thus an Rh-positive person may have either of two genotypes, $RhRh$ or $Rhrh$; but a negative person can only be $rhrh$. Soon, however, it became evident that different Rh antigens and antisera were not equally reactive. There seemed to be a family of three Rh antigens, which Wiener called Rh_o, Rh', and Rh'', together with a corresponding group of antisera. Hence he postulated a series of six alleles as follows: Rh_o, Rh', Rh'', Rh_1 (antigens Rh_o and Rh'), Rh_2

(antigens Rh_o and Rh''), and rh. Thus there is a complex series of multiple alleles, with twenty-one possible genotypes leading to eight distinguishable phenotypes. But with all of this complexity, only the original alternative of Rh positive or negative has any clinical importance.

THE C-D-E SYSTEM OF FISHER The situation was soon complicated by discovery (by Levine) that Rh-positive blood contained antibodies capable of agglutinating Rh-negative cells. This looked like a sort of backward reaction, and it was named Hr. Further study showed that, like the Rh antigens, there were three Hr antigens. And the two sets showed a reciprocal relationship, such that, if a person had a particular Rh antigen, he would not have the corresponding Hr antigen. As there were three sets of such alternative pairs, the English biometrician, R. A. Fisher, drew the conclusion that the Rh–Hr complex was probably determined by three pairs of allelic genes, which he called $C\text{-}c$, $D\text{-}d$, and $E\text{-}e$. This would lead to the same eight phenotypes which Wiener had derived with multiple alleles. Of the possible genotypes, only $ccddee$ would be negative (but having all of the Hr antigens), while the others would correspond to the array of positive types in Wiener's system. But why should these be inherited as a unit, confusable with mono-factorial inheritance? Fisher believes that the $C\text{-}D\text{-}E$ genes are located very close together in the same chromosome, much as discussed above in connection with color blindness. Decisive data are not yet available to decide between the hypotheses of Fisher and Wiener. At present the consensus among specialists seems to favor the Fisher system, but majorities have not always been right, and when all of the evidence is in, Wiener's system may very possibly be vindicated. At present, it is customary to label typing antisera according to both methods.

RÉSUMÉ Because any gene may mutate

in more than one way, series of multiple alleles are quite common. While there is no theoretical limit upon the number of alleles of a single gene which may be present in a population, only two can be represented in any individual, because the chromosomes exist only in pairs, and there can be only one gene of each kind in a single chromosome. Typically, the wild type allele of a series is dominant over all of the others, while the compounds of any two recessives in the series lead to intermediate phenotypes. In some instances, however, the alleles of a series can be arranged in such an order that each is dominant over those which follow it. Multiple allelism is well known in man, just as in other organisms. The best known examples in man are the blood groups, which have been very intensively studied because of their clinical and legal importance.

Questions and Problems

1. Define:

Antibody	Compound (genetic, not chemical)
Antigen	Immune reaction
	Multiple allele

What would be the outcome, genotypically and phenotypically, of the following crosses:

1. $c^{ch}c^{ch} \times c^{ch}c^a$ (rabbit coat color)
2. $c^{ch}c^a \times c^{ch}c^a$
4. $Cc^{ch} \times c^hc^a$
5. $WW \times wO$ (*Drosophila* eye color)
6. $w^aw^a \times w^{ch}O$
7. $w^ew^a \times WO$
8. $Srsr \times sr^wsr^d$ (sun-red in corn)

9. Blood tests are made to determine whether a certain man has fathered a certain child. The mother's blood is group A; the child's is also group A; and the putative father's is group O. Discuss the meaning of these data from both genetic and legal viewpoints.

10. Two couples both claim the same child.

Blood tests are made, and it turns out that the child is O-MN-Rh+. Mr. and Mrs. X are A-MN-Rh+ and B-M-Rh− respectively, while Mr. and Mrs. Y are AB-M-Rh+ and O-N-Rh+. Whose is the child? Explain your answer, giving genotypes of all persons as completely as the data will permit.

11. Mr. and Mrs. W belong to groups B and A respectively, while Mr. and Mrs. Z belong to groups B and AB. The two couples have a total of four children, one in each of the four blood groups. Assign these children to the correct parents as far as possible, show the genotypic basis of the assignment, and indicate why any others cannot be assigned with certainty.

What types of children could result from the following marriages:

12. $L^AL^AMmRhrh \times L^AL^BMMrhrh$
13. $L^AL^BMmrhrh \times L^BL^BmmRhrh$
14. $llmmRhrh \times L^AL^BMMrhrh$
15. $L^{Al}MmRhrh \times llmmrhrh$

References

Fisher, R. A., 1947. The Rhesus factor. A study in scientific method. American Scientist, 35:95–102. A presentation of the C-D-E system by one of its major protagonists.

Landsteiner, Karl, 1945. The Specificity of Serological Reactions. Harvard University Press, Cambridge. The man who started it all summarizes his science.

Potter, Edith L., 1947. Rh. Yearbook Publishers, Chicago. An excellent, comprehensive review of the problem.

Race, R. R. and Ruth Sanger, 1950. Blood Groups in Man. C. C Thomas Co., Springfield.

Wiener, A. S., 1943. Blood Groups and Transfusion. Third edition. C. C Thomas Co., Springfield.

———— 1945. Recent Advances in Knowledge of Rh Blood Factors, with Special Reference to the Clinical Applications. Transactions and Studies of the College of Physicians of Philadelphia, Series 4, vol. 13:105–122. A good, concise summary of the multiple allele theory on Rh.

CHAPTER 9

Modifications of Mendelian Inheritance

VI: Collaboration of Genes

A whole series of modified Mendelian ratios arises from the fact that the combined effects of two or more pairs of genes may be necessary to produce a single phenotype. The simplest problems in heredity were, quite naturally, the first to be successfully attacked, and in these there seemed to be a $1:1$ correlation between genes and phenotypic characters, with each gene subserving a definite character which was independent of all others, the various characters being related to the organism much as the separate pieces of a mosaic are related to the whole picture. This concept became entrenched in genetic thinking under the name of the *one gene—one character* theory of genic action. Because of this, when examples of collaboration of different genes to produce one phenotype were discovered, they were thought to be exceptional. But their importance has increased until now collaboration of genes appears to be one of the most typical phenomena in genetics.

23. COLLABORATIVE GENES

COMPLEMENTARY GENES   The experiments of Bateson and Punnett on the genetics of chickens constituted the first proof that Mendelian principles applied to animals as well as to plants. In the course of their investigation of plumage colors, they tried crossing different breeds of white chickens. In most of these crosses, white behaved as a simple recessive to colored patterns. However, when they crossed White Silkies with another (unspecified) white breed the F_1 was all colored and the F_2 included colored and white birds in a ratio of nine to seven. As nine plus seven equals sixteen, they believed that they must be dealing with a dihybrid cross. They reasoned that color must depend upon interaction of two substances, each dependent upon a different gene. They suggested that one of these might be a *chromagen*, a protein which is colorless when reduced and colored when oxidized; and that the second might be an oxidase, that is, an oxidizing enzyme. Each of these was dependent upon the presence of the corresponding dominant gene, C and O respectively, with each of the parental strains lacking one of the dominants. Thus the cross becomes:

P $CCoo \times ccOO$ white parental varieties

F_1 $CcOo$ colored F_1

F_2 9 $C?O?$: 3 $C?oo$: 3 $ccO?$: 1 $ccoo$

   colored   7 white

The ordinary dihybrid segregation, then, leads to the nine to seven ratio, because each of the last three classes lacks one or both of the dominant genes.

Actually, this example is disappointing, because the second white variety was not specified, and more recent attempts to duplicate the cross have failed. But the principle that a ratio of nine to seven is given when complementary dominant genes are necessary to produce a given phenotype is well established. The same authors did extensive experiments on the genetics of the sweet pea (*Lathyrus odoratus*). Again, when two white-flowered varieties were crossed, the F_1 consisted of purple-flowered varieties, like the wild sweet peas of Sicily, from which the cultivated English varieties were known to have been derived. In the F_2, a ratio of nine purple-flowered to seven white-flowered plants was obtained. These results were again interpreted in terms of two substances, each determined by a different dominant gene, being necessary for the development of color. *C* and *P* were used as gene symbols, and if these be substituted for *C* and *O* in the diagram above, it will not differ from the genotypic diagram for the chicken color example.

A suggestive analogy is afforded by the relationship between the indicator, phenolphthalein, and a base like KOH. In a neutral solution, phenolphthalein is colorless, but it becomes red if KOH be added to the solution (fig. 55). Thus both substances, colorless separately, are essential for the production of red color. That this may be more than an analogy is suggested by an experiment of

Blakeslee on the yellow daisy, *Rudbeckia hirta*. A cross was made between two races characterized by yellow seed cones. In the F_1, all plants had purple seed cones, while in the F_2 a ratio of nine purple to seven yellows was obtained. Now if the seed cones of the parental races were treated with alkali, one turned to a reddish color while the other turned black. When the F_2 yellows were similarly treated, a ratio of three red to four black was obtained. Clearly, this means that the modification of the $9 : 3 : 3 : 1$ ratio depends upon the method of diagnosing the phenotype. As judged by the color of the growing plant the last three classes are added together to give a $9 : 7$ ratio; but if the yellows are treated with alkali, then the last two differ from the second class, giving a ratio of $9 : 3 : 4$. It is also clear that we are dealing here with a physiological, or biochemical character, the relative concentrations of two similar but different indicator pigments, and probably also the pH of the cell sap.

COLLABORATION OF FACTORS A somewhat more complicated type of collaboration was discovered in chickens by Bateson and Punnett, and was called by them the collaboration of factors. Here, a whole series of phenotypes depended upon the interplay of two pairs of genes. They had several pure breeding strains of chickens which differed in comb form (fig. 56). Of these, *single* comb was believed to be the wild type, as it is characteristic of the wild fowl of Malay, from which domestic chickens have been derived. *Rose* and *pea* combs

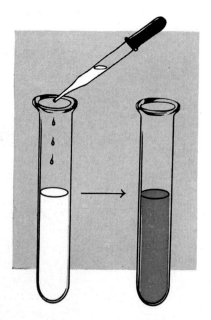

Fig. 55. *If a few drops of KOH (colorless) be added to a test tube filled with phenolphthalein (colorless), the result is a bright red fluid.*

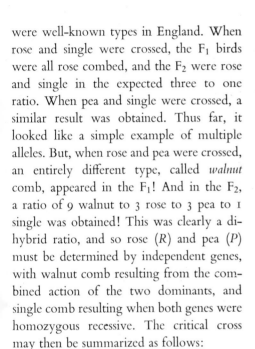

Fig. 56. *Comb types. Upper left, single; upper right, rose; lower left, walnut; and lower right, pea.*

were well-known types in England. When rose and single were crossed, the F_1 birds were all rose combed, and the F_2 were rose and single in the expected three to one ratio. When pea and single were crossed, a similar result was obtained. Thus far, it looked like a simple example of multiple alleles. But, when rose and pea were crossed, an entirely different type, called *walnut* comb, appeared in the F_1! And in the F_2, a ratio of 9 walnut to 3 rose to 3 pea to 1 single was obtained! This was clearly a di-hybrid ratio, and so rose (R) and pea (P) must be determined by independent genes, with walnut comb resulting from the combined action of the two dominants, and single comb resulting when both genes were homozygous recessive. The critical cross may then be summarized as follows:

P $RRpp$ $\times$ $rrPP$
      rose   pea

F_1 $RrPp$
        walnut

F_2 9 $R?P?$: 3 $R?pp$: 3 $rrP?$: 1 $rrpp$
     walnut   rose   pea   single

Now, suppose that the stocks available for investigation had included only rose and single. The only possible series of crosses would have been: $RRpp \times rrpp \rightarrow F_1$ $Rrpp$ $\rightarrow F_2$ 3 $R?pp$: 1 rrpp. In this sequence, the segregation of the R gene is quite evident,

but there is no indication at all that a second pair of genes is influencing the form of the comb. Had no further evidence been available, the second pair of genes would have remained unknown, although fully effective and necessary for normal comb development. This suggests the possibility that there may be additional comb form genes which are unidentifiable because they are homozygous throughout the species. There appears to be no theoretical limit to the number of genes which might influence a particular character, and some highly complex examples will be given below. But frequently, one or a few genes will have major effects upon a character, while numerous others have minor effects, which alter the phenotype in a plus or minus way. One speaks of such minor genes as "modifiers," and their control is important for genetic research. If one is dealing with a pair of major genes, especially for a quantitative character, evaluated by measure, the phenotypes associated with the different genotypes can be properly compared *only if the constellation of modifiers be identical in each case.* In order to do this, it is necessary to build up stocks homozygous for the modifier complex. This is done by inbreeding, a very simple statement of what may be a difficult job.

PLEIOTROPIC GENES   Collaboration of

factors and modifying genes have turned out to be the rule rather than the exception, and this has led to the concept that every character is actually the product of the whole genotype of the organism. Stated in another way, the complex processes of embryological development which terminate in the adult phenotype result from the cooperative action and interaction of the entire constellation of genes. The whole genetic complex tends to result in the development of a normal, wild type, organism. But if a mutated gene is present, in addition to its collaboration in the production of the entire organism, it may cause a deviation from the usual pattern of development in some specific organ, and we then speak of a color gene, or an eye form gene, or a comb form gene. But actually, the mutant gene has simply acted as a differential factor, causing a specific deviation from the normal pattern of development.

Another line of evidence for this viewpoint is afforded by the phenomenon of *pleiotropic* (Greek—*pleion,* many + *tropē,* change) *genes.* A pleiotropic gene is one which has more than one phenotypic effect. Almost any gene that is adequately studied is likely to fall in this class. The gene for vestigial wings in *Drosophila* also causes changed orientation of the bristles on the scutes, slower than normal development, divergence of the wings, reduced size of the balancers, and decreased viability. The gene is named for its most obvious effect, yet some of these "secondary" effects may be as important or more important to the organism. Similarly, the gene for red eye in the flour moth, *Ephestia,* also makes optic ganglia red instead of brown, makes the testes colorless, reduces the pigmentation of the skin and ocelli, slows down the rate of development, and reduces the viability. In general, the earlier in development a particular gene exerts its major effect, the more extensive will be its pleiotropic effects. This is well illustrated by a study of the primrose, *Primula,* for the effects of ten different mutant genes upon the leaves and upon the various parts of the flowers. In every case, it was found that genes with major effects upon the leaves (which develop before the flowers) had supplementary effects upon the flowers (fig. 57), while those with major effects upon the flowers lacked supplementary effects upon the leaves.

Thus the facts of collaboration of factors and pleiotropy reinforce one another in suggesting that the whole genotype collaborates in the production of a normal organism, while the differential effects of a particular gene upon a particular character may be relatively large, making it possible to speak of eye color genes, wing form genes, and other special types.

HIERARCHIES OF GENES   The early studies in genetics were quite naturally concentrated upon the most obvious problems. For students of mammalian genetics, the coat colors of rodents such as mice provided an obvious starting point, and an immense literature upon this subject developed rapidly. It soon became evident that coat color is simple only insofar as it is superficial on the animal, but its inheritance depends upon many pairs of genes which are functionally related in such a way that the expression of one gene in the series depends upon those which precede it, a relationship which is called a *hierarchy of genes.* At the top of the hierarchy is the *albino* series, with the gene c preventing the development of any color whatever (other than respiratory pigments), while the gene C permits full development of such colors as may be determined by other genes in the hierarchy. There are also some intermediate alleles. Because this gene permits or precludes the expression of the remaining genes in the series, it is said to be *epistatic* to them. The *agouti* series (studied above in connection with multiple alleles and lethal genes) includes A, which causes the normal salt-

Fig. 57. *Pleiotropy in the primrose,* Primula sinensis. *Each horizontal row shows the phenotype of leaf, calyx, and flower under the influence of a single gene, which has been named for its effect upon the leaves. Top row,* chch, *stellata; second row,* oo, *oak; third row,* tt, *tongue; fourth row,* 22, *claw; and bottom row,* ChCh, *sinensis. (Redrawn from Anderson and de Winton.)*

and-pepper agouti pattern, and *a,* which causes each hair to be uniformly colored, lacking the usual yellow band near the tip. *B* determines the formation of black pigment (but only if *C* is also present), while *b* determines brown pigment. Whatever the pigments, *D* causes full intensity of color, while *d* causes a paler, dilute color. Thus the hierarchy goes to genes of progressively lesser effect until so minor a gene is reached as *P,* determining normally pigmented iris, and its allele *p* determining pink eyes, like those of an albino.

The hierarchy of coat color factors looked

like a rather complex case of collaboration of factors even when a mere half dozen color genes had been investigated. But Gruneberg now lists no less than fifteen pairs of major coat color genes. If we substitute in the expression 3^n to determine the number of genotypes that could be formed from such a series we get the staggering figure of 14,348,000 (as calculated by logarithms)! Of course, many of these genotypes would be identical phenotypically, as, for example, all of the genotypes homozygous for c would be albinos irrespective of the rest of the genotypes. But the case is further complicated by the existence of series of multiple alleles of three of these genes, C, A, and P. In addition there are several genes controlling spotting. Obviously, it has been possible to test experimentally only a small portion of coat color genotypes.

As might be expected in so complicated a hierarchy, some rather surprising ratios may be obtained in crosses between strains of different color patterns. In making such crosses, it is necessary that the stocks used be isogenic, usually being homozygous dominant for those genes not under study. Thus, if one crosses an albino and a black, the F_1 mice are all agouti, while the F_2 gives agoutis, blacks, and albinos in a ratio of 9 : 3 : 4. This is easily understandable when the cross is represented in symbols:

$$P \quad ccAA \times CCaa$$
$$\quad \text{albino} \quad \text{black}$$

$$F_1 \quad CcAa$$
$$\quad \text{agouti}$$

$$F_2 \quad \begin{array}{ll} 9 \ C?A? & \text{agouti} \\ 3 \ C?aa & \text{black} \\ 3 \ ccA? & \left. \right\} \ \text{albino} \\ 1 \ ccaa \end{array}$$

As all genes in the series other than the two pairs segregating are assumed to be homozygous dominant, it is not necessary to write them out. But it is important to remember

that B is among them, so that any mouse of genotype $C?aa$ will be black. In the F_2, the last two categories are identical phenotypically because they are homozygous for albinism. Hence the ratio of 9 : 3 : 4. Many other atypical ratios are possible in so complicated a hierarchy.

ALEURONE COLORS IN CORN Another remarkable hierarchy of genes has been worked out in corn, and controls the colors of the aleurone, which are so striking in Indian maize. But first a brief digression on the structure of the corn seed (fig. 58) may be in order. The most essential part of the seed is, of course, the *embryo*. The main mass of the seed, the *endosperm*, is made up of fleshy cells and provides food for the embryo. It may be noted here that the cells of the endosperm are triploid. The outermost layer of cells of the endosperm is called the *aleurone* (a-lur'-ōne) layer. These cells are oriented as a very regular surface layer, and they have certain characteristics, including color, which contrast with the rest of the endosperm. Finally, the entire seed is surrounded by a thin, transparent seed coat.

If certain varieties of white corn are

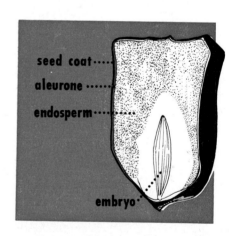

Fig. 58.   *The structure of a corn seed, showing the embryo imbedded in the endosperm. The aleurone layer is formed by the outermost layer of endosperm cells. Surrounding the entire structure is the seed coat.*

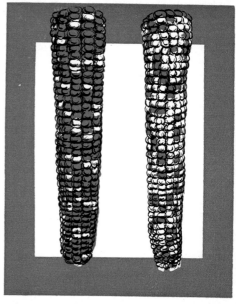

Fig. 59. Ears of corn showing segregation for dominant and recessive whites. On the left, recessive white; on the right, dominant white.

crossed with colored corn, the F_1 is all white, and the F_2 gives a ratio of three white to one colored (fig. 59). It is evident that white is dominant over colored, and the genes are designated *I* and *i* respectively. (The letter *I* stands for *inhibitor*. It is used on the grounds that evidence indicates that the necessary biochemical apparatus for pigment formation is present, but is inhibited by a product of this gene.) When a second white variety was crossed with colored corn, however, the F_1 was colored, and the F_2 ratio was three colored to one white (fig. 59). Hence it is clear that a second pair of genes influences color, with white now behaving as a recessive. This gene pair is designated by the letters *A* and *a*. Two more recessive whites are known, independent of each other and of *a*. These are called *c* and *r*, respectively. If a plant has the genotype *i i A A C C R R*, a fifth pair of genes determines whether the color shall be purple (*P*) or red (*p*). Thus there is a hierarchy of five pairs of major genes, as well as some modifiers and spotting genes.

This hierarchy of genes provides the basis for some highly modified ratios, and a few of these may be explained. A cross between any two of the three recessive whites proves their independence. For example:

P   *aaCC* $\times$ *AA c c*
           a-white   c-white

F_1 *AaCc*
             colored

F_2 9 A?C?   3 A?cc : 3 aa C? : 1 *aacc*
       _____
       colored   7 white

The ratio of 9 : 7 proves that a dihybrid segregation has occurred. A cross of a dominant white to a purple gives a ratio of three white to one purple in the F_2, because only one pair of genes is segregating. But a cross of dominant white times red gives an F_2 ratio of 12 white : 3 purple : 1 red! This may be easily understood if the cross be set up in symbols:

P *IIAACCRRPP* $\times$ *iiAACCRRpp*

As only the first and last of these genes show factor differences, the expression can be simplified by omitting the others:

P   *IIPP* $\times$ *iipp*
                 white   red

F_1 *IiPp*
                  white

F_2 9 I?P? : 3 I?pp : 3 iiP? : 1 *iipp*
      _____ _____ _____
        12 white   3 purple   1 red

Trihybrid ratios are also modified, as might be expected, for example, the cross *IIAACC* $\times$ *iiaacc* leads to a ratio of 55 white to 9 purple in the F_2.

CONSTELLATIONS OF BIOCHEMICAL MUTANTS IN *NEUROSPORA* A particularly important type of hierarchy of genes has recently been found to control the biosynthesis of essential amino acids and other nutritional compounds in microorganisms. The most important work in this field has been done by G. W. Beadle and his collaborators, first at Stanford University and now at California Institute of Technology, using a species of bread mold, *Neurospora crassa*. But before discussing these experiments, a digression on the life cycle of *Neurospora* may be worth while.

Like other molds, *Neurospora* can reproduce either sexually or asexually. An asexual spore, or *conidium*, can divide mitotically to produce a *mycelium*, or mass of haploid cells. Such mitotic division of haploid cells may lead to large masses of genetically identical mold, a convenient fact for biochemical or other study. As long as a *clone*, the asexually produced descendants of a single spore, is maintained in isolation, reproduction occurs only by mitosis. However, the clones belong to two different mating types, *A* and *a*, and if mycelia from the two types of clones are mixed, sexual reproduction occurs. (As the two mating types are not distinguished morphologically, nor by the type of gamete, they are not referred to as male and female. The mating types must be physiologically differentiated, however, for otherwise intraclonal matings should occur.) When mating types *A* and *a* are mixed, some of their cells fuse two-by-two to form zygotes, which are therefore diploid. *But the zygote is the only diploid cell in the entire life cycle, for the meiotic divisions follow immediately.* As these divisions occur within a long, narrow capsule (ascus), the resulting four spores are held in alignment in the order of their formation, like an idealized diagram of meiosis. Finally, each spore undergoes a mitotic division, so that a mature ascus contains eight spores, comprising four pairs of genetically identical cells. These spores are normally scattered by the bursting of the ascus wall, and each spore gives rise to another haploid mass of mycelia. However, it is possible to dissect the spores out of the ascus and grow separate clones from each one, and this technique has yielded valuable genetic and cytological information.

Wild type *Neurospora* can synthesize all of its nutritional requirements, except biotin, from carbohydrate and inorganic salts. Hence a *minimal medium*, containing only carbohydrate, salts, and biotin, is adequate for the growth of a culture of the mold, unless a mutant gene has altered the nutritional requirements of the organism. Actually mutations can be induced by subjecting the culture to x radiation. If an irradiated culture fails to grow on the minimal medium but does grow on a complete medium containing all of the essential amino acids and vitamins, then one knows that the irradiation has caused the loss of the ability to synthesize some essential nutritional substance. Its hereditary nature may be tested by crossing it with wild type in much the same fashion as in other Mendelian crosses. This has been done with a large number of nutritional mutants, and they generally turn out to be simple recessive genes.

The next question to be investigated is that of the specific nature of the induced nutritional deficiency. This may be done by growing the mold on a variety of culture media, each of which contains the minimal medium plus one of the essential amino acids or vitamins. If the culture fails to grow on any medium except the one, let us say, to which tryptophan has been added, then it is clear that the induced mutation must block the synthesis of this amino acid. By this method, genes affecting almost every nutritional requirement of *Neurospora* have been identified. Actually, several tryptophan requiring mutants have been obtained. Of course, a complicated structure like tryptophan is not synthesized at one step, and the study of the different tryptophan-requiring mutants has thrown light on the actual course of the biosynthesis of the compound. One such mutant will grow if tryptophan is added to the minimal medium, but indole, a simpler nitrogenous compound, then accumulates in the medium. It appears that tryptophan is formed by the condensation of indole and serine (a simpler amino acid). This reaction is catalyzed by an enzyme which is inactivated by the tryptophan-requiring mutant. But another tryptophan-requiring mutant will grow if indole, but not tryptophan, is added to the culture. This indicates that the enzyme which couples indole and serine is functional, but that the synthesis of indole is blocked. In this instance, anthranilic acid accumulates in the culture, and so this substance must be the precursor from which indole is made. Similar evidence indicates that phenylalanine is the precursor of anthranilic acid. Thus three steps in the biosynthesis of tryptophan have been identified by means of mutant genes which block the specific enzymes controlling each step. In this series each gene may be considered epistatic (expressed to the ex-

clusion of a non-allelic gene—see below) to those which follow it.

But this is not the end of the tryptophan story, for there is a group of mutant genes known which permits growth if either tryptophan or nicotinic acid is added to the medium. Hence the mold must be able to synthesize one when supplied with the other. Two intermediates in the synthesis of nicotinic acid from tryptophan have been identified. The evidence indicates that tryptophan is first converted into kynurenine. This is in turn converted into 3-hydroxy-anthranilic acid, which finally yields nicotinic acid. Thus the tryptophan cycle, as now known, runs in six steps from phenylalanine to nicotinic acid, as illustrated in figure 60. Genes are known which specifically block five of the six steps. It appears, then, that the biochemical reactions of organisms are based upon constellations of specific enzymes, each of which is produced under the influence of a particular gene. This has led Beadle and his collaborators to formulate the *one gene—one enzyme* theory of genic action. While it would be very difficult, if not impossible, to

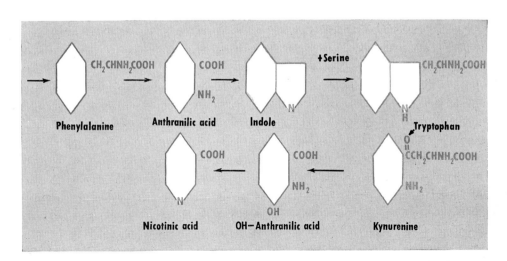

Fig. 60. *The tryptophan cycle in* Neurospora. *Mutants are available which interfere with each step in this extensive series of biosyntheses, with the exception of the conversion of tryptophan to kynurenine. (Modified from Horowitz in* Advances in Genetics, *vol. 3.)*

test this theory in relation to the morphological mutants with which most geneticists have dealt, yet its applicability may well be very much broader than the type of data upon which it is based. Further consideration of this subject will be deferred to the chapter on the theory of the gene.

24. MULTIPLE FACTORS

Several types of collaborative actions of genes have been discussed above, in each of which two or more independent pairs of genes contributed to the formation of a single phenotypic effect. In these, each gene pair appeared to have a different, though supplementary effect. Thus, one gene determined a colorless protein while a second gene determined an enzyme capable of converting the protein to a pigment. But the experiments of H. Nilsson-Ehle, a Swedish pioneer of genetics, showed that, in wheat, there appeared to be non-allelic genes of *identical* effect. These he called *multiple factors*. This term should be contrasted with multiple alleles. The latter are, of course, series of different mutants of the same gene, and will give monohybrid ratios in crosses.

Multiple factors, on the other hand, are independent genes which, although identical in effects, will give dihybrid or polyhybrid ratios in crosses.

DUPLICATE FACTORS   When Nilsson-Ehle crossed a variety of wheat with red-seed coats to one with white-seed coats, the F_1 was all red, and he naturally expected a three to one ratio in the F_2. What he actually obtained, however, was a ratio of fifteen reds to one white! He saw that there must be two independent gene pairs for the red-white alternative, with red being produced when either or both pairs included a dominant. Thus the first three members of the dihybrid ratio of 9 : 3 : 3 : 1 all led to the same phenotype, red, while only the last member produced its alternative, white.

A similar case was found by G. H. Shull in the shepherd's purse, *Capsella bursa-pastoris*, a common weed throughout much of the United States (fig. 61). In this plant the seed capsules are generally triangular, but occasionally plants occur with oval seed capsules. When a cross between the two varieties was made, the F_1 had only triangular capsules, but the F_2 yielded fifteen triangular to one oval. Upon selfing the F_2 plants with

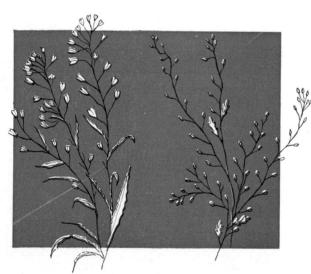

Fig. 61.   *The shepherd's purse, showing triangular seed capsules on the left, and oval seed capsules on the right. (Drawn from specimens in the Nieuwland Herbarium of the University of Notre Dame.)*

P $T_1T_1T_2T_2 \times t_1t_1t_2t_2$
         triangular   oval

F_1 $T_1t_1T_2t_2$
            triangular

F_2 15 triangular:

      1 $T_1T_1T_2T_2$ ⎫
      1 $T_1T_1t_2t_2$ Breed
      1 $t_1t_1T_2T_2$ true
      2 $T_1T_1T_2t_2$ in F_3
      2 $T_1t_1T_2T_2$ ⎭
      1 oval:
           $t_1t_1t_2t_2$ Breeds true

      2 $T_1t_1t_2t_2$ ⎫   3 : 1
      2 $t_1t_1T_2t_2$ ⎭   in F_3

      4 $T_1t_1T_2t_2$ 9 : 3 : 3 : 1 in F_3

triangular capsules, some bred true, some segregated in a three to one ratio, and some segregated in a fifteen to one ratio, thus proving conclusively that duplicate genes were involved. If the two gene pairs be represented as T_1—t_1 and T_2—t_2, then the cross appears as shown at the top of this page.

TRIPLICATE GENES Surprisingly enough, Nilsson-Ehle found that his wheat color example was capable of still further complications. For when certain varieties of red wheat were crossed to white, an F_2 ratio of sixty-three to one was obtained. This looked like a trihybrid ratio, and it was tested by breeding an F_3 from the F_2 reds. As expected, monohybrid, dihybrid, and trihybrid ratios were obtained from different plants. It was clear, then, that there were actually three independent pairs of genes for the red-white alternative, with one dominant gene in any one of them being sufficient to produce red color in the grain.

MULTIPLE FACTORS AND POLYPLOIDY All three of the examples of multiple factors discussed above are taken from the plant kingdom. This is not simply a poor sample: although this type of inheritance is not unusual in the plant kingdom, it is almost unknown among animals. Why this difference should exist demands an explanation, and an explanation may be found in the chromosomal complements of the species concerned. As explained in chapter 3, the gametes of a typical species contain one chromosome of each kind, the haploid chromosome set. These unite in pairs to form zygotes with two chromosomes of each kind, and such an organism is said to be diploid. However, the chromosome numbers of related species of plants are often most suggestive. Thus among the wheats, *Triticum monococcum* has seven pairs of chromosomes, while *T. durum* has fourteen pairs, and *T. vulgare* has twenty-one pairs. It is difficult to avoid the inference that the higher numbers have been formed by duplication of whole sets of chromosomes. Detailed evidence (to be presented in a subsequent chapter) indicates that such is actually the case, and such plants, characterized by multiples of a basic chromosome set, are called *polyploids* (Greek—*polyplous*, manyfold). With this knowledge at hand, one need not look far for an explanation of multiple factor inheritance: there may be expected to be as many identical pairs of genes as there are basic sets of chromosomes. Actually, this theoretical expectation may be reduced by independent mutation in the different chromosome sets.

But why should multiple factors, so common among plants, be rare or non-existent among animals? Polyploidy itself is rare among animals, probably because polyploidy would upset the balance of the sex chromosomes. The majority of plants are monoecious, that is, both sexes are represented in one individual, and hence no sex chromosome mechanism is necessary. It is noteworthy that among those relatively few plants in which the sexes are separate polyploidy is rare; while the scattered cases of polyploidy in the animal kingdom are concentrated among those exceptional species which ordinarily reproduce parthenogenetically or hermaphroditically.

The above discussion is applicable to duplicate and triplicate factors, the kind of multiple factors originally studied by Nilsson-Ehle. But one also speaks of multiple factors when several nonallelic genes of a single chromosome set influence a single character in an additive way. This has nothing to do with polyploidy, and so is as common among animals as among plants. As such multiple factors are the basis of inheritance of quantitative characters, the discussion of this topic will be deferred to the following chapter.

25. HETEROZYGOUS EXPRESSION

Mendelian ratios will also be modified whenever the phenotypic expression of the heterozygote differs from both homozygous

types. Actually, the first example taken up in chapter 2 was of this type. Red and white flowering varieties of four-o'clocks were crossed. The F_1 plants were all pink-flowering, there being no dominance. In the F_2, a ratio of one red to two pink to one white was obtained, because the expression of the heterozygote differed from that of either pure type. This subject does not logically belong in a chapter on collaborative effects. However, the major example is concerned with endosperm characters of maize, to which much attention has been given above. Hence this seems to be a convenient place to discuss the subject of heterozygous expression.

Simple lack of dominance is perhaps the commonest type of heterozygous expression. It is easily recognizable through the intermediacy of the heterozygotes. But a more specialized type occurs with regard to certain endosperm characters. Before going into this, however, it may be advisable to

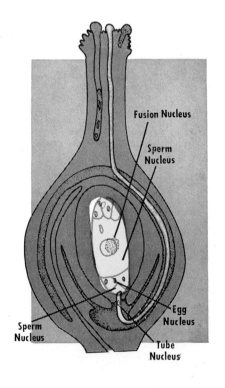

Fig. 62. *Fertilization in a flowering plant. Note that one sperm nucleus unites with the egg nucleus, while the other unites with the fusion nucleus.*

review certain facts from elementary botany. The end products of the maturation divisions of a plant are megaspores (female) and microspores (male), each of which is initially a single, haploid cell. The microspore nucleus then divides mitotically and one of the daughter nuclei divides a second time. The result is a pollen grain containing three haploid nuclei, all of which are genetically identical. Two of these are sperm nuclei, while the third is the pollen tube nucleus. Each megaspore nucleus undergoes a series of three mitotic divisions, resulting in an ovule containing eight haploid nuclei. Again, all of these must be genetically identical, because they are the mitotic products of one original haploid nucleus. But their prospective fates are not alike. Only one of the eight is the real egg nucleus. Two more fuse together to form the diploid *fusion* nucleus, which plays an essential role in the formation of the seed. The other five ovule nuclei deteriorate without forming definitive structures.

When fertilization (fig. 62) occurs, the pollen tube enters the ovule and *both* sperm nuclei migrate in. One unites with the egg nucleus to form the zygote nucleus which leads to the formation of an embryo. The second sperm nucleus unites with the fusion nucleus to form a triploid fertilization product. From this triploid nucleus is formed the endosperm, the main nutritive mass of the seed. And because it is triploid, each gene is represented three times, one gene from the pollen parent, and two identical genes from the ovule parent. Two possibilities are evident when such a triploid nucleus is heterozygous. Dominance of an endosperm gene could be absolute, so that even a single dominant gene would be expressed over two recessive genes. Or dominance could be relative, so that whichever gene was present in duplicate would be expressed to the exclusion of the other one. Actually, both

occur, and both will be exemplified below.

The first type has already been exemplified above with the hierarchy of color characters. In the case of the *C* gene, for example, endosperms will be colored with either genotype *CCc* or *Ccc* while only those with *ccc* will be white. The influence of the sperm nucleus, when it carries a dominant gene, in determining a character even in the triploid endosperm, was discovered by Correns, and was called by him *xenia*. The full color of grains of genotype *Ccc* is an example. The second type is exemplified by a pair of characters concerned with the texture of the endosperm, flinty and floury. If a cross be made between a flinty plant, *FF*, and a floury plant, *ff*, then the resulting F_1 plants will all be heterozygous, *Ff*, but the endosperms of the seeds from which they arise will have the genotype *FFf* and the phenotype flinty. In the reciprocal cross, *ff* × *FF*, the progeny will again be the monohybrids, *Ff*, but the endosperms of the seeds from which they grow will have the genotype *ffF* and the phenotype floury. Because of this type of functional relationship between the alleles, the F_2 gives an unusual ratio (which is identical from either of the above mentioned F_1's). In order to understand this, a Roman square should be made with two columns for the pollen parent and *four* columns for the female parent, two for the egg nuclei and two for the fusion nuclei. The third column thus indicates the fusion nucleus which corresponds to the egg nucleus of column one, while the second and fourth columns have a similar correspondence. Hence the first two columns show the constitutions of the zygotes, and will indicate their potential breeding behavior in producing an F_3. But the last two columns show the genotypes of the F_2 endosperms. Those having genotypes *FFF* or *FFf* have flinty endosperm, while those with genotypes *ffF* or *fff* have floury endosperm. Thus the F_2

phenotypic ratio is actually 1 to 1:

P flinty ♀ FF × floury ♂ ff

F$_1$ Ff (flinty—endosperm FFf)

F$_2$ ovules

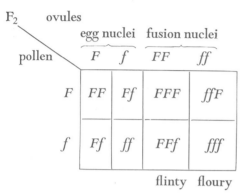

flinty floury

1 : 1

Thus the tabulation of genotypes and phenotypes shows that the phenotype depends upon the relative *quantities* of the two alleles.

26. TYPES OF FACTOR INTERACTION

The earliest studies in genetics led to a conception of gene action in which each pair of genes produced its phenotype independently of all others. An organism was thus regarded as a mosaic of independent characters. Interaction between the members of one pair of genes seemed to be limited to simple dominance, with one member of a heterozygous pair being expressed to the exclusion of the other.

Because of the phenomena discussed above, this simple conception has been abandoned. With respect to dominance, which De Vries described as a "law," it is now clear that this is not the universal, inexorable phenomenon which it at first appeared to be. In many cases, simple intermediacy occurs, as in the case of the pink four-o'clocks, so that the concept of dominance is not applicable at all. In the case of some endosperm characters, like the flinty-floury alternative, dominance is shown, but it is a simple quantitative matter: the allele which is present twice is expressed to the exclusion of the one which is present only once, regardless of which is which. Thus it appears that dominance is not an integral characteristic of the gene itself, but rather a characteristic of the phenotype which can be influenced by the quantitative balance among the genes, and by other factors as well. Again, in the inheritance of quantitative characters (to be discussed in the next chapter) dominance is commonly not apparent. In spite of all of these qualifications, dominance is a very widespread phenomenon, but it is not as universal as it appeared at first.

We have seen several types of interaction between non-allelic genes. One gene may be expressed to the exclusion of another. It looks like dominance, but dominance is by definition a relationship between members of a pair of alleles. The masking effect between genes of two different pairs is called *epistasis*. Thus the gene for albinism is epistatic over all the rest of the coat color hierarchy in rodents. Or different pairs of genes may collaborate more or less equally in the

Fig. 63. *Hooded rats, with varying degrees of extension.*

formation of a single phenotypic character, as in the case of comb form in fowl. Finally, one major gene may determine a character, while a whole series of independent genes alter its expression, usually in a quantitative way. Such minor genes are called modifiers. For example, in the rat, a major gene is responsible for the hooded coat pattern, in which the pelage is generally white, but the head and shoulders are black (fig. 63). A series of modifying genes can cause the extension of the black hood over more and more of the body until an almost solid black results if all of the modifiers are favorable to hood extension. The effect of each gene pair is small, but additive.

Thus collaborative actions of genes, which were once supposed to be exceptional, have now been shown to be the norm.

Questions and Problems

1. Define:

Aleurone	Heterozygous expression
Biochemical mutants	Hierarchy of genes
Chromagen	Hyposta ic
Collaboration of factors	Minimal medium
Complementary genes	Modifier
Duplicate factors	Multiple factors
Endosperm	Oxidase
Epistatic	Pleiotropy

What progenies will result from the following crosses:

2. $CCPP \times ccpp$ (flower color in sweet peas).
3. $CCpp \times ccPP$
4. $CcPp \times CcPp$
5. $CcPp \times ccpp$
6. $RRpp \times rrpp$ (comb form in fowl)
7. $Rrpp \times rrpp$
8. $rrPp \times rrPp$

9. $RrPp \times RrPp$
10. $IIAACCRRPP \times iiaaccrrpp$ (aleurone color in corn)
11. $IiAaCcRrPp \times IiAaCcRrPp$
12. $iiAaCcRRPP \times iiaaccRRPP$
13. $iiAACCrrPP \times iiAACCRRpp$

14. Two hens with walnut comb are mated to the same pea-combed rooster. The following offspring are obtained:

From hen 1: 3 walnut, 3 pea, 1 rose, and 1 single.
From hen 2: 5 walnut and 3 pea.

What are the genotypes of the parents? Write the crosses in Mendelian symbols.

15. A walnut-combed hen lays a single egg, from which a single combed chick hatches. What is the genotype of the hen?

16. A cross is made between flinty and floury wheat, then the F_1 is backcrossed to floury. What will the backcross generation be with respect to genotype and phenotype? For the genotype, consideration must be given to both germinal tissue and endosperm.

References

Caspari, Ernst, 1952. Pleiotropic gene action. Evolution, 6:1–18. A brief but thoughtful and provocative review of the subject.

Grüneberg, Hans, 1952. Genetics of the Mouse. Second edition. Martinus Nijhoff, The Hague. A comprehensive summary of our knowledge of inheritance in mice.

Horowitz, N. H., 1950. Biochemical genetics of *Neurospora*. In Advances in Genetics, 3:33–71. A very readable and clear presentation of some of the important work in this field.

Hutt, F. B., 1949. Genetics of the Fowl. McGraw-Hill Co., New York. A clear, comprehensive treatment of genetics in chickens and other domestic fowl.

Punnett, R. C., 1927. Mendelism. Seventh edition. The Macmillan Co., London. The classic experiments of Bateson and Punnett recounted by their co-author.

CHAPTER 10

Modifications of Mendelian Inheritance

V: Quantitative Inheritance

The character pairs discussed in the preceding chapters have generally presented clear-cut, easily diagnosed alternatives. Thus Mendel's tall peas were no less than six feet tall, while his dwarf peas were never taller than a foot and a half. Both varieties varied in height somewhat, but the tallest dwarf could not possibly be confused with the shortest of the tall peas. The currant moths had dark wings or they had milky colored wings. Snails were dextrally coiled or they were sinistrally coiled. In every case, there is a sharp discontinuity between the alternative members of a pair. Such discontinuous types are said to differ *qualitatively*.

Mendel's success was due in part to his selection of such qualitative differences for his experimental material, and the early Mendelians of the present century followed his example. However, not all of the differences between organisms fall into such neatly separable classes. Many differences are best expressed by *measurement*, and the measurements of a large number of individuals are likely to range by imperceptible steps between the extremes. Quetelet's data on French soldiers exemplify this nicely. In such a *continuously varying* series, any assignment to classes must be arbitrary. The analysis of such continuous variation is the problem of quantitative inheritance. This type of inheritance has great practical importance, for it is quantitative characters like crop yield, milk production, size of cattle or hogs, and egg production upon which agriculture depends.

27. THE BASIS OF QUANTITATIVE INHERITANCE

Actually, quantitative inheritance had been studied intensively even before the rediscovery of Mendelism. Sir Francis Galton, a cousin of Charles Darwin, made very extensive studies in this field in the last half of the nineteenth century. Darwin believed that continuously varying characters were the ones which had most importance for evolution. In his efforts to develop this thesis, Galton made no progress toward the solution of the problems of heredity, but he did devise excellent biometrical tools for the description and analysis of variation. When Mendelian heredity came to the fore with its emphasis on sharply discontinuous unit characters, it appeared that this was completely disharmonious with the Galtonian studies, and the belief was widespread that quantitative inheritance could not be understood in Mendelian terms. It is to the credit of Nilsson-Ehle and the American E. M. East (of Harvard) to have proposed independently the *multiple factor hypothesis,* according to which quantitative inheritance could be analyzed in Mendelian terms if it be assumed that numerous independent pairs of genes, lacking dominance, each contribute a small amount to the determination of a quantitative character. Examples from the work of each of these men will be presented below.

INHERITANCE OF COLOR IN WHEAT Nilsson-Ehle's study of triplicate factor inheritance of grain color in wheat, as summarized in the preceding chapter, was already oversimplified, for only two color classes, red and white, were recognized. But, actually, the reds varied from an intense red through an array of lighter reds and pinks to a very light pink, almost an off-white. About one plant in every sixty-four produced white seed, while the same proportion produced seed of the deepest red. The majority of the plants yielded seed in the middle of the color range, but the adjacent color classes blended with one another so that an exact enumeration of the plants by classes was not possible.

Nilsson-Ehle saw that these results could be understood only if one discarded the notion of dominant and recessive alleles, and instead thought of them as *plus* (R_1, R_2, and R_3) and *minus* (r_1, r_2, and r_3). Thus a plant of genotype $r_1r_1r_2r_2r_3r_3$ has white seed, and each plus gene substituted in the genotype adds a small amount of redness, their effects being additive. Because there is no dominance, a plant of genotype $R_1R_1\ r_2r_2r_3r_3$ produces seed which is twice as red as does one of genotype $R_1r_1r_2r_2r_3r_3$, and equal in redness to one of genotype $R_1r_1R_2r_2r_3r_3$. In other words, the degree of redness is a simple function of the number of plus genes for color. On the other hand, this character like most others is subject to environmentally caused fluctuations, and, as the effect of each individual plus gene is small enough to

be masked by these fluctuations, the observed color range is a continuous spectrum in which sharply defined classes simply do not appear.

But, although phenotypic classes cannot be accurately separated, knowledge of trihybrid segregation makes it possible to determine the proportions of F_2 plants which ought to have any particular number of plus genes. Thus if a cross is made between an intensely red variety ($R_1R_1R_2R_2R_3R_3$) and a white variety ($r_1r_1r_2r_2r_3r_3$), the F_1 should all have three plus genes, $R_1r_1R_2r_2R_3r_3$, and actually the color is intermediate. The expected results in the F_2 can be determined by making a progression table. The essential data are summarized in table 8.

Table 8. Relative Intensity of Color

No. of plus genes	6	5	4	3	2	1	0
No. of plants per 64	1	6	15	20	15	6	1

It may be noted that this distribution of plus genes describes a normal probability curve, as illustrated in figure 64.

INHERITANCE OF FLOWER SIZE IN TOBACCO The principles of quantitative inheritance are perhaps even more clearly demonstrated by East's study of size in tobacco. The tobacco flower (fig. 65) consists of a long, nar-

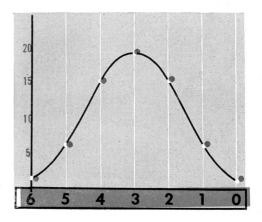

Fig. 64. *Curve of distribution of genes for color in the F_2 of Nilsson-Ehle's trihybrid cross. The abscissa indicates the number of plus genes in the genotype, while the ordinate indicates the number of plants out of 64.*

row tube, the *corolla*, from the end of which five petals extend, like a star, in one plane. East had one variety with short corollas, averaging only 25.6 millimeters in length, and another variety with long corollas averaging 78.8 millimeters. Each of these was moderately variable, the standard deviations being 2.27 and 5.38, respectively. Upon crossing these two varieties, the F_1 was approximately intermediate, with an average corolla length of 44.3 millimeters and a standard deviation of 3.67. In the F_2 (of 828 plants) the mean was about the same, 49.9 millimeters, but the range of variation was very much greater (fig. 66), including both of the original parental types and having a standard deviation of 11.26. In this broadening of the base of the curve he saw (correctly) evidence of the segregation and recombination of numerous independent Mendelian genes. East's data are summarized in table 9 and in figure 66.

Fig. 65. *East's flower-size cross in* Nicotiana. *1, the large parental type; 2, the small parental type; 3, the* F_1; *and 4–9, F_2 segregants. (From East, in the Botanical Gazette, vol. 55.)*

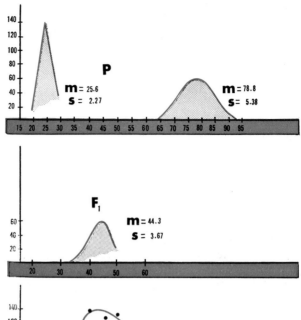

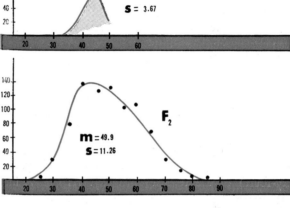

Fig. 66. *A series of curves summarizing East's data on inheritance of corolla length in* Nicotiana.

Table 9. Frequency Distributions for Length of Corolla in a Cross Between Two Varieties of <u>Nicotiana</u> (Tobacco)

Modified from East

PLANTS	CLASS CENTERS IN MILLIMETERS														
	20	25	30	35	40	45	50	55	60	65	70	75	80	85	90
Short parent	9	133	28												
Long parent										1	19	50	56	32	9
F_1				3	30	58	20								
F_2			5	27	79	136	125	132	102	105	64	30	15	6	2

What is going on here can be easily understood if it is presented as a series of segregating Mendelian genes with plus and minus effects. Let us assume for simplicity that only three pairs of genes are segregating. The genotype *aabbcc* will then determine a certain minimal length of the corolla, averaging about 25 millimeters. In such an instance in which a complete array of minus genes leads to a positive quantity, one speaks of the *residual heredity*, and each plus gene which is substituted then adds a certain amount to this minimum. The other parental type has all of the plus genes, $AABBCC$. The F_1 would then be the trihybrid, $AaBbCc$, so it is plain that such plants should be relatively uniform trihybrids. The F_2 should therefore be a typical trihybrid segregation, the progression table for which has been given in table 2 on page 41. The great variability of the F_2, then, depends upon the fact that a trihybrid segregation yields no less than twenty-seven different genotypes! These are, of course, not all phenotypically different, for all those with the same number of plus genes are alike. Thus a trihybrid for a quantitative character leads to a progeny with seven classes, ranging from six plus genes to none, as shown above in table 8.

ESTIMATING THE NUMBER OF GENES SEGREGATING Is the above supposition, that three pairs of genes are segregating for corolla length, a reasonable one? If it is, then either of the parental extremes should be recovered to the extent of about one sixty-fourth of the total F_2 progeny. As there were 828 plants in the F_2, this means that the parental extremes should have been represented by about thirteen plants each ($828/64 = 12.9$). Actually, the extremes are fewer. But if five pairs of genes were segregating, then each parental extreme should make up $1/1024$ of the total progeny. In short, it would be quite likely to be missing from a progeny of only 828 plants. Hence East concluded that there were most probably four pairs of genes segregating for corolla length.

To put the above operation in more general terms, it may be said that the number of genes segregating is a function of the minimum size of population which is necessary in order to recover the parental extremes. These extremes are completely homozygous for all of the plus genes or for all of the minus genes. The frequency with which such a homozygote will be formed is $1/4^n$, where n is the number of genes segregating.

Thus the frequencies of reappearance of parental extremes for various numbers of segregating genes may be summarized as follows:

Number of pairs	Relative Frequency
1	$1/4$
2	$1/16$
3	$1/64$
4	$1/256$
5	$1/1024$
6	$1/4096$
7	$1/16384$
8	$1/65536$
9	$1/262,144$
10	$1/1,048,576$
n	$1/4^n$

Because of the immense numbers of progeny which would have to be raised in order to get decisive results where more than a very modest number of genes are segregating, the method has very limited applicability. For the same reason, studies in quantitative inheritance are likely to lead to conclusions such as that the number of genes for oil content of corn is "at least of the order of 20–40, possibly of 200–400, and not at all likely to be of the order of 5–10." Sewall Wright of the University of Chicago has subjected this problem of numbers of genes segregating to a brilliant mathematical analysis.

SOME ODDS AND ENDS A few minor points should be considered before leaving the corolla length study. It was stated above that the F_1 was intermediate between the parental varieties. This is not quite true, for the arithmetical average of the two parental means is 52.2, while the F_1 mean actually obtained was only 44.3, a significantly lower value. But there are other kinds of means besides the arithmetical. Growth of a plant is of course a three dimensional thing, and it is hardly to be expected that a simple linear process like addition would give a good measure of it. A *geometrical mean* can be calculated by multiplying the two parental averages and then extracting the square root. This gives a value of 44.9, which is certainly not significantly different from the experimentally obtained F_1 mean of 44.3. For many problems involving growth, geometrical means have proved more useful than the more usual arithmetic means.

Examination of the F_2 curve in figure 66 will show that it is not a true, symmetrical normal probability curve, like those discussed in chapter 4. Instead, it is definitely skewed to the left. East thought that this too might depend upon the geometrical character of growth processes, so that there ought to be fewer classes with the size of the class intervals increasing with the size of the flowers. So he recalculated his data, starting with a four millimeter class interval, and increasing each class interval by one millimeter over the preceding one. Plotted in this way, a very good normal probability curve was obtained. In other cases, however, it may be much more difficult to find so successful a method of handling the data.

THE INHERITANCE OF EAR LENGTH IN CORN
Another famous example of quantitative inheritance which has been quoted and requoted was also originally studied by East, together with R. A. Emerson. This is the case of inheritance of ear length in corn. The short eared parent used in the study was a commercial variety known as Tom Thumb pop corn. The range of variation in length was from 5 to 8 centimeters, with a mean of 6.6 and a standard deviation of 0.81. The long eared variety was Mexican Black corn,

with a range of variation from 12 to 21 centimeters, a mean of 16.8, and a standard deviation of 1.87.

The question may well be asked, is Mexican Black corn really more variable than Tom Thumb popcorn, or is the greater apparent variability simply a geometric consequence of the greater total size? This question can be answered by calculating the coefficients of variability $(V = 100s/m)$. They turn out to be 12.2 for Tom Thumb popcorn and 11.1 for Mexican Black corn. Hence the inherent variability of the two strains is not very different, and actually the smaller variety is the more variable of the two.

The cross is summarized graphically in figure 67. The F_1 again is roughly intermediate between the parents, and is rather uniform. In the F_2, the mean is roughly the same as in the F_1, but the range of variation is very much greater, including one of the parental extremes. Plainly this is the result to be expected if many genes with small, additive effects but no dominance are segregating. Hence the inheritance of ear length in corn agrees in principle with the inheritance of corolla length of tobacco flowers and of color intensity in wheat.

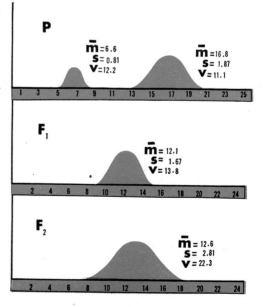

Fig. 67. *Graphical presentation of the cross between Tom Thumb popcorn and Mexican Black corn.*

28. TRANSGRESSIVE VARIATION AND HYBRID VIGOR

The assumption implicit in the above discussion, that one of the parental varieties must carry all of the plus genes and the other all of the minus genes, is not a necessary assumption, nor even a probable one if one deals with any variety of organism that has not been intensively inbred. Hence, when crosses between different varieties are followed with respect to a quantitative character, it not infrequently happens that the F_1 or subsequent generations exceed one or both of the original parental stocks. This may be easily understood in terms of the wheat color cross. Assume that a cross is made between a dark-red variety of genotype $R_1R_1R_2R_2r_3r_3$ and a light-red variety of genotype $r_1r_1r_2r_2R_3R_3$. The F_1 would all be trihybrids, and should be phenotypically intermediate between the parents. But the F_2 should include the whole array of genotypes ranging from all plus genes to all minus genes, and exceeding the phenotypes of the parental strains at both ends of the color range. This phenomenon is called *transgressive variation*, and it is very common in quantitative inheritance.

With only three pairs of genes segregating, it is to be expected that the extremes would be included in a moderate sized F_2. But suppose that there had been seven—or seventeen—pairs of genes, so that the extremes could be expected to appear only to the extent of a few in a very large progeny. In such cases, the base of the population curve broadens at every generation, as a result of segregation and recombination, until the extremes are reached, indicating that more and more of the potential genotypes are being realized at each successive generation. Such a series is diagrammed in figure 68. This type of behavior is really more characteristic of quantitative inheritance than the examples discussed previously, because generally rather large numbers of genes are involved. Because these numerous genes with

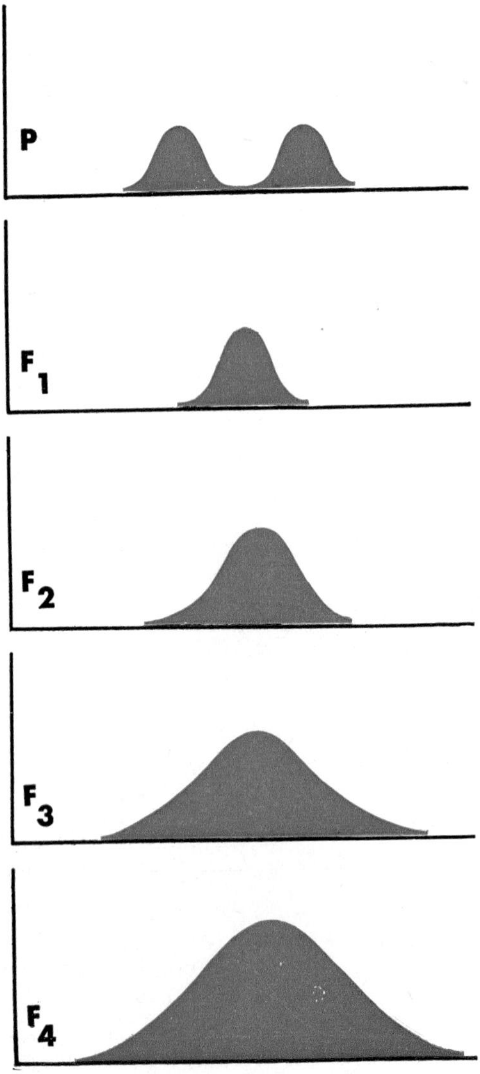

Fig. 68. *Transgressive variation. The P generation consists of two samples which differ widely, with the F_1 being intermediate. In the F_2 and succeeding generations, the base of the curve broadens and finally exceeds the two parental extremes.*

such small individual effects are not separately identifiable, Kenneth Mather, who has studied the problem intensively, prefers to speak of them as *polygenes*. But any inference that the polygenes differ fundamentally from genes with larger individual effects is unjustified by the available data.

HYBRID VIGOR OR HETEROSIS   More striking than transgressive variation is the occasional occurrence of an F_1 which far surpasses the parental lines in quantitative characters, including general vigor. This may be well illustrated by a cross between two varieties of a species of tobacco, *Nicotiana rustica*. The two varieties used contrasted in average height of the mature plant, in number of leaves, in length and breadth of leaves, and in the time required to mature. Plant height will typify this array of quantitative characters. Strain *A* averaged 49.9 inches in height, while strain B averaged 29 inches. The F_1, far from approximating the average of the two, actually approximated the average of the taller parent, with an average height of 48.5 inches, and individual F_1 plants exceeded the taller parental average. Now the tallest F_1 plants were selected for further breeding, and Smith was able to select out relatively pure-breeding strains which far surpassed the taller of the original parents. This is strikingly illustrated in figure 69, which shows the two parental plants, an F_1 plant, and a plant from the sixth generation of selection.

Two principal theories have been proposed to explain the facts of hybrid vigor. The simplest is that hybrid vigor results when one allele in each of the segregating pairs is *dominant* over the other. Relatively pure-breeding varieties would generally include some homozygous recessive genes, and crosses between different varieties would be likely to yield more *pairs* with dominants than had characterized either of the parents. Thus *AABBccdd* and *aabbCCDD* might be phenotypically similar, while their progeny

Fig. 69.   *Heterosis in tobacco. Left to right: the tall and short parental strains, the F_1 showing mild heterosis, and a plant from the sixth generation of selection for large size.*
(*From Smith, in Heterosis, Iowa State College Press.*)

119

AaBbCcDd would be much larger because every pair of genes includes a dominant. This *dominance theory of heterosis* is not in keeping with the statement above that polygenes are characterized by lack of dominance. But there is no reason why the relationship between the members of a pair of alleles should be the same for all genes influencing quantitative characters; and the fact that heterosis is not a universal phenomenon in itself indicates that genic action differs in different quantitative characters. This dominance theory of heterosis has achieved very widespread acceptance because of its plausibility, yet critical data to test it are very difficult to obtain because of the fact that individual polygenes are not readily identifiable.

The second theory is that *heterozygosity itself* causes a physiological stimulus which results in an organism superior to either of the homozygous types. This is sometimes called *overdominance*. While this theory has received less support than has the dominance theory, yet direct evidence for it is available in certain cases in which heterozygotes for unit factors are superior to the homozygotes. For example, the effects of certain chromosomal rearrangements (see chapter 12) on egg laying in a fruit fly, *Drosophila persimilis*, have been investigated. These chromosomal patterns are characterized by differences in the order of genes in the chromosome. One arrangement is called *ST* and the other is called *CH*. Females of genotype *ST/ST* lay nearly twice as many eggs per day as do females of genotype *CH/CH*. But heterozygous females, *ST/CH*, lay even more eggs than do the more prolific kind of homozygotes. This looks very much like overdominance. This example is by no means isolated, yet it is not clear that conclusions can be extended from such simple cases to typical cases of quantitative inheritance. This subject will be developed somewhat further below in connection with hybrid corn.

29. HYBRID CORN

The most important crop plant in the United States is *Zea mays*, corn or maize. To some this statement may sound surprising, for the average American eats a few ears of sweet corn-on-the-cob in the summer and a little canned corn during the rest of the year. But we eat wheat daily in bread, cereals, spaghetti, noodles, and other food products. Wheat is also valuable as a source of alcohol, both for industrial and beverage purposes. Incidentally, the dried stems of the plants are used for straw carpets, basketry, certain kinds of hats, and various other minor purposes. Can maize really be used more than wheat? The answer is unequivocally "yes." Annual production figures give an indication of the relative importance of the two. In 1947, 74,389,000 acres were sown in wheat in the United States. The resulting crop totaled 1,367,186,000 bushels. In the preceding year, 88,489,000 acres were planted in corn, and the crop totaled 3,249,950,000 bushels. Where does it all go? The greater part of it goes into feed for livestock. One cannot eat beef, pork, chicken, eggs, milk, or butter without eating corn, first passed through the digestive tract of an animal and converted into animal products of many different types.

One of the primary objectives of plant breeding is to get superior varieties of agricultural plants in pure-breeding (homozygous) form. The basic method is to inbreed the variety (by self-fertilizing when possible) and to select progeny with the desired characters for further breeding stock. In this way, homozygosity is achieved in a few generations. Because of the great importance of corn in our economy, its improvement has long been an important objective of the plant breeders. But it became apparent many years ago that the usual method of inbreeding and selection would not work in the case of corn. Even the best varieties of corn deteriorate rapidly when inbred. Often, the inbred lines show as little as 50 per cent of the productivity of the out-crossed parental varieties. In addition to this their general vigor is much reduced.

PRODUCTION OF HYBRID CORN Nonetheless, the Mendelian plant breeders of the early years of the present century continued to investigate inbred lines of corn for the knowledge to be gained from them. It was G. H. Shull who first realized, in 1905, that the problems of deterioration of inbred lines and of hybrid vigor were related. Upon crossing different inbreds, he obtained a progeny of excellent general vigor and with superior yield and grain characteristics. But it was not feasible to use this hybrid corn commercially, because the poor yields of the parent plants would keep the seed scarce. It was twelve years more before Donald F. Jones made practical the utilization of hybrid vigor in corn by the invention of the "double-cross" method. In this method, four inbred strains, which may be designated here as strains A, B, C, and D, are used. In the first year the crosses $A \times B$ and $C \times D$ are made. This leads to two different hybrids, AB and CD, each a vigorous and high-yielding type, greatly superior to its inbred parents, but small in quantity because of the poor seed production by the parents. In the second year, the two hybrids are crossed, with the result that a large crop of superior "double-cross" corn is obtained (fig. 70). This is the seed which is now sold to the farmer to produce the next year's crop.

THE NATURE OF HYBRID VIGOR IN CORN The exploitation of hybrid vigor in corn has been a major—perhaps the major—triumph of modern, genetically directed plant breeding. The principal theoretical knowledge upon which hybrid corn is based was all available by 1917, yet it began to appear on the market in appreciable quantities only in 1933. Its use increased rapidly, so that by 1943 about 98 per cent of the corn belt acreage was planted to hybrid corn. Yields often increased by as much as 50 per cent over the older varieties. As the increases never exceeded 25–30 per cent in the agricultural experiment stations, it appears that hybrid corn must have acted as a sort of catalyst to speed up the adoption of sound, scientific farming methods generally. The result was that during the three war years 1942–1944, in spite of drought and reductions in manpower and of acreage under cultivation, the farmers of America produced almost as much corn as in the *four* preceding years of peace. And because of this great abundance, the American dietetic standard was not only largely maintained (and improved for many people), but large quantities of food were shipped to our allies. And thus, because armies (production armies as well as military armies) march upon their stomachs, it may well be said that genetics played an important, possibly even decisive, role in winning the war.

This is a most impressive achievement, and its explanation must have great theoretical importance. Two theories of heterosis were introduced above, and each may be assessed for its ability to explain the facts of hybrid corn. Corn is normally a wind-pollinated plant, and hence is typically out-crossed and highly heterozygous. East, Shull, and others demonstrated many years ago that the deterioration of inbred lines was accompanied by the segregation of many different pure lines. But any one pure line will be homozygous for some plus genes and for some minus genes, and with many genes present, a great array of different pure lines is possible. Crossing different pure lines will then bring together complementary dominants. Now, if this is the basis of heterosis, use of part of the hybrid crop for seed for the next year should result in a poorer crop, because segregation should break up the favorable gene complexes. Traditionally, farmers have always saved a portion of each crop for next year's seed. They learned to their sorrow that that cannot be done with hybrid corn, for farmers who actually tried it (against the advice of the seed companies) harvested very poor crops in the second year, as should be expected on the theory of complementary dominant genes. This is most agreeable to the seed producers, who are assured of a good sale every year. It is also agreeable to the farmers, because their hybrid crops are so superior to the old open pollinated varieties that they can well afford to buy new seed every year.

Evidence for the theory of overdominance, which attributes a special value to the heterozygous state as such, is less direct. Its advocates point out that, if the theory of complementary dominants is correct, then

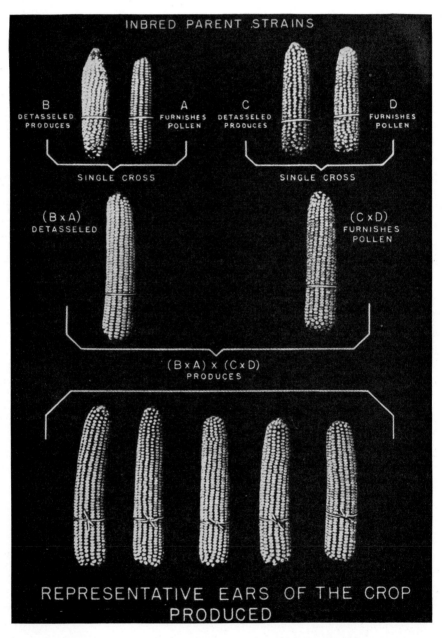

Fig. 70. *Hybrid corn and its ancestry. (U. S. Depart. of Agriculture.)*

it should be possible to segregate out the types with all or most of the plus genes. Thus superior, pure breeding types would be available. Yet this has never been possible: homozygous lines of corn always seem to be degenerative. Hence, it is argued, the superiority of the hybrids must be due to overdominance. While very plausible, there are two serious obstacles to the acceptance of this reasoning. First, the hybrids are not necessarily quantitatively superior to all outbred corn. The hybrids do not exceed the very best performance of the older varieties. But the hybrids uniformly achieve this excellence, while all of the open-pollinated varieties are highly variable. The literature is charged with the inference that the superiority of the hybrids is almost a mystical thing, yet comparison of hybrids to the best of varietal corn has led some investigators to the opinion that hybrid corn is uniformly "normal," while other corn is in one degree or another "subnormal."

The second difficulty is inherent in the multiple factor nature of quantitative inheritance. It was pointed out above that very large numbers of genes may be involved in a single quantitative character. But the heterosis of corn involves many independent characters, so that the number of gene pairs segregating must be great indeed. How probable is it that a pure line (inbred) with all or most of the plus genes could be segregated out? Singleton has calculated that, if only thirty pairs of genes were involved, it would require two thousand times the total area of the earth to grow enough corn to have a fifty-fifty chance of recovering a plant completely homozygous for all of the plus genes. Thus the failure to get such pure-breeding superior plants is really not serious evidence against the theory of complementary dominants. At present, the consensus among geneticists favors this theory but there is no unanimity, and the positive evidence is less strong than might be desired.

30. SUMMARY AND ADDENDA

All of the phenomena of quantitative inheritance can be understood in terms of the multiple factor hypothesis. This hypothesis is that quantitative characters depend upon the segregation of many different pairs of genes with plus and minus effects, and generally lacking dominance. Because the effect of each individual allele is small, on the order of environmentally caused fluctuations, the appearance is one of continuous variation, in which discrete phenotypes, corresponding to specified genotypes, cannot be identified. Because of this, quantitative inheritance must be studied primarily with the tools of biometrical analysis.

The characters which are inherited upon the basis of such swarms of minor genes (the polygenes of Mather) include all of those innumerable biological properties which are best defined by measurement rather than by a qualitative naming, such as intensity of color; size of the whole organism, or of its component parts; concentration of particular substances like an oil, a vitamin, or butterfat; yield of milk by dairy cattle; or yield of grain per acre. Such a list could be extended indefinitely, and would include practically all agriculturally important characteristics of domestic plants and animals. Numerous characters of man are probably also inherited in this way, such as height, intelligence, basal metabolic rate, longevity, and many others.

If crosses are made between plus and minus individuals, the F_1 should have an intermediate number of plus genes, and so is generally phenotypically intermediate. Then in the F_2, segregation results in a broad spectrum of phenotypes. Because the number of genes segregating may be too great for the whole range of possible genotypes to segregate out in a moderately sized F_2 population, the common result is that the base of the curve (that is to say, the range of variation) broadens at each successive generation until the extremes are reached. Selection at any point will establish a new curve, with its mean shifted in the direction of selection. These facts are summarized in figure 71.

In connection with heterosis, it became apparent that intermediate inheritance of quantitative traits is not universal, but rather dominance may occur. Another sort of evidence of dominance is obtained when the curve of an F_1 population is *skewed*, that is, its mode shifted away from the center to give an asymmetrical curve. If it is shifted to the left (as in the case of crosses involving extreme differences in human height), it indicates dominance of the minus genes; while a shift to the right would indicate dominance of the plus genes. But commonly the mode of the F_1, although skewed toward one of the parental modes, does not reach it, and one may then speak of *partial dominance* or *incomplete dominance*.

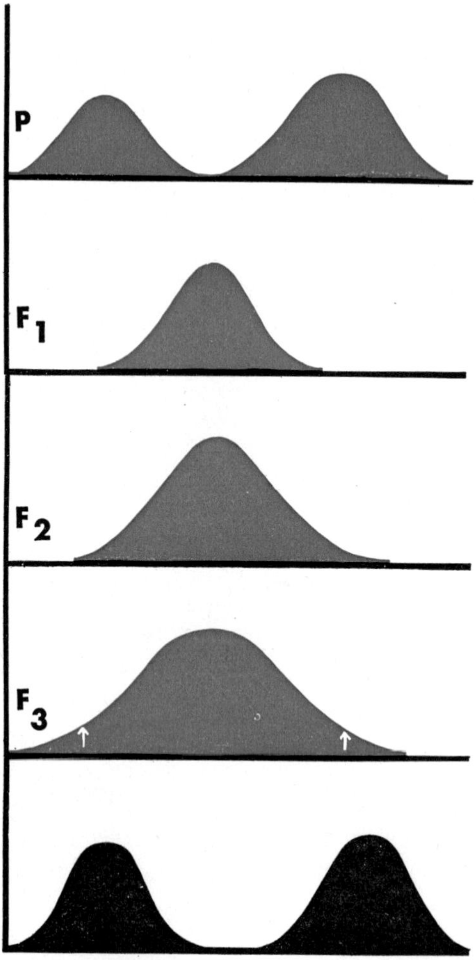

Finally, it was assumed above that all of a myriad of genes influencing a particular quantitative character have about equal effects. The evidence available indicates that this is often true, perhaps even usually true. But there are certainly instances in which it is not true, and certain genes have major effects, while numerous other genes behave as modifiers for the major genes. The *tall-dwarf* alternative in Mendel's original experiments represents such an example. In man, height is influenced by numerous anatomical components, such as size and shape of the skull, thickness of the centra of the vertebrae, thickness of the intervertebral discs, length of the long bones of the legs, and other minor factors. Obviously, any gene influencing length of the long bones will have a much greater effect on total height than will any gene influencing the other components mentioned.

Questions and Problems

1. Distinguish between quantitative and qualitative characters.
2. Define:

Arithmetic mean	Polygenes
Geometric mean	Residual heredity
Hybrid vigor (heterosis)	Transgressive variation
Multiple factor hypothesis	

Fig. 71. *A summary of quantitative inheritance. The P generation consists of two samples differing widely for a quantitative trait. The F_1 is intermediate and fairly uniform. In succeeding generations, the base of the curve broadens progressively until all possible genotypes have been formed. The arrows on the F_3 curve indicate selection at their respective levels, and the next generation shows the response to selection.*

3. A long-eared and a short-eared variety of rabbits are crossed. The F_1 is intermediate, with small fluctuation about the mean. The F_2 is also intermediate, but with more fluctuation. The shortest-eared F_2 individuals are selected for further breeding, and in the F_3 a few out of hundreds are as short-eared as the original parents, and these breed true in the F_4. Explain these data in genetic terms, with formulas and curves.

4. A small race of plants averages 20 centimeters in height, while a tall one averages 32. On crossing, the F_1 has a mean of 26 centimeters with a moderate variation. The F_2 also has a mean of 26 centimeters, but the range of variation is much greater. In fact, out of about 4000 plants, a very few reach or closely approach the parental extremes. Draw curves to illustrate these data.

5. Now estimate the number of pairs of genes segregating in problem 4.

6. Now add genetic symbols to explain why the curves of problem 4 go as they do.

7. A strain of cattle averaging 6 quarts daily milk yield is crossed with a strain averaging 12 quarts. Draw a series of curves showing the probable results of such a cross, assuming random mating among the progeny in each successive generation.

8. A small strain of beans with a mean length of 12 millimeters and a range of 10 to 14 mm. is crossed with a large strain with a mean of 16 mm. and a range of 12 to 20 mm. The F_1 is approximately intermediate, while the F_2 yields the following results:

BEAN LENGTH	NUMBER
11	3
12	9
13	34
14	131
15	251
16	330
17	323
18	138
19	40
20	7

Draw curves for this series of crosses, and calculate the mean and standard deviation for the F_2. How many genes for size would you estimate to be segregating in these beans?

References

East, E. M., 1913. Inheritance of flower size in crosses between species of *Nicotiana*. Botanical Gazette, 55:177–188. The co-discoverer of the principles of quantitative inheritance analyzes a case simply and clearly.

Gowen, John W. (editor), 1952. Heterosis. Iowa State College Press. A collection of essays on special aspects of the problem by some of its most distinguished students.

Jones, D. F., 1917. Dominance of linked factors as a means of accounting for heterosis. Genetics, 3:159–192. This is the paper that opened up the possibilities of the hybrid corn industry.

Mangelsdorf, P. C., 1952. Plants and Human Affairs. University of Notre Dame Press. Includes a very effective and readable treatment of hybrid corn.

Mather, Kenneth, 1951. The Progress and Prospect of Biometrical Genetics. In "Genetics in the 20th Century." A thoughtful evaluation.

Shull, G. H., 1946. Hybrid seed corn. Science, 103:547–550. A brief review by one of the pioneers of corn breeding.

Smith, H. H., 1944. Recent studies of inheritance of quantitative characters in plants. The Botanical Review, 10:349–382. An excellent summary of research up to the date of publication.

Whaley, W. G., 1944. Heterosis. The Botanical Review, 10:461–498. An excellent brief summary, with an extensive bibliography.

CHAPTER 11

Linkage and Crossing Over

The Law of Independent Assortment, as indicated in chapter 4, depends upon the location of the different pairs of segregating genes in non-homologous chromosomes. The garden pea has only seven pairs of chromosomes, and Mendel was fortunate in selecting (quite by chance) seven pairs of genes no two of which are located in the same pair of chromosomes. But there are around fifty pairs of genes which have been thoroughly studied in peas, as well as numerous others which have been casually studied, and undoubtedly many more which have not been studied at all. *Drosophila* has only four pairs of chromosomes, and hundreds of pairs of genes have been studied. Around 400 pairs of genes are known in maize, yet there are only ten pairs of chromosomes. Stern estimates the total number of pairs of genes in man as "probably not less than 5000 or more than 120,000."[*] But man has only twenty-four pairs of chromosomes. Thus it is obvious that numerous pairs of genes must be located in each pair of chromosomes.

31. LINKAGE DEFINED

If a dihybrid cross be made between any two pairs of genes which are located in the same pair of chromosomes, it is plain that independent assortment could not occur, for both pairs of genes depend upon the same factor, namely the meiotic distribution of a single pair of chromosomes. They are like passengers on the same bus, who must go in the same direction. The existence of numerous pairs of genes in the same pair of chromosomes is called *linkage*, and the behavior of linked genes will be the subject of the present chapter.

INHERITANCE OF LINKED GENES   The phenomenon of linkage was discovered by T. H. Morgan in 1910. The discussion of his first example will be deferred, as it also included sex linkage. Two third chromosome genes, hairy (*h*), a bristle mutant, and approximated (*app*), a wing vein mutant, may serve as an example of linkage between autosomal genes.

But before giving the details of a cross involving these two genes, it may be well to introduce a type of genetic notation which is better adapted to linkage studies than that used up to this point. A pair of chromosomes may be represented by a line, with the genes of one member of the pair being written above the line, and those of the other member being written below the line. Thus a fly homozygous for both *hairy* and *approximated*, written hh app app in the older notation, now becomes $\frac{h\ app}{h\ app}$. Yet another convention has been found useful by the *Drosophila* geneticists. As mutants in general may be thought of as deviations from normalcy, the normal or wild type alleles are conveniently designated simply by a plus sign, +. Thus a fly heterozygous for

[*] From Principles of Genetics by Curt Stern. W. H. Freeman and Company, 1949.

the genes mentioned above may be indicated by the formula, $\dfrac{h\ app}{+\ +}$. There is, of course, a possibility of confusion as to which "plus" corresponds to which mutant. This can be avoided by adding the "plus" as a superscript to the gene symbol, as h^+ and app^+.

In using these symbols, there is no implication that the normal allele is necessarily dominant and the mutant recessive. Although this is commonly true, it need not be. Thus in *Drosophila*, the gene for lobe eyes is obviously abnormal, a mutant from the more typical condition. So the gene for normal eyes (recessive) is indicated by +, and that for lobe eyes by the symbol L. Thus it is the *normal* or *wild type* condition that is designated by the plus sign, irrespective of which allele is dominant. Finally, it may be mentioned that this practice, originally used only by the *Drosophila* geneticists, has become very widespread.

To return to the problem of the inheritance of linked genes, a cross may be made between a hairy, approximated stock of flies and a normal stock. All of the progeny will be normal but heterozygous, with both of the mutants in one chromosome, and both of the normal alleles in the other. In symbols, this becomes:

$$\frac{h\ app}{h\ app} \times \frac{+\ +}{+\ +} \rightarrow \frac{h\ app}{+\ +}$$

The heterozygous condition of the F_1 flies can be tested by backcrossing such F_1 females to males from the recessive stock:

$$\frac{h\ app}{+\ +} \times \frac{h\ app}{h\ app}$$

If the chromosomes of the hybrid females remain unmodified, only two kinds of eggs can be formed: those containing the two normal alleles (+ +), and those containing the two mutant genes ($h\ app$). The male parent can, of course, produce only gametes with the two recessives. Fertilization then leads to two kinds of zygotes in equal numbers, and these are identical with the parents of the backcross generation, $\dfrac{h\ app}{+\ +}$ and $\dfrac{h\ app}{h\ app}$. They are also identical in phenotype with the original parents, and so these are called the *parental* types.

CROSSING OVER When the above series of crosses is made, it turns out that the backcross generation is made up of these parental types to the extent of 90 per cent of the flies. But the remaining 10 per cent are new combinations, either normal bristled with approximated wing veins or hairy with normal wing veins. The occurrence of such *recombination* types can be understood only on the assumption that there is an interchange of genes between the two third chromosomes of the heterozygous F_1 females. Thus an exchange occurs between the two chromosomes as indicated by an X, and so $\dfrac{h}{+}\times\dfrac{app}{+}$ leads to the formation of eggs of constitutions $h+$ and $+app$, and to zygotes of constitutions $\dfrac{h+}{h\ app}$ and $\dfrac{+\ app}{h\ app}$. As this *crossing over* occurs in only 10 per cent of the eggs, the total backcross progeny consists of 90 per cent parental types and 10 per cent recombination types. Thus all phenotypes which could have appeared with independent assortment also appear when the genes are linked. But, where a dihybrid backcross would give a ratio of 1 : 1 : 1 : 1 with independent assortment, in the case of linkage two equal parental classes comprise almost all of the backcross generation, while the recombination classes are very much less frequent. The above example is summarized in figure 72.

RECIPROCAL CROSSES The next logical question is, what would the result have been had the original cross been hairy-normal

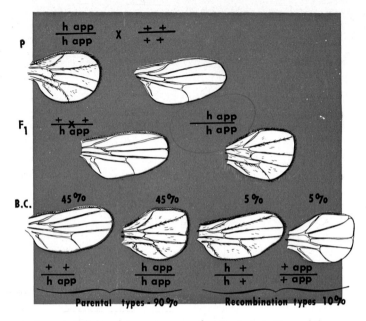

Fig. 72. *A cross to demonstrate linkage between two genes for wing traits in* Drosophila. *Note that the B.C. ratio is far off from the 1:1:1:1 which would be expected if independent assortment occurred.*

veined X normal bristled-approximated, $\frac{h+}{h+} \times \frac{+app}{+app}$? The F_1 now becomes $\frac{h+}{+app}$ and the backcross $\frac{h\ +}{+\ app} \times \frac{h\ app}{h\ app}$. It turns out that the backcross progeny includes 90 per cent hairy-normal veined and normal bristled-approximated veined flies, while only 10 per cent of the backcross progeny show both mutants or both normal alleles. In other words, no matter in what combination a cross be made involving these two pairs of genes, linkage acts as a conservative agent preserving the parental types (whatever they may have been) in 90 per cent of the backcross progeny, while crossing over results in recombination types to the extent of 10 per cent.

ADDITIONAL EXAMPLES If two different pairs of linked genes are involved in such a series of crosses, the results are similar in kind, though different numerically. Thus if the cross were made between yellow (body

color) and white (eye color), the parental types would comprise 98.5 per cent of the backcross generation, while the recombination types would comprise only 1.5 per cent. Such a cross (Morgan's original example) may be represented in symbols as shown at the top of page 129.

If a similar series of crosses be made involving yellow and cut (a recessive wing mutant, *ct*), then the parental types would be recovered in 80 per cent of the backcross generation, while the remaining 20 per cent would be recombination types. Thus the percentage of recombination is typical for any two pairs of linked genes.

It may be seen that the principles of linkage and crossing over apply whenever two pairs of genes in a dihybrid cross are both in the same chromosome. Autosomal and sex-linked genes behave alike in this regard. But notice that in all of the examples discussed above the backcross was made between heterozygous F_1 females and males homozygous for both recessives. There is, of

P $\dfrac{y\ w}{y\ w} \times \dfrac{+\ +}{o}$ (These genes are sex-linked.)

F$_1$ ♀♀ $\dfrac{y\ w}{+\ +}$ ♂♂ $\dfrac{y\ w}{o}$

F$_1$ eggs $\quad y\ w,\ +\ +,\ y\ +,\ +\ w$

B.C. progeny ♀♀ $\quad\dfrac{y\ w}{y\ w}\quad \dfrac{+\ +}{y\ w}\quad \dfrac{y\ +}{y\ w}\quad \dfrac{+\ w}{y\ w}$

♂♂ $\quad\dfrac{w\ y}{o}\quad \dfrac{+\ +}{o}\quad \dfrac{y\ +}{o}\quad \dfrac{+\ w}{o}$

Parental types   Recombination types
98.5%   1.5%

course, no other possibility when sex linkage is involved. However, the same procedure is necessary in studies of autosomal linkage. The reason for this is that, in *Drosophila*, crossing over does not occur in the male, even between autosomal genes. Why this should be true is obscure, to say the least. This is an unusual feature of the genetics of *Drosophila*. It has been found in a few other species of Diptera (flies and their allies), and in silkworms and a few other Lepidoptera (butterflies and moths). In the latter, however, it is the females in which no crossing over occurs. But in general, crossing over occurs equally in both sexes, except for the sex-differential chromosomes.

COUPLING AND REPULSION Actually, the statement above that linkage and crossing over were discovered by Morgan is not strictly true, although he was the first to understand it. Bateson and Punnett had observed similar facts in sweet peas several years earlier, but they were unable to interpret their data correctly because they did not appreciate the role of the chromosomes in heredity. One of their original examples will add another instance of the basic facts, as well as exemplifying their own interpretation of these facts. In sweet peas, purple flower color, *B* (for blue), is dominant over red, *b* (fig. 73). Fresh pollen is always round, but when dried, it may remain round, or it may become oval, in which case it is called long pollen. Long pollen, *L* is dominant over round, *l*. When the dihybrid cross, *BBLL* × *bbll*, was made, the F$_1$ all had purple flowers

Fig. 73. *A sweet pea.*

Table 10. Bateson and Punnett's Experiment on Linkage in the Sweet Pea

	P	Purple-long × red-round			
	F₁	Purple-long			
	F₂	Purple-long	purple-round	red-long	red-round
Observed		4831	390	393	1338
Expected if on basis of 9 : 3 : 3 : 1		3910	1304	1304	434
Expected if gametes are in ratio of 7 : 1 : 1 : 7		4814	408	408	1332

and long pollen, and of course the genotype $BbLl$. When these were backcrossed to the recessive parental type, a ratio of 1 : 1 : 1 : 1 was expected. But the results were about 7 purple-long to 1 red-long to 1 purple-round to 7 red-round. It was plain that the hybrids produced gametes of types BL and bl about seven times as frequently as those of types Bl and bL. Hence Bateson and Punnett suggested that these dominants of the two pairs must in some way be *coupled*, so that they tended to pass into the same gametes at gametogenesis.

When a corresponding cross was made, $BBll \times bbLL$, the F₁ was again heterozygous for both genes, and phenotypically the plants showed both dominant characters. But this time the backcross yielded 1 purple-long to 7 purple-round to 7 red-long to 1 red-round. Now it appeared that gametes of types Bl and bL were seven times as abundant as those of types BL and bl. Hence a *repulsion* between the two dominant genes was postulated. The nature of these forces of coupling and repulsion was not suspected, and the entire theory was soon superseded when Morgan demonstrated that the facts were easily explainable by the location of the genes on the chromosomes, with interchange of genes between the chromosomes accounting for the production of recombination gametes. Thus the coupling cross was

$$\frac{BL}{BL} \times \frac{bl}{bl} \rightarrow \frac{BL}{bl},$$

while the repulsion cross was

$$\frac{Bl}{Bl} \times \frac{bL}{bL} \rightarrow \frac{Bl}{bL}.$$

AN F₂ WITH LINKAGE   The above examples are all based upon backcrosses of F₁ organisms to the homozygous recessive parental type. The results of such a backcross give easily interpretable data from which the proportions of each type of gamete produced by the heterozygous parent can be readily calculated.

Nonetheless, linkage can be recognized in an F₂ by the same fundamental characteristic: significant deviation from the results expected with independent assortment. It was actually such an F₂ that Bateson and Punnett first studied. The example introduced above will illustrate the present problem also. When pure-breeding purple-long sweet peas $\left(\dfrac{BL}{BL}\right)$ are crossed with pure-breeding red-rounds $\left(\dfrac{bl}{bl}\right)$, the resulting F₁ plants are all purple-long, but heterozygous for both genes $\left(\dfrac{BL}{bl}\right)$. A large F₂ of 6952⁓

Table 11. Calculation of an Example of the F$_2$ of a Dihybrid When the Two Pairs of Genes are Linked

$$P \quad \frac{Og\ Li}{Og\ Li} \times \frac{og\ li}{og\ li}$$

$$F_1 \quad \frac{Og\ Li}{og\ li}$$

F$_2$ Zygotes and proportions:

	Og Li	Og li	og Li	og li
	0.44	0.06	0.06	0.44

	Og Li	Og li	og Li	og li
Og Li 0.44	$\frac{Og\ Li}{Og\ Li}$ .1936	$\frac{Og\ li}{Og\ Li}$ .0264	$\frac{og\ Li}{Og\ Li}$ .0264	$\frac{og\ li}{Og\ Li}$ .1936
Og li 0.06	$\frac{Og\ Li}{Og\ li}$ .0264	$\frac{Og\ li}{Og\ li}$ .0036	$\frac{og\ Li}{Og\ li}$ .0036	$\frac{og\ li}{Og\ li}$ .0264
og Li 0.06	$\frac{Og\ Li}{og\ Li}$ .0264	$\frac{Og\ li}{og\ Li}$ .0036	$\frac{og\ Li}{og\ Li}$ .0036	$\frac{og\ li}{og\ Li}$ .0264
og li 0.44	$\frac{Og\ Li}{og\ li}$ .1936	$\frac{Og\ li}{og\ li}$ .0264	$\frac{og\ Li}{og\ li}$ .0264	$\frac{og\ li}{og\ li}$ .1936

Frequencies of the four F$_2$ phenotypes:

Og Li	Og li	og Li	og li
9 squares:	3 squares	3 squares	1 square
0.1936	0.0036	0.0036	0.1936
0.1936	0.0264	0.0264	
0.1936	0.0264	0.0264	
0.0264	0.0564	0.0564	
0.0264			
0.0264			0.6936
0.0264			0.0564
0.0264			0.0564
0.0036			0.1936
0.0036			
0.6936			1.0000

∴ the proportional parts are correct.

plants was grown from this cross. Independent assortment would have led one to expect the four phenotypes in a ratio of 9 : 3 : 3 : 1, or 3910 : 1304 : 1304 : 434. This typical dihybrid ratio is based upon the assumption that the four types of gametes (BL, Bl, bL, and bl) are formed in equal numbers. Actually, however, the F$_2$ consisted of the following: purple-long, 4831; purple-round, 390; red-long, 393; and red-round, 1338. This obviously could not be a random deviation from the results of independent assortment. The chi-square value is enormous. However, Bateson and Punnett saw that the results were interpretable on the assumption that gametes of classes BL and bl were produced seven times as abundantly as those of classes Bl and bL. The mathematical basis of this analysis is rather complicated, and is not generally useful. Suffice it to say that the results of the backcross, which was made later, verified the conclusion. This cross is summarized in table 10.

While it is difficult to calculate the degree of linkage from F$_2$ data, it is easy to calculate what the F$_2$ must be if the degree of linkage (proportion of parental and recombination gametes) is already known. Thus in maize the genes for old gold stripe, Og, and lineate stripe, li, are twelve units apart in chromosome number 10. If the cross $\frac{Og\ Li}{Og\ Li} \times \frac{og\ li}{og\ li}$ is made, then the F$_1$ plants must all be $\frac{Og\ Li}{og\ li}$. The F$_2$ may now be obtained by the Roman square method. But previously, this method has been used with the tacit assumption that all four classes of gametes are produced in equal numbers. This is not a valid assumption in the present instance. The parental type gametes $Og\ Li$ and $og\ li$, are known to comprise 0.88 of the total, or 0.44 each; while the recombination types $Og\ li$, and $og\ Li$, are known to comprise 0.12 of all gametes, or 0.06 each. And so these coefficients are written with the appropriate gametic types, and are multiplied in the squares to get the frequency of each zygotic type. If the frequencies of zygotic types of like phenotype are then added, the relative proportions of the four phenotypes in the F_2 will be obtained. The whole operation is presented in table 11. In the present example, the proportions are approximately 35 : 3 : 3 : 10, a very great deviation indeed from a ratio of 9 : 3 : 3 : 1.

32. LINKAGE AND THE CHROMOSOMES

The cytological basis for crossing over was known even before Morgan published the first reports of genetic crossing over. In 1909, F. A. Janssens, a Belgian Jesuit, published a description of the formation of *chiasmata* in the tetrads during spermatogenesis in salamanders. Each chiasma, as explained in chapter 3, represents a break in two of the four chromatids which make up the tetrad, with the chromatids rehealing in different combinations than the original. This is illustrated in figure 74. It should be added that chiasmata can form without crossing over, if the chromatids exchange partners without breaking. It has been demonstrated that this is a common phenomenon in the spermatogenesis of *Drosophila*, although crossing over does not normally occur in male *Drosophila*. In his original paper, Janssens pointed out that, if the chromosomal theory of heredity should be proven correct, then such exchanges between the chromosomes should provide an additional mechanism for reshuffling the hereditary characters. Confirmation of this insight was not long delayed, for it was only a year later that Morgan demonstrated the fact of genetic crossing over in *Drosophila*. Thus, like independent assortment, crossing over is based upon a visible feature of the behavior of the chromosomes.

MAPPING THE CHROMOSOMES The demonstration that chiasma formation is the basis of crossing over proved that whole segments of chromosomes are exchanged when crossing over occurs. Furthermore, it was explained above that the percentage of crossing over is constant between any two pairs of genes, but is different between different sets. Thus the rate of crossing over between *yellow* and *white* in *Drosophila* is 1.5 per cent, while the rate between *hairy* and *approximated* is 10 per cent. It is plain that it is very much easier for a crossover to occur between *hairy* and *approximated* than between *yellow* and *white*. Sturtevant, originally a student of Morgan and for many years his collaborator, reasoned that these data could most easily be explained by two assumptions. First, each gene has a definite position or *locus* in its chromosome. And second, the place where a chiasma occurs is a matter of chance, and therefore the fre-

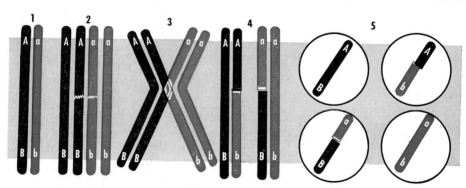

Fig. 74. *A diagrammatic representation of the chromosomal basis of crossing over.*

quency with which crossing over occurs between any two loci is proportional to the linear distance separating them in the chromosome. Hence the reason that crossing over occurs between *hairy* and *approximated* with about seven times the frequency that it occurs between *yellow* and *white* is that the *hairy* and *approximated* loci are about seven times as far apart as are the *yellow* and *white* loci.

From the concepts that the genes occupy definite loci along the length of the chromosomes and that the distances separating the genes are proportional to the rate of crossing over between them, it is only a short step to the mapping of the chromosomes. How this is done may be illustrated for the X chromosome of *Drosophila*, using the data given above for the *yellow*, *white*, and *cut* loci. It need only be added here that 1 per cent of crossing over is considered to indicate one unit of length in the chromosome. Such a unit is purely relative, and cannot be restated in micra, Angstrom, or other physical length units. Because 1.5 per cent crossing over occurs between the *yellow* and *white* loci, they may be said to be 1.5 units apart in the chromosome. Similarly, *yellow* and *cut* are said to be 20 units apart. If a line diagram of the chromosome is now set up, *y* and *ct* may be represented as 20 units apart, but when *w* is added at a distance of 1.5 units from *y*, it could be in the same direction as *ct*, or it could be in the opposite direction:

$$\overline{\quad\underset{w?\;y\;w?}{\rule{0pt}{0pt}|\;\;|\;|}\hspace{4cm}\underset{ct}{|}\quad}$$

How can it be determined which of these alternatives is the correct one? If *w* and *ct* lie on opposite sides of *y*, then a crossover test between *w* and *ct* should give 21.5 per cent of crossing over, that is, the sum of the rates in the separate segments. But if *w* lies between the other two, then the crossover rate between *w* and *ct* should be only 18.5

per cent, the difference between the rates in the separate segments. Actually, the latter is the case, and so it is certain that the order of genes in the chromosome runs *y—w—ct*.

By considering the known genes in each linkage group three at a time, it has been possible to build up extensive chromosome maps for organisms such as *Drosophila* and maize which are thoroughly known genetically. In the case of the X chromosome of *Drosophila*, all of the numerous genes which have been localized have proven to be on the same side of *y* as are *w* and *ct*. Hence it has been concluded that the *y* locus must be at or very near the end of the chromosome. Arbitrarily, *y* is said to mark the *left* end of the chromosome, and all other genes are said to be so many units to the right of *y*. Terms such as right and left cannot have any but arbitrary significance for chromosomes, which are oriented differently in neighboring cells. But it is a convention of chromosome mapping that the first "end" gene to be found in any particular chromosome is designated as the left end of that chromosome, and the other loci are numbered as so many units to the right of that zero point.

THE THREE POINT CROSS In point of fact, chromosome mapping is not usually done in the fashion indicated above, requiring three series of crosses. The same results (better, actually) can be obtained with much less work by means of one series of crosses involving all three loci at once. Continuing the same example discussed above, the initial cross would be set up as follows:

$$\frac{y\;w\;ct}{y\;w\;ct} \times \frac{+\;+\;+}{0}$$

All of the female offspring must be heterozygous, $\dfrac{y\quad w\quad ct}{+\;+\;+}$; while the males must be simplex for all of the recessives. These are now bred together (which is, it will be recalled, equivalent to a backcross in this unique case), and the backcross progeny are then classified by phenotypes. Because it is a three point cross, the results are rather complicated, there being in addition to the parental classes those with crossovers between *y* and *w*, those with crossovers between *w* and *ct*, and those with crossovers in *both* segments at once.

The results of such a cross are tabulated in table 12. In the first column, the various possible phenotypes are listed, together with a genotypic description of the *egg* giving rise to it. These occur always as two reciprocal classes, simultaneous products of crossing over. In the next column are the numbers of each type, followed by the sums of each pair of reciprocal classes. Finally, there is a series of three columns in which the apparent crossovers are listed. Thus, for example, there are twelve flies in the reciprocal classes *gray-white-cut* and *yellow-red-normal wing*. The *y* and *w* were linked together in the original cross, but now they are separated, so these twelve flies are entered in the column for apparent crossovers between *y* and *w*. The same is true for *y* and *ct*. But *w*

and *ct* are still in the parental relationship, and therefore a zero is entered in that column.

Now each of the vertical columns is totaled, and the three loci are mapped on the basis of these totals. Thus there are a total of 15 apparent crossovers between *y* and *w* out of 1000 progeny. This is 1.5 per cent, so the loci are 1.5 units apart. There are 185 apparent crossovers between *w* and *ct*, and this corresponds to a map distance of 18.5 units. There are 194 apparent crossovers between *y* and *ct*, corresponding to 19.4 units. Thus *y* and *ct* are the most distant points, and *w* must lie between them. But if this is the case, the distance from *y* to *ct* should be the sum of the distances *y–w* and *w–ct*, which is 20 units. The apparent distance is only 19.4 units. Where has the other 0.6 unit gone? The answer may be found at the bottom of the table, where *double* crossovers are found. If a crossover occurs in the segment *y–w*, it rearranges *y* and *ct* with respect to one another. A second crossover occurring simultaneously in the segment *w–ct* then restores

Table 12.   A Three Point Cross in Drosophila

$$P \quad \frac{y \; w \; ct}{y \; w \; ct} \times \frac{+\,+\,+}{o} \to F_1 \; \frac{y \; w \; ct}{+\,+\,+}, \; \frac{y \; w \; ct}{o}$$

B.C. (F$_1$ ♀ × F$_1$ ♂):

Phenotypes	Ova	Nos.	Totals	Apparent c.o. between:		
				y-w	w-ct	y-ct
No crossovers						
yellow-white-cut	y w ct	399	803	0	0	0
gray-red-normal	+ + +	404				
1 crossover						
gray-white-cut	+ w ct	5	12	12	0	12
yellow-red-normal	y + +	7				
yellow-white-normal	y w +	89	182	0	182	182
gray-red-cut	+ + ct	93				
2 crossovers						
gray-white-normal	+ w +	2	3	3	3	0
yellow-red-cut	y + ct	1				
			1000	15	185	194

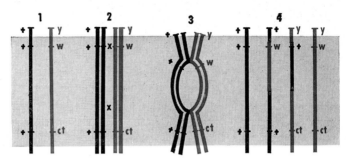

Fig. 75. *A diagrammatic presentation of double crossing over.*

the original relationship between *y* and *ct*, as shown in figure 75. The double crossovers are identifiable only when a third pair of genes is present between the other two. Thus the six exchanges in the bottom line of the table (three double crossovers) must be added to the total of apparent crossovers between *y* and *ct*. This makes a total of 200 out of 1000, or 20 map units, which is the expected figure.

At this point, it may be well to add two precautions which are important in the mapping of the chromosomes. First, the three point cross is not only more convenient than the two point cross, but it is more accurate, as it makes possible the detection of double crossing over. Second, maps should be based upon tests over fairly short segments wherever this is possible, not only because this reduces the rate of double crossing over, but because loci separated by as much as fifty units should be separated by chiasmata as often as not. As a result, their transmission simulates independent assortment.

DOUBLE CROSSING OVER In the above discussion, it has been tacitly assumed that more than one crossover can occur simultaneously in the same pair of chromosomes. This assumption is justified by available facts. Genetic data show that as many as five crossovers may occur simultaneously in the larger chromosomes of *Drosophila*. And many more chiasmata have been observed in the long chromosomes of some amphibians. In general, the number of chiasmata that occur in a particular tetrad is constant,

and this number is directly proportional to the length of the chromosome.

INTERFERENCE AND COINCIDENCE If it is simply a matter of chance where a chiasma occurs, and if crossing over between loci *a* and *b* is independent of crossing over between *b* and *c*, then application of the multiplication theorem should give the rate of double crossing over. Thus if the rates of crossing over in segments *a–b* and *b–c* are 5 and 10 per cent, respectively, the rate of double crossing over should be 1/2 of 1 per cent ($0.10 \times 0.05 = 0.005$). Actually, something less than the calculated amount of double crossing over is usually obtained. This indicates that the separate chiasmata are not entirely independent of one another, but rather that one chiasma interferes with the occurrence of a second one. The phenomenon is called, quite simply, *interference*. The longer the segment *a–c*, the more nearly do the actual values approach the calculated values. In *Drosophila*, for example, interference is complete in segments of 10 units or less; but there is no interference at all in segments of 45 units or more. Intermediate segments show all degrees of interference, according to their length.

There is a very simple measure of the degree of interference. It is called *coincidence*, and is defined as the ratio of observed rate of double crossing over to the calculated rate (coincidence $= \dfrac{\text{observed double crossing over}}{\text{calculated double crossing over}}$). Thus, if 6 per cent were the expectation and 3 per cent were actually observed, coincidence would be $3/6 = 0.5$. Thus coincidence varies from o (no double crossing over at all) in very short segments to 1 (no interference) in very long segments. The name is somewhat misleading, but the concept is so simple and obvious that a poorly chosen name cannot obscure it.

The problem of the cause of interference is a very difficult one. It was originally assumed that it was a simple mechanical effect of the rigidity of the chromosomes. A model might be made by twisting various lengths of wire about one another: long pieces may be easily intertwined while short ones are very difficult to twist. But microdissection experiments have demonstrated that the chromosomes are characterized by great plasticity. Thus W. R. Duryee of the Carnegie Institution found that the chromosomes of oocytes of the salamander *Triturus* could be stretched as much as 300 per cent and still return to the original length upon release of tension. He was able to stretch them as much as 800 per cent without breakage. As a result of these and other comparable observations, most cytologists are gravely skeptical whether the chromosomes could be sufficiently rigid to account for the facts of interference. It is an observed fact that the chromosomes are coiled like a helix spring, the degree of coiling varying with the stages of the chromosomal cycle. Occurrence of a chiasma at one point in a pair of such coils might tend to hold homologous points apart for some distance so that a second exchange would be inhibited. This coiling theory of interference is now generally held, not so much because it is supported by positive evidence, as because no serious negative evidence is at hand and no competing theory is in the field.

However unsatisfactory our knowledge of the mechanics of interference may be, the known facts of interference and coincidence have some important consequences. First, they prove that each crossover results in the exchange of whole blocks of genes rather than single gene loci. While this seems obvious on the basis of the cytologic behavior of chiasmata, yet every line of evidence that can be brought to bear upon the correlation of genetics and cytology is important. Second, these facts show that crossover data are valid for purposes of mapping the chromosomes only if the segment tested is short enough that interference is complete, or if an adequate test is made for double crossing over.

EXAMPLES OF CHROMOSOME MAPS Numerous experiments on linkage and crossing over, three point crosses and the other topics discussed above, have resulted in a considerable extension of the available knowledge of the transmission of hereditary characters and of the organization of the chromosomes. Among the important formal results of these studies are the chromosome maps which have been compiled, with varying degrees of completeness, for many organisms. Probably the most complete map is that for the chromosomes of *Drosophila*, which is presented in figure 76. Probably the second best map is that for the chromosomes of maize, which is represented in two figures, 77 and 78. Maps for other organisms are generally much less complete as, for example, Hutt's map of six of the twenty pairs of chromosomes in the chicken. Another important outcome of these studies is the fact that the number of linkage groups never exceeds the haploid number of chromosomes. Thus in *Drosophila* and maize the haploid numbers are four and ten respectively, and these are also the numbers of linkage groups characterizing these species. The number of known linkage groups may be less than the haploid number of chromosomes. Thus the mouse has twenty pairs of chromosomes, but only eight linkage groups are known. The tomato has twelve pairs of chromosomes, and only ten linkage groups are known (fig. 79). This may be attributed

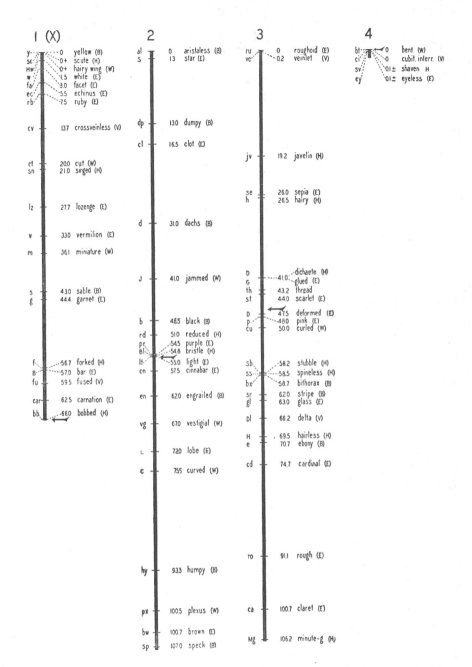

Fig. 76. *The four linkage groups of* Drosophila melanogaster, *showing some of the better known loci.* (*After Bridges, from* Sturtevant and Beadle, *Introduction to Genetics, W. B. Saunders Co.*)

Fig. 77. *A living chromosome map for corn, as set up for the Sixth International Congress of Genetics at Ithaca, N. Y. At each "locus" is a plant showing the appropriate mutant. (From the Journal of Heredity, vol. 23.)*

to incomplete and inadequate knowledge of the species concerned. But however thoroughly a species may be known, the haploid chromosome number always appears as the limit of the number of linkage groups. This fact is an important support for the chromosome theory of inheritance.

ASSIGNING A NEW GENE TO ITS LOCUS When a new gene is under study, one of the first objectives is to determine its proper position in the chromosome set. How does one go about it? The most obvious method is to test for linkage with known genes in each chromosome, one at a time, until one is found which gives a significant deviation from the results expected with independent assortment. This method is laborious, as many series of crosses may be required if one is not fortunate enough to test the right chromosome first. Also, it may be misleading, for even if the new gene and the test gene in a particular chromosome are linked, this fact will not be shown in the data if they are on the order of fifty units or more apart.

A more convenient method of assigning a

new gene to its chromosome is by the use of *marked* test organisms. The method may be illustrated by a hypothetical example from *Drosophila*. The X chromosome may be marked by the pattern of sex-linked inheritance. The second chromosome may be marked by the dominant mutant Star, S, in which the facets of the eye are defective, giving the eye a starry appearance. The third chromosome may be marked by the dominant mutant Dichaete, D, a bristle and wing mutant. The fourth chromosome need not be marked, because any gene which is not located on I, II, or III, must be on IV. S and D are particularly useful as markers because they are lethal when homozygous. For this reason, any fly showing these phenotypes is known to be heterozygous for these chromosomes.

Let us assume that the new mutant is a recessive, m. One begins by crossing a homozygous m female to a male of the marked stock. Two results are possible in the F_1. If all of the sons show the m phenotype and all of the daughters are normal,

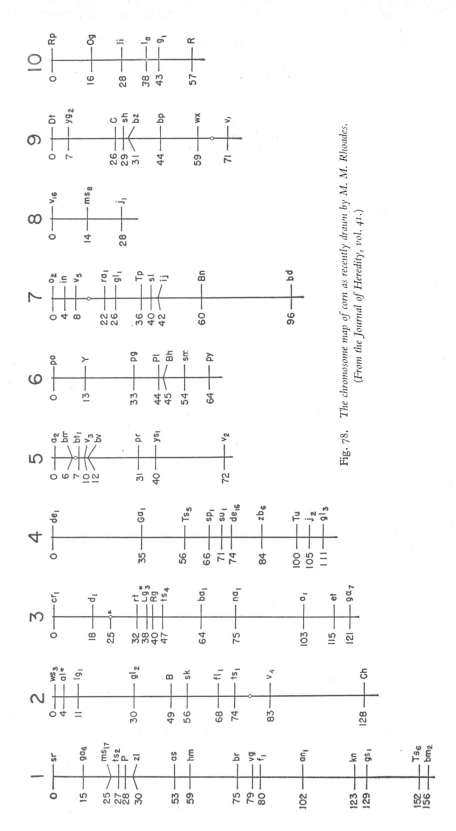

Fig. 78. *The chromosome map of corn as recently drawn by M. M. Rhoades.*
(From the Journal of Heredity, vol. 41.)

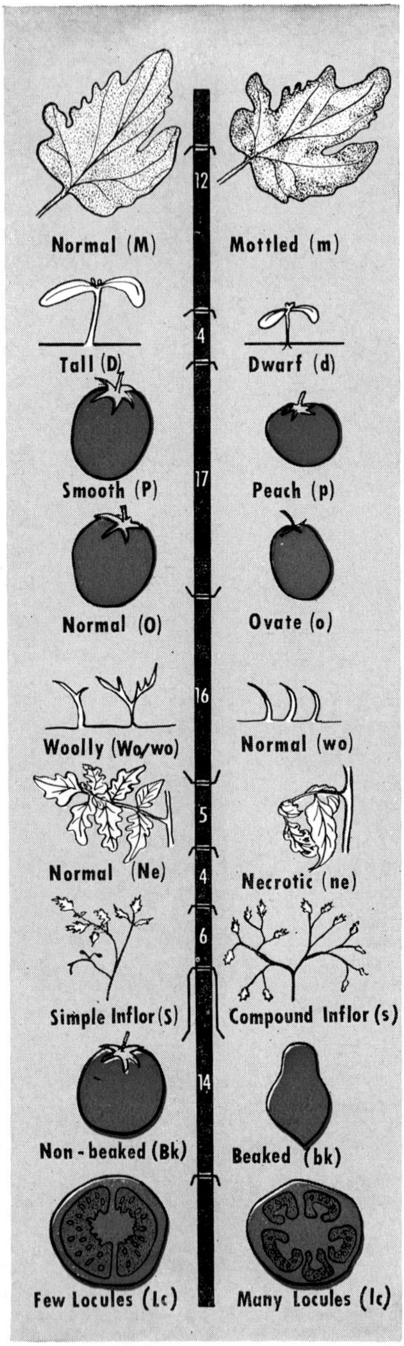

Fig. 79. *A map of chromosome 1 in the tomato.* (*Redrawn from Butler.*)

then *m* must be located on the X chromosome, as otherwise this criss-cross inheritance could not occur. On the other hand, all of the F₁ flies might be normal. This would mean that the gene must be autosomal, and heterozygous in all of the F₁ flies.

Star-Dichaete F₁ males are now backcrossed to females homozygous for *m*. In order to simplify the explanation, let us now assume that *m* is actually on chromosome II. One of the pair will then carry *S* and *m⁺*, while the other will carry *S⁺* and *m*. Because the male heterozygote is used, the recombinations *S m* and + + do not occur. But this pair of chromosomes shows independent assortment with respect to the third pair. Hence four types of sperm are formed as shown in figure 80. Fertilization of eggs carrying all of the recessives leads to the four types of zygotes shown in figure 80. They show various combinations of *S*, *D*, and *m*. Note that *m* may appear phenotypically either with or without *D*, showing independent assortment. But if a fly is *S*, it is not *m;* and if it is *m*, it is not *S*. They are mutually exclusive, not independent.

Hence, in the actual experiment, if *m* and *S* are mutually exclusive, *m* is located on chromosome II. But if *m* and *D* are mutually exclusive, the same reasoning leads to the conclusion that *m* must be on chromosome III. Finally, if *m* shows up either with or without both *S* and *D*, then it must be located upon chromosome IV. Once it is determined upon which chromosome the gene is located, its exact locus can be determined by the appropriate three point crosses.

Another convenient method of marking the chromosomes is available for some polyploid plants. Frequently, a single chromosome may be missing, so that the genes carried in that pair are all simplex. Such a plant is called a *monosomic* (see chapter 14). At meiosis, half of the ovules get the monosome, while half are deficient. If the latter

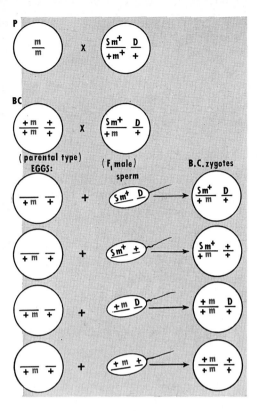

P

BC

(parental type)
EGGS:

(F₁ male)
sperm

B.C. zygotes

Fig. 80. *The Star-Dichaete test for localizing genes.*

are fertilized by pollen carrying a recessive gene on that chromosome, the recessive will show up because no other allele is present at all. Now if a complete series of monosomics is available (as is the case in tobacco), a new recessive may be crossed to each of the monosomic types. In the progeny of one of these crosses, the recessive gene should show up. The monosomic concerned is then the one carrying the gene under study.

33. EXPERIMENTAL INFLUENCE UPON CROSSING OVER

A basic goal in the study of any natural phenomenon is its experimental control. Toward this end, the influence of many experimental tools upon crossing over has been tested. A number of these have proved to increase the rate of crossing over. These include high

and low temperature, heat shock, x-radiation, other high energy radiation, and certain chemical treatments, such as mustard gas and ethyl carbamate. By means of cold, crossing over has even been induced in male *Drosophila*. None of these agencies is selective in the sense that crossing over can be increased between predetermined loci.

34. LINKAGE IN MAN

The study of linkage in man is particularly difficult, because of the large number of chromosomes and because experimental crosses cannot be made. There must of course be twenty-four linkage groups, corresponding to the twenty-four pairs of chromosomes. Because of the difficulties of obtaining adequate data for linkage studies in man, the objective sought is usually a much more modest one than in comparable studies upon experimental organisms: the demonstration of the mere fact that two genes are linked is the goal, with the rate of crossing over usually being disregarded. Complex formulas for extracting this meager return from scanty data have been devised. As a result of these studies, a few autosomal linkages have been demonstrated in man. But progress in this field may be expected to be very slow, and a useful map of the autosomes of man is far in the future.

With respect to the sex-differential chromosomes of man, the situation is quite different, and much more encouraging. Because of the unique pattern of inheritance of sex-linked genes, it is easy to assign such a gene to its chromosome. And because it is so much easier to gather data, some progress has been made toward mapping the sex chromosomes of man. But because the explanation of this map involves some principles not yet discussed, it will be deferred to a later chapter.

RÉSUMÉ Linkage is thus a simple consequence of the fact that the number of genes exceeds the number of chromosomes. Hence each chromosome must include many genes, and these tend to be inherited as a group. They are not assorted independently. Nonetheless, segments may be interchanged between the homologues during meiosis, and this results in recombinations among the linked genes. Because each gene has a definite locus in the chromosome, and because the rate of crossing over between any two loci is proportional to the distance between them, crossover data offer a basis for the mapping of the chromosomes. Linkage has been demonstrated in man as in other organisms, but it is very difficult to study autosomal linkage in man. Sex linkage, however, is much more readily studied, and considerable progress has been made in the mapping of the sex-differential chromosomes of man.

Questions and Problems

1. Define:

Chiasma	Locus
Coincidence	Map unit
Crossing over	Marked chromosome
Interference	Three point cross
Linkage	

2. A female *Drosophila* heterozygous for sex-linked recessives a, b, and c is backcrossed to a male which is simplex for all three of these recessives. The following are the progeny:

+ + +	390
a b c	360
a + +	42
+ b c	32
a b +	30
+ + c	34
a + c	2
+ b +	3

If *a* be regarded as point 0 on the map, what are the loci of *b* and *c*?

3. Normal maize was crossed to a stock homozygous for three recessive mutants: brown midrib, *bm*; red aleurone, *p*; and virescent, *v* (light yellow seedlings). The F$_1$ plants were backcrossed to the recessive parental type, and the following results were obtained:

+ + +	232
bm p v	235
+ p v	84
bm + +	77
+ + v	201
bm p +	194
+ p +	40
bm + v	46

Explain the meaning of these data. Make the appropriate calculations, and map the chromosome.

4. Ruby (*rb*) and vermilion (*v*) are recessive mutants in *Drosophila*. A ruby, vermilion fly is crossed to a wild type fly. The F$_1$ females are then backcrossed to ruby, vermilion males. The B.C. includes 176 Rb-V, 80 Rb-v, 76 rb-V, and 168 rb-v. Discuss the significance of these results, including the degree of reliability.

5. Flies homozygous for echinoid (*ed*) and dachs (*d*) are crossed to normals. The progeny are all normal. Upon backcrossing to the recessive parental type, the following offspring are obtained: ed d, 117; ++, 126; ed +, 30; + d, 28. What is the recombination rate between these loci?

6. Could the data of problem 5 be used in mapping the chromosome? Justify your answer in a sentence or two.

7. Assuming the same number of offspring, what should the results have been if the loci had been independent?

8. Now assume that, although these genes are actually linked, they are 50 units apart, so that the results simulate independent assortment. How could you prove the fact of linkage? You may design an additional experiment in answering this question.

9. "Cabbage" is a recently discovered mutant in the tomato. It is characterized by compact, dark foliage, and inconspicuous flowers and fruit. Plants homozygous for cabbage and non-yellow (*cbcbyy*) were crossed to plants homozygous for the dominant alleles. F$_1$ plants, which were all normal, were then backcrossed to the recessive parental type. The following offspring were obtained: ++, 28; + y, 14; cb +, 3; and cb y, 16. Are these genes most probably linked or independent? Calculate the rate of recombination between the loci.

10. Using the data of problem 9, calculate the ideal distribution of the 61 plants, assuming linkage of the degree calculated. Now test the probability that the observed deviations are random, using the chi-square test.

References

Duryee, W. R., 1941. The Chromosomes of the Amphibian Nucleus. In the University of Pennsylvania Bicentennial Conference on Cytology, Genetics, and Evolution, pp. 129–141. A clear and interesting account of microdissection experiments upon isolated nuclei.

Emerson, R. A., G. W. Beadle and A. C. Fraser, 1935. A Summary of Linkage Studies in Maize. Memoir 180, Cornell University Agricultural Experiment Station.

Janssens, F. A., 1909. La theorie de la chiasmatypie. La Cellule, 25:387–413. For students who read French with facility, the first paper by the man who started it all has considerable interest.

Mather, Kenneth, 1938. Crossing over. Biological Reviews of the Cambridge Philosophical Society, 13:252–292. A scholarly review, emphasizing the cytological and statistical aspects of the subject.

Morgan, T. H., C. B. Bridges and A. H. Sturtevant, 1925. The Genetics of Drosophila. Bibliographia Genetica, 2:1–262. Includes a treatment of the materials of this chapter by three of the prime movers in the field. Much other valuable material is included.

Owen, A. R. G., 1950. The theory of genetical recombination. In Advances in Genetics, 3:117–157. A very thorough and thoughtful treatment of the problems of linkage and crossing over, but difficult reading for those who are not mathematically inclined.

Punnett, R. C., 1927. Mendelism. Seventh edition. The MacMillan Co., London. A last presentation of the views of this pioneer of genetics.

CHAPTER 12

Architectural Changes in the Chromosomes

The fact that it has been possible, by crossover tests, to map the chromosomes of some species in considerable detail is one of the most impressive achievements of genetics. But a very fundamental question remains: crossover tests measure the ease of crossing over between different loci; this is a purely relative measure; how closely does the map based upon such tests correspond to the real chromosome? The problem may be visualized readily by means of an analogy originally proposed by A. H. Sturtevant, to whom we are indebted for the first steps toward the mapping of the chromosomes. Suppose that a railroad were to be mapped, with no data available other than the times of arrival at various cities of a train running the length of the line. Let us say that the train leaves A at 8 A.M. and arrives at B at 12 M.; at C at 4 P.M.; and at D at 8 P.M. The data leave no doubt that the order of cities along the line is A—B—C—D rather than A—C—D—B, or any other imaginable arrangement. And if one assumes that the distances between cities are simply proportional to the traveling times between them, then the successive cities would have to be equidistant.

However, the last proposition is not necessarily true. Suppose, for example, that the run from A to B goes through several urban areas for which the train must slow down and through country areas with frequent turns which prevent the train from reaching top speeds. As a result the train averages only thirty miles per hour. But between B and C the train traverses a broad plain with few towns and a fast roadbed all the way, so that it averages sixty miles per hour. Finally, between C and D the train passes through rugged mountains with steep grades and sharp turns, so that it can only average fifteen miles per hour. Thus, although the traveling times for the three segments of the trip are equal, segment A—B is twice as long as segment C—D, and only half as long as segment B—C.

One has no assurance that differences along the length of the chromosome, comparable to the different types of terrain over which the train runs, may not also cause differences in the rates of crossing over in different segments of the chromosome. In the railroad analogy, it is easy to measure the actual mileage from city to city. As the gene loci are not directly visible, the analogous measurement cannot be made in the chromosome. But, if some method could be devised for correlating visible points in the chromosome with known gene loci, then this would give some insight into the relationship between the genetic map and the real chromosome. Fortunately, such a method is available, as will be shown below.

35. THE ARCHITECTURE OF THE CHROMOSOMES

That the chromosomes must have a longitudinally differentiated structure is a minimum conclusion from the facts of linkage and crossing over. However, this had al-

144

ready been demonstrated by cytological methods. While the chromosomes at metaphase may look highly uniform, this is not true at all stages in the chromosomal cycle. Especially during the prophase of the first meiotic division, much detail of structure can be seen in the chromosomes. In the leptotene stage (see chapter 3 and fig. 18), when the chromosomes are extremely extended, each chromosome has much the appearance of a string of beads. The various beads, called chromomeres, differ in size and shape. Synapsis is absolutely specific, homologous chromomere synapsing only with homologous chromomere. This demonstrates that the visible differentiation of the chromosome is paralleled by a physiological differentiation.

INVERSION The specificity of synapsis and the fact that there is a serial architecture characteristic of each pair of chromosomes is especially well demonstrated when the material of one member of the pair becomes rearranged. Several types of chromosomal rearrangements are known, but the first to be discussed is a type called an *inversion*. This is a simple reversal of a segment of the chromosome. If, for example, a series of markers have been demonstrated to be in the order A B C D E F G H I J K, and if the segment D to H is inverted, the order in the rearranged chromosome will be A B C H G F E D I J K. This inverted order, if heterozygous, results in a visible change in the behavior of the chromosomes at synapsis, because the synaptic attraction is still strictly specific, homologous point for homologous point. The result is that synapsis can be completed only if one of the homologues forms a twisted loop, while the other homologue loops around this one without twisting. This may be visualized with the aid of figure 81.

Inversions can be detected by several means. Crossovers within an heterozygous inversion lead to grossly abnormal chromo-

somes which are lethal, and hence the crossover products do not appear among the progeny. The details of this belong in courses on cytogenetics. For the present, it is sufficient to note that inversions act as crossover suppressors. When first discovered, the cytological nature of inversions was not understood at all, and they were referred to simply as crossover inhibitors. Because there are other conditions which inhibit crossing over, however, other evidence is needed to prove that an inversion is present. If an inversion can be made homozygous, there is no inhibition of crossing over, and so the reversed order of factors can be demonstrated. Frequently, however, inversions are lethal when homozygous. Thus the conclusive demonstration of the presence of an inversion is ordinarily made by the examination of a cytological preparation of the chromosomes of an heterozygous individual.

The data of classical genetics led to the conclusion that the presence of a particular gene under normal circumstances results in the corresponding phenotype. No notation of the position of the gene in relation to others is necessary. Thus in 1927 Babcock and Clausen were able to write that ". . . . for development the important desideratum is the presence of the factors; their position in the genetic system appears to be of little consequence."[*] Another geneticist has said that the nucleus is essentially an unordered system. And so it may come as a surprise to learn that inversions may have phenotypic effects, that is, they behave as if they were mutations. Thus *Curly* (Cy), a dominant wing defect of *Drosophila*, is based upon a large inversion in the second chromosome. Because such "genes" are also crossover inhibitors, they make good markers.

DEFICIENCY OR DELETION Sometimes a segment of a chromosome may be missing

[*] Genetics in Relation to Agriculture, p. 286, McGraw-Hill Book Co., 1927, New York.

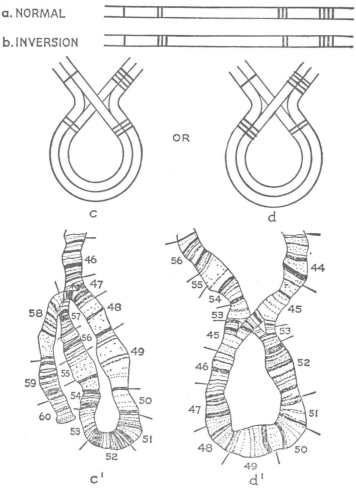

Fig. 81. *Heterozygous inversion in the salivary gland chromosomes. a–d, diagrammatic; c′ and d′, actual chromosomes. (From Altenburg, Genetics, Henry Holt and Co.)*

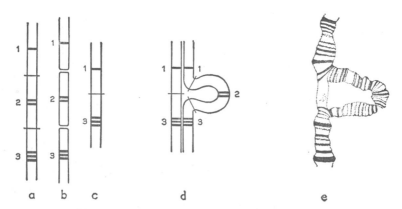

Fig. 82. *Heterozygous deficiency in the salivary gland chromosomes. a–d, diagrammatic; e, actual specimen. (From Altenburg, Genetics, Henry Holt and Co.)*

altogether, and then one speaks of a *deficiency* or deletion. Returning to the hypothetical chromosome A B C D E F G H I J K, if there were a deficiency for the segment D to H, the chromosome would have the constitution A B C I J K. Again, it is the specificity of synapsis which makes the presence of the deficiency readily visible in the heterozygous condition. Because each point in the deficient chromosome synapses with its homologous point in the normal chromosome, the segment D to H of the normal chromosome must project off to one side as an unpaired loop. This is illustrated in figure 82.

Like inversions, deficiencies can be detected by genetic means as well as by cytological observation. At the outset, it is obvious that there could be no crossing over within the deleted segment, and hence crossover tests between loci on opposite sides of a deficiency will lead to apparent distances which are shorter than the standard map distances. Thus if loci *a* and *b* are 15 units apart, and if a deficiency for a 5 unit segment occurs between them, subsequent tests will indicate that they are even less than 10 units apart because of impairment of synapsis.

The most elegant test for a deficiency may be illustrated by an actual example. *Notch* wing is a dominant, sex-linked mutant which has occurred repeatedly in *Drosophila*. When notch females are crossed to normal males, a ratio of one notch female to one normal female to one normal male is obtained. The two to one sex ratio shows that

the gene is lethal in the simplex condition, hence only females can show the character, and these are always heterozygous. Now, if a white eyed male is mated to a notch female, the offspring are in the ratio of one notch-white female to one wild type female to one wild type male. These results are not in line with the principles of sex-linkage as developed in chapter 6. All of the female offspring from this cross should have been *heterozygous* for the eye color gene, and therefore red-eyed. The fact that some are actually white-eyed can only mean that they are *simplex* for this locus, in other words the normal allele is missing from the notch chromosome (see fig. 83). Pseudodominance is a convenient term to designate this phenomenon. This experiment has been repeated with several sex-linked genes from the left end of the X chromosome. It turns out that *w* is the first gene which will show up in the notch females, and *abnormal abdomen* (*Ab*) is the last. As *w* is located at 1.5 and *Ab* at 4.5 on the chromosome map, this indicates that the notch deficiency must be three units long.

Like inversions, deficiencies are usually lethal when homozygous.

DUPLICATION   Just as a segment may be missing from a chromosome, so also a segment may be repeated, and one then speaks

Fig. 83.   *A diagram of the Notch deficiency in Drosophila. Note the pseudodominance of alleles opposite the deficiency. (Modified from Babcock and Clausen.)*

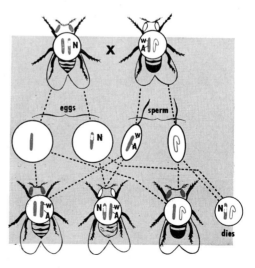

of a duplication. Again using the model introduced above a duplication for segment D to H gives a chromosome of constitution A B C D E F G H D E F G H I J K. In an heterozygous organism, synapsis looks very much as it does in deficiency heterozygotes, with an unpaired loop projecting to one side of the chromosome. The two chromosomes of the pair synapse perfectly point for point, but because material present only once in the normal chromosome is present twice in the other, the duplicated segment cannot pair, and so forms the loop.

Genetic evidence of duplication is given when it is attempted to localize a gene in the duplicated segment. An inexact result is obtained because the gene is actually present twice, at two different places in the chromosome. Like inversions and deficiencies, duplications may have mutant effects which do

not depend upon the genes included. One of the most intensively studied mutants in *Drosophila*, the sex-linked dominant for bar-eye (narrow) is actually a duplication for a small segment of the right end of the X chromosome. This example will be discussed in detail in a later chapter.

TRANSLOCATION   The final type of architectural rearrangement is the transfer of a section of one chromosome to another non-homologous chromosome. This is called a *translocation*. By far the commonest type is reciprocal translocation, in which segments are exchanged between two non-homologous chromosomes. This is often referred to as illegitimate crossing over. This again results in an easily recognized pattern of synapsis because of the fact that homologous point still synapses with homologous point. Thus the translocation binds together two

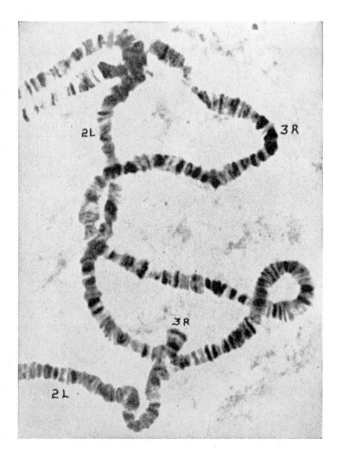

Fig. 84.   *A heterozygous translocation in the salivary gland chromosomes. (Courtesy of Dr. B. P. Kaufmann, Carnegie Institution of Washington, Cold Spring Harbor, New York.)*

different tetrads during the first meiotic division.

The mode of distribution of the chromosomes of such translocation complexes is noteworthy, and may be understood with the help of figures 84 and 136. Independent assortment may lead to four types of gametes, as follows: the first includes an unmodified chromosome from each tetrad. Another includes both of the translocated chromosomes, and between the two of them an entire chromosome of each kind is represented. But the other two include one normal and one translocated chromosome. Upon fertilization of such a series of eggs by normal sperm, the first yields an entirely normal zygote; the next yields a zygote with two complete pairs of chromosomes, two members of which are reciprocally translocated; but the other two have each a large duplication for one pair of chromosomes and a large deficiency for the other. Since large duplications and large deficiencies are both lethal, these do not appear among the progeny. Hence a translocation reduces the viable seed set by 50 per cent.

Translocations can be identified cytologically by the appearance of such tetrads which are joined together by the translocated members, or genetically by dominant lethality of the unbalanced types. An additional genetic test is afforded by the change in linkage relations. If there is, for example, a translocation between chromosomes II and III in *Drosophila*, then tests will show not only the usual linkage groups, but also linkage between markers for II and III. Thus the linkage groups appear to be branched rather than linear.

Finally, it may be mentioned that translocations, like other architectural changes in the chromosomes, may have mutant effects. Thus a particular translocation between chromosomes I and II in *Drosophila* results in a diminution of pigments, and is called "blond." Or a translocation may change the expression of another gene. For example, cubitus interruptus (*ci*) is a fourth chromosome recessive in *Drosophila*, which, when homozygous, causes a break in one of the wing veins. But if a translocation break occurs near this gene, it behaves as a dominant. This phenomenon is called *dominance modification*.

36. CORRELATION OF GENETIC AND CYTOLOGICAL MAPS—SALIVARY GLAND CHROMOSOMES

This chapter began with the question of whether it might be possible to compare the genetic chromosome map, based upon crossover tests, with the actual positions of the genes in the chromosomes. Before this could be done, it was necessary to make a cytological map, localizing genes on the visible chromosomes. This was first undertaken, principally by Dobzhansky, for the mitotic chromosomes of *Drosophila*.

METAPHASE MAPS The architectural changes in the chromosomes listed above offer a means of localizing genes on the cytologically observed chromosomes. Assume, for example, that genetic tests show that translocation has occurred at or near a particular locus. One can examine the metaphase chromosomes of an heterozygous individual and see where, on the actual chromosome, the break has occurred. This then marks the locus of the gene in the metaphase chromosome. End points of all four types of rearrangement can be correlated with specific loci. When a series of points along the length of the chromosome have been localized in this manner, the resulting map can be compared with the genetic map.

The method is not an easy one. Few organisms are known both genetically and cytologically in sufficient detail to permit construction of useful maps for such studies. *Drosophila* is better known genetically than

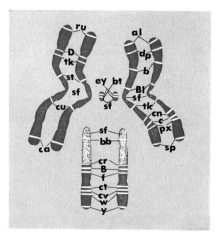

Fig. 85. *Metaphase map of the chromosomes of* Drosophila. (*Modified from Dobzhansky in* Duggar, Biological Effects of Radiation.)

independent of one another, it is of high theoretical interest that in every case the order of genes in the two kinds of maps is identical. But the relative distances between the genes need not be the same. In some instances, genes which appear widely separated on the genetic map may be clustered close together on the cytological map; while in sections of the chromosome in which the genes appear close together on the genetic map, they may be widely separated on the real chromosome (fig. 86). This can only mean that, as suggested by the railroad analogy above, crossing over occurs much more readily in some sections of the chromosome than in others. It appears that the euchromatic sections are characterized by a high crossover rate, while the heterochromatic sections are characterized by a low rate.

any other organism, but its chromosomes are small and difficult to study. Only the larger rearrangements can be seen satisfactorily in the metaphase chromosomes. Of the large rearrangements available for study, not all will have genetically known loci at their end points.

In spite of these difficulties, and by dint of much labor, Th. Dobzhansky succeeded in mapping the metaphase chromosomes of *Drosophila* for a fairly large number of points throughout the chromosome set. His map is reproduced in figure 85. As the methods of making genetic and cytological maps are

While slow progress was thus being made in the comparison of genetic and cytological maps, it was often regretted that *Drosophila*, which seemed to be the ideal animal for genetic research, was nonetheless a very poor animal for cytological research because of the very small size of its chromosomes. Then in 1933 it turned out that, quite the contrary, *Drosophila* was an ideal organism for chromosomal studies, because the salivary glands of its larvae have giant chromosomes.

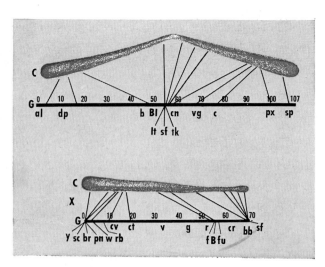

Fig. 86. *A comparison of cytological and genetic (crossover) maps of the X chromosome and the second chromosome of* Drosophila. *In each case, C is the actual chromosome, and G the genetic map. (Modified from Dobzhansky, in Duggar.)*

SALIVARY GLAND CHROMOSOMES Actually, this was not a new discovery. As long ago as 1881, very coarse, coiled threads had been observed in the nuclei of living, unstained salivary gland cells of a midge. But nothing further was done with these large structures until 1933, when it was demonstrated that these were actually chromosomes. It was found that the giant chromosomes could be easily studied by crushing the salivary glands between a slide and cover slip. The giant chromosomes of the salivary glands characterize most Diptera, including *Drosophila*. Once the nature of the structures was made known, T. S. Painter, an American cytologist, realized at once that such large chromosomes must afford a unique tool for the correlation of genetic and cytological information, and he soon published data comparable to those of Dobzhansky, but based upon the salivary gland chromosomes. Many others soon joined in this work, among whom Calvin Bridges of the Carnegie Institution deserves especial mention.

The most striking characteristic of the salivary gland chromosomes is their immense size. They may reach as much as 300 micra in length—nearly a third of a millimeter long—and a proportional thickness! This is large enough that, if they were opaque, they could be seen with the naked eye. How great the size increase is as compared to the ordinary mitotic chromosomes may be seen in figure 87, for a metaphase chromosome is about the size of one of the heavier cross bands which appear in the photograph of the salivary gland chromosomes.

As the diploid number for *Drosophila* is eight, one might expect to see eight strands in each salivary gland nucleus. But this is not the case: one sees only six which extend out from a heavy mass, the *chromocenter*. Why?

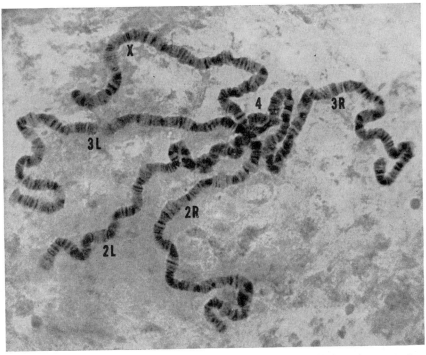

Fig. 87. *The salivary gland chromosomes of* Drosophila *as they appear in a typical smear preparation. Numbers and letters identify the six arms of the set.*
(*Courtesy of Dr. Berwind P. Kaufmann, Carnegie Institution of Washington, Cold Spring Harbor, New York.*)

First, it is generally characteristic of the Diptera that homologous chromosomes are loosely paired even in somatic tissues. In the salivary gland chromosomes, this tendency is carried further, and the homologues are closely synapsed, so that one cannot distinguish the synaptic partners from one another. This should result in four visible strands. But the largest heterochromatic masses tend to join together without respect to homology or the lack of it, and thus they form the chromocenter. Because the main masses of heterochromatin are located at one end of chromosomes I and IV (the end with the centromere), these chromosomes appear as single strands extending from the chromocenter. But the long chromosomes II and III have their main heterochromatic segments located centrally (again about the centromeres), with the result that each of these chromosomes appears to be divided into two by the chromocenter. And thus six chromosome arms appear in preparations of salivary gland chromosomes.

BANDING Typical metaphase chromosomes, including those of *Drosophila*, are more or less uniform rods, bent into various shapes according to the location of the centromeres, which stain uniformly and intensely with basic dyes, such as hematoxylin and carmine. In contrast to this, the salivary gland chromosomes show a regular and detailed pattern of differences along their length. There are regularly situated bulbs and constrictions which aid in the identification of particular chromosomes. But, more important, there are alternating stainable bands and non-stainable interband spaces. These bands differ in thickness, intensity, spacing, and other easily observed characteristics, as can be readily seen in figure 87. The sequence of bands has been worked out in detail, principally by Bridges, and it is possible to identify any section of the salivary gland chromosomes by reference to Bridges' map. To facilitate this, the entire chromosome set has been arbitrarily divided into 102

segments. Within each numbered segment, smaller groups of bands are designated by letters, and any particular band within a lettered group may again be identified by a number. Thus, for example, if a cytogeneticist refers to an abnormality at 52-F-3, anyone can identify the band designated by reference to Bridges' map.

It is noteworthy that the salivary gland chromosomes do not simply show on a large scale structures which are already visible on a smaller scale in ordinary mitotic chromosomes. The finest structural units which can be made out in ordinary chromosomes are the chromomeres in the early stages of meiosis. In *Drosophila*, there are about 150 of these. But well over 5000 bands appear in the salivary gland chromosomes. Thus these giant chromosomes reveal a wealth of fine detail which was utterly unsuspected when only the ordinary chromosomes were studied.

CHROMOSOMAL REARRANGEMENTS IN THE SALIVARY GLAND CHROMOSOMES Architectural rearrangements of the chromosomes, often called chromosomal aberrations, were introduced above as a means of localizing genes on the visible chromosome. But in the ordinary chromosomes, such a localization can be made only very crudely. A break may be designated as "near the right end," or "about a third of the way from the left end to the centromere." But exact localization is not possible, and very small rearrangements cannot be used at all. However, the same rearrangements are also visible and easily identifiable in the salivary gland chromosomes. And because the chromosomes are so much enlarged, it is possible to study rearrangements which are impossibly small for study in ordinary chromosomes. In fact, deletions for only a single band have been identified. This would correspond to a very small fraction of a single chromomere, already the smallest identifiable part of the ordinary chromosome.

The method of correlating the salivary

gland chromosomes with the genetic map does not differ in principle from that described above for correlating the metaphase and genetic maps. One simply looks for rearrangements near the ends of which there are known genes. Thus it is possible to limit the locus of each gene to a small segment of the chromosome. But now, instead of describing the locus crudely as, for example, "near the left end of the X chromosome," one can specify just what bands may be involved. The Notch case was described above. In the salivary gland chromosomes of females heterozygous for Notch, there may be seen a small deficiency in sections 1 and 2, at the left end of the X chromosome. Its partner buckles off to one side as an unpaired bulge. One knows that the genes w and Ab, as well as the intervening recessives which show pseudodominance, must all be located in this short segment. If a particular gene shows pseudodominance in the presence of either of two overlapping deficiencies, then its locus must be in the segment of overlap. By this method, it has been claimed in some cases that the locus of a gene has been definitely assigned to a single band in the salivary gland chromosomes.

THE VISIBLE CHROMOSOME AND THE CROSSOVER MAP Since the introduction of cytogenetic studies of the salivary gland chromosomes in 1934, an immense amount of work has been done to correlate the visible bands of these giant chromosomes with the crossover map. The formal result is summarized in part in Bridges' map, in which crossover maps and the salivary gland chromosomes are drawn on the same scale. This has made possible a very much more extensive and precise comparison than was ever possible with the metaphase maps, yet it is an important and striking fact that the conclusions differ not in kind but only in the degree of assurance with which they can be stated. The major facts which emerge are still that the order of genes is always the same in genetic and cytological maps; and

that the relative spacing of loci may be quite different in the two kinds of maps.

EUCHROMATIN AND HETEROCHROMATIN Relative spacing of loci appears to depend upon the distribution of euchromatin and heterochromatin in the chromosomes. The different types of chromatin were introduced in chapter 6, where it was pointed out that the Y chromosome, with its paucity of known mutants, is mainly heterochromatic, while the X chromosome, with its abundant mutants is mainly euchromatic. The distinction between these two kinds of chromatin was originally made on the basis of a difference in staining reaction during mitosis. Heterochromatin appears first in prophase and disappears last in telophase. In meiosis, heterochromatic chromosomes may begin the anaphasic movement earlier or later than the others. In other words, the heterochromatin is generally out of step as compared to the "typical" chromatin, the euchromatin.

When the euchromatin and the heterochromatin were first studied genetically, it became apparent that the known mutants were almost always in the euchromatin. So rare were the heterochromatic mutants that many geneticists concluded that the apparent exceptions must be based upon small segments of euchromatin inserted into generally heterochromatic regions. Euchromatin was defined as "genetically active" and heterochromatin as "genetically inert." This is not strictly true, because studies in the physiology of the gene have shown that heterochromatin may exercise a considerable influence upon the expression of genes. Nonetheless, mutation is rare in the heterochromatin, and possibly it is non-existent.

Another difference between the behavior of euchromatin and heterochromatin lies in the much greater susceptibility of the former to crossing over. This would be of little importance if heterochromatin were confined to the Y chromosome. However, smaller segments of heterochromatin are scattered through the entire chromosome set (fig. 88). In *Drosophila*, each chromosome has a large mass of heterochromatin about the centromere, and smaller segments are widely distributed. Because crossing over is rare in the heterochromatin, loci which are widely separated by heterochromatic segments may appear close together on a genetic map. Similarly, loci separated by purely euchromatic segments will appear relatively far apart genetically.

37. CYTOLOGICAL PROOF OF CROSSING OVER

When the salivary gland chromosomes were discovered, it was hoped that they would permit a direct demonstration of the correlation between genetic crossing over and cytological exchange of segments between homologues. This was, however, a vain hope, for it turned out that the giant chromosomes, being fully synapsed, show no evidence whatever of crossing over.

But a very clever method of supplying this evidence was devised by Curt Stern, using stocks of flies marked both with specific genes and chromosomal rearrangements. Altogether, three marked stocks were used. Stock 1 had the hook of the *Y* chromosome translocated on to the *X*, so that females appeared to have a pair of *Y* chromosomes, but this stock was normal with respect to genes. Stock 2 had a portion of the *X* chromosome translocated on to IV, so that it looked as though the *X* was split. One segment included the genes for carnation eye color (*cr*) and for bar eye shape (*B*).

Stock 3 had normal *X* chromosomes with the two marker genes present in the recessive form (*cr* and *B+*). All stocks are diagrammed in figure 89.

First, stocks 1 and 2 were crossed. All of the female offspring from this cross had to have one split *X* chromosome with the mutant genes *cr* and *B*, and one hooked *X* chromosome with the normal alleles *cr+* and *B+*. Such females were then crossed to males from stock 3, having a normal *X* chromosome with the two recessive alleles. The results of such a cross are diagrammed in figure 89. Parental type female offspring should have a normal *X* chromosome from the father and a translocated one from the mother. If the latter is the split chromosome, the flies should be carnation and bar. If it is the hooked *X*, then the flies should show the two normal characters (red eyes of normal, oval shape). But if a crossover should occur between *cr* and *B*, then the maternal chromosome should be either a normal appearing one with the two recessive alleles, so that the flies would show the recessive characters; or it should be both split and hooked and carry the two dominant alleles. These flies should have red, bar shaped eyes.

Thus, if crossing over is based upon exchange of segments of the chromosomes, the following should be obtained among the female offspring from the second cross described above. All carnation-bar-eyed flies should have one split *X* chromosome and one normal chromosome, while those with red, oval eyes should have one hooked *X* chromosome and one normal one. These are the parental types. The cross-over types

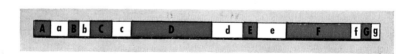

Fig. 88. *Map of the main segments of euchromatin (colored) and heterochromatin in the* X *chromosome of* Drosophila. (*Modified from Kodani, in the* Journal of Heredity, *vol. 32.*)

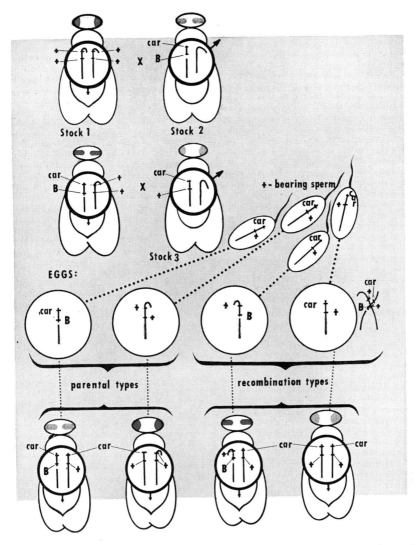

Fig. 89. *Stern's proof that crossing over is based upon exchange of segments between the chromosomes of a pair. See text for discussion.*

are red-bar and carnation-oval. The first should have a split *and* hooked X chromosome paired with a normal one, while the second should have a pair of normal X chromosomes. Stern compared phenotypes and chromosomal configurations of 364 flies. In 359 instances, the expected results were actually obtained, while only five flies yielded discordant results. Stern concluded that these five must have been based upon experimental errors of some sort. Certainly,

agreement with prediction in 359 out of 364 examples is an impressive record, and it may be regarded as proven that crossing over is based upon exchange of segments of chromosomes.

RÉSUMÉ While the genes are ordinarily localized in a definite serial order in the chromosomes, nonetheless, the architecture of the chromosomes can be rearranged in several ways. A segment may be inverted, that is, broken out of the chromosome and then rejoined in the reversed position. Or a segment may be deleted from the chromosome entirely. Or a segment may be duplicated. Finally, segments may be interchanged between non-homologous chromosomes. Each rearrangement leads to a typical pattern of synapsis which is readily recognizable in heterozygotes. Whenever a known gene is located at or near an end of such a rearrangement, the gene can be approximately localized in the visible chromosome. Thus a comparison of crossover maps with the real chromosome becomes possible. This kind of work was greatly facilitated by the discovery of the salivary gland chromosomes, giant chromosomes of *Drosophila* and some other Diptera. The order of the genes has proved to be identical in the crossover maps and in the real chromosomes, but the spacing is often different. It appears that crossing over occurs more readily in the euchromatin than in the heterochromatin.

Questions and Problems

1. Define:

Chromocenter	Heterochromatin
Chromomere	Inversion
Deficiency	Metaphase map
Duplication	Salivary gland chromosome
Euchromatin	Translocation

2. Sketch clearly, and large enough to show the features intended, the mitotic and salivary gland chromosome sets of *Drosophila*. Label all essential features.

3. Now sketch diagrams of the principal types of chromosomal rearrangements.

4. In the X chromosome of *Drosophila*, vermilion (*v*), miniature (*m*), dusky (*dy*), and wavy (*wy*) are located at 33.0, 36.1, 36.2, and 41.9, respectively. A female homozygous for these mutants is crossed to a normal male which has been subjected to x-radiation. Male offspring should all be simplex for the recessives, while female offspring should be heterozygous and should show the wild type characters. But a few of the females showed the miniature and dusky characters. How can you account for this in terms of the present chapter?

5. In a stock of *Drosophila*, chromosome I is marked by yellow (*y*), chromosome II by brown (*b*), chromosome III by ebony (*e*), and chromosome IV by eyeless (*ey*). Upon crossing a female homozygous for these markers to an irradiated male, and backcrossing the F_1 to the marked parental stock, only about half as many offspring are obtained as in control crosses. Of these, yellow and gray body, eyeless and normal eyes appear in the expected 1 : 1 ratios. But homozygous brown flies and ebony flies are rare or absent from the progeny. How can you account for these data?

6. In the X chromosome of *Drosophila*, the following genes are located as indicated: yellow (*y*), 0.0; white (*w*), 1.5; ruby (*rb*), 7.5; crossveinless (*cv*), 13.7; and cut (*ct*), 20. A female heterozygous for these mutants was crossed to a male with all of the recessives. In the progeny, white, ruby, and crossveinless always remained together, but yellow and cut recombined freely with each other and with the other loci mentioned. Furthermore, the rate of recombination between yellow and cut appeared to be only 7.8 per cent. What is the explanation of these data?

References

Bridges, C. B., 1935. Salivary chromosome maps. Journal of Heredity, 26:60–64. A classic, including the standard map.

Dobzhansky, T., 1936. Induced Chromosomal Aberrations in Animals. In B. M. Duggar, Biological Effects of Radiation, 2:1167–1208. A general review of the problem, including the author's work on metaphase maps.

Painter, T. S., 1934. Salivary chromosomes and the attack on the gene. Journal of Heredity, 25:465–476. A preliminary review by the man who introduced the giant chromosomes into cytogenetic research.

Stern, C. 1931. Zytologisch-genetische Untersuchungen als Beweise für die Morgansche Theorie des Faktorenaustausch. Biologisches Zentralblatt, 51:547–587. For those who read German well, the original account of Stern's proof of the correlation between crossing over and exchange of chromosomal segments holds considerable interest.

CHAPTER 13

Mutation

Throughout the preceding chapters, the phenomenon of mutation has been assumed, but it has not been directly treated. Mutation is a permanent change in a gene. As such, it is the basic phenomenon both of genetics and of evolution: of genetics because inheritance can be studied profitably only when different alleles of the same gene are available for use in breeding experiments; of evolution, because inheritable variability is the only possible substrate for the action of natural selection in differentiating species.

If a population under study were completely homozygous for, let us say, a particular color gene, then all members of that population should be identical, save for minor, environmentally produced fluctuations in intensity and distribution of the pigment. From this fact, one might get considerable strength of conviction that the color character in question was, in fact, inherited. And it might further be concluded that reproduction of the organisms was paralleled by a remarkably exact and invariable reproduction of the units of inheritance. But this is all the information that such observations could yield. No insight could be obtained into the number of units involved, or the mode of inheritance, whether qualitative or quantitative, dominant or recessive, sex-linked or autosomal. The permanence of the gene would not only emerge as its major property, but it would tend to mask all others except reproducibility.

Permanence is, indeed, one of the important properties of genes. But they are occasionally reproduced inexactly, so that a changed or *mutant* gene results. The mutant gene is now reproduced with the same fidelity as was the original, or *wild type*, gene, and together they constitute an allelic pair, the basic unit of genetic experimentation. While the relative permanence of the gene has been assumed without proof in the preceding chapters, nonetheless the data reported have been obtainable only because mutations have occurred from time to time. There is no other means by which allelic pairs could have been established. And thus insight into the details of the mechanism of heredity depends upon the fact of mutation.

38. BASIC ASPECTS OF MUTATION

While the significance of mutations has been understandable only since the rise of modern genetics, the occurrence of mutant individuals has long been known. Taxonomy has been a fundamental branch of biology for two hundred years, and the taxonomists have always had to deal not only with the typical members of the species studied, but also with those more striking variants which we would now call mutants. While these were always found in greater or lesser proportion in natural populations, the taxonomists called them *aberrations*, thereby indicating that they did not regard them as being of any importance in the economy of nature. Plant and animal breeders have also been familiar with mutants since remote antiquity. The Mendelian breeders of today treasure their mutants as reservoirs of new and potentially valuable variability, but the pre-Mendelian breeders called them *sports,* indicating that they regarded them as capricious freaks of nature. They often killed their mutants and kept their occurrence secret, on the grounds that the sports reflected upon the purity of their breeding stock.

THE FREQUENCY OF MUTATION The greater portion of elementary genetics emphasizes the idea of the permanence of the gene, and even professional biologists are likely to think of mutation as a rare thing— something which could be important only if time be available on a geological scale. Most realize that more mutant types have been discovered in *Drosophila* than in any other organism, but they are likely to estimate the number of mutants known in this genus as on the order of 1000 or less. Yet W. P. Spencer has stated that "actually the number of natural and induced mutations found in this genus would be much closer to 100,000 and probably in excess of this figure."[*]

Actually, mutation does occur with measurable frequency, and the rate has been measured in several instances under natural and experimental conditions. Some of the specific data will be summarized here. At the outset, it should be pointed out there is no single mutation rate which is generally applicable. A more or less general average would be about one mutation in every 100,000 gametes, but every possible type of deviation from average is known. Thus Spencer found in 1935 that the rate of mutation in *Drosophila* varies from time to time. This he attributed to the influence of the environment. Later, Demerec demonstrated that different strains of *Drosophila* show inheritable differences in mutation rate even when grown simultaneously in one laboratory. This led to the concept of genes controlling the rate of mutation. Recently,

[*] Advances in Genetics, vol. 1, p. 359, Academic Press, Inc., New York.

"mutator" genes have been investigated in wild populations of *Drosophila*. These cause a very striking elevation of the mutation rate, and have been regarded as a fundamental factor in evolution.

It may be regarded as demonstrated, then, that the rate of mutation is variable even within a single species. Further, it varies markedly from one gene to another. This was evident even before the experimental analysis was begun, because some mutants, like white eyes, recur frequently in *Drosophila* stocks, others appear rather rarely and still others are known only from single records. But the most impressive study yet reported on this subject is one by L. J. Stadler on the rates of mutation of eight genes in maize. Well-known and easily identifiable characters were selected for study (see table 13). Plants homozygous for the normal dominant alleles were crossed to test plants homozygous for the recessives. Any F_1 plant showing a mutant phenotype must have resulted from a mutation in a gamete of the dominant parent. An immense number of progeny were examined, and the results then expressed as so many mutations per million gametes tested. As

Table 13. Mutation Frequencies of Eight Common Genes in Maize

(Modified from Stadler, Spragg Memorial Lectures, Third Series, 1939. Michigan State College Press)

GENE	NUMBER OF GAMETES TESTED	NUMBER OF MUTATIONS	FREQUENCY PER MILLION GAMETES
R	554,786	273	492
I	265,391	28	106
Pr	647,102	7	11
Su	1,678,736	4	2.4
C	426,923	1	2.3
Y	1,745,280	4	2.2
Sh	2,469,285	3	1.2
Wx	1,503,744	0	0

shown in the table, a great range of mutation rates was found among these seven genes. The third member of this series, *Pr* (purple), approximated the general average of one mutation in 100,000 gametes. The first in the series, *R* (colored endosperm) mutated at the rapid rate of 492 mutations per million gametes, or approximately one mutation in every 2000 gametes. Yet the last gene in the series, *Wx* (non-waxy) was characterized by so low a rate that not a single mutation was observed in over 1,500,000 gametes tested.

Mutation rates also differ between closely related species. Thus two species of snapdragon, *Antirrhinum majus* and *A. siculum*, were studied over a period of many years. Regularly, the progeny of normal *A. majus* included 5 to 7 per cent of mutant types. While this was undoubtedly based in part upon recombination of recessives that had been carried in the heterozygous state for many generations, yet long-continued intensive selection for the normal alleles should have eliminated such genes unless new mutation were proceeding at least as rapidly as selection. Yet during twenty years of breeding and observing, not a single mutant of *A. siculum* was observed! Mutation, then, proceeds at measurable rates, rates which vary from one locus to another in a single species, from one time to another in a single race, between different genetic races of any species, and between different species of a genus.

MUTABLE LOCI   A special case of extremely rapid mutation rate is presented by the so-called *mutable loci*, or *unstable genes*, which mutate numerous times during the development of a single individual, so that a somatic mosaic results. The best known example is that of the variegated plants (fig. 90), which are characterized by green foliage with splotches of white. Variegations of foliage or flower colors make up most of the known examples, no doubt because these are most easily observed. Almost all of the known examples occur in plants.

Fig. 90.   *Variegated leaves of* Polygonum, *the knot weed.*
(*From Imai, in Cytologia, Fujii Memorial volume.*)

Typically, the direction of mutation is from an unstable recessive allele to a dominant which is then as stable as are most genes. But in some instances, unstable genes have been reported which mutate from dominant to recessive, and even two-way mutation has been reported.

The basis for such extraordinary mutation rates is not known, but there has been no dearth of theories. One of the earliest theories suggested that an unstable gene is a diseased gene. Another suggestion is that the gene may be made up of subgenes, or genomeres, which may be of different types, with intragenic segregation during mitosis accounting for the appearance of a high mutation rate. A third, and more generally accepted theory, is that an unstable gene is characterized by a physicochemical structure which is unstable in a molecular sense, with the stable form to which it mutates representing a more stable chemical state. Most of the literature on this subject is rather old, and the whole subject should be reinvestigated by modern methods.

MEASUREMENT OF MUTATION RATES Most of the above discussion infers the use of methods for the quantitative study of mutation rates, yet an actual method was mentioned only in the case of Stadler's study of the rates of mutation of particular genes. Where the rate of mutation in general is sought, rather than that of specific genes, the problem is more difficult, and cannot be covered comprehensively; however some examples will be described. Usually it is necessary to set up the experiment to test for some particular class of mutations, as lethal or visible, sex-linked or autosomal. What is required is an experimental tool which will make the class of mutants under study easily identifiable in the experimental population.

DETECTION OF SEX-LINKED VISIBLE MUTATIONS The use of attached-X chromosomes provides a simple and direct method for the detection of sex-linked visibles. Many years ago L. V. Morgan (Mrs. Thomas Hunt Morgan) discovered a female *Drosophila* which passed *all* of her sex-linked traits to her daughters and none to her sons. Further breeding from her progeny showed a regular mother-to-daughter and father-to-son pattern of inheritance of sex-linked characters. Mrs. Morgan reasoned that this

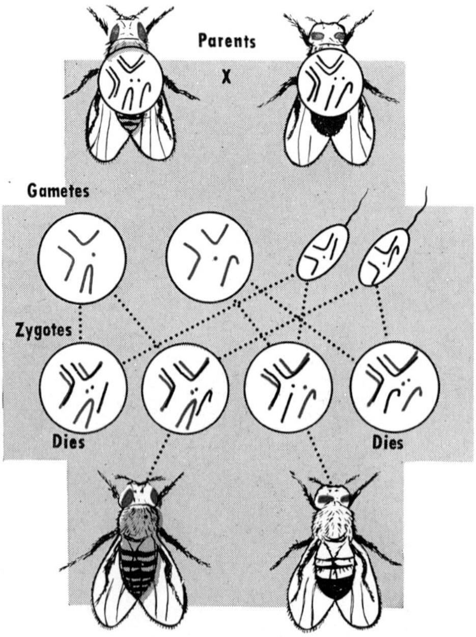

Fig. 91. *Attached-X inheritance. Yellow body color, the usual marker for attached-X chromosomes, is here indicated by the very pale pink. Bar eye is used as a marker for the X chromosome in the males. Note that inheritance of these sex-linked traits follows a mother-to-daughter and father-to-son pattern.*

could be explained *if the two X chromosomes of the female be attached together* (symbolized $\widehat{XX}$). Cytological examination proved this to be the case. Such females also carry a Y chromosome. They produce two kinds of eggs, $\widehat{XX}$ and Y. Upon fertilization by normal sperm, the following array of zygotes is formed: $\widehat{XXX}$, $\widehat{XXY}$ XY, and YY. The first of these is usually inviable, while the last always is. The second is again an $\widehat{XX}$ female, and shows only maternal sex-linked characters. The third is a normal male, *but* the Y chromosome is derived from the mother and the X from the father, hence only paternal sex-linked traits show up. In order that the $\widehat{XX}$Y females may be easily recognizable the $\widehat{XX}$ chromosomes are usually marked with a pair of homozygous recessive genes, commonly yellow body (yy). This pattern of inheritance is diagrammed in figure 91.

With such a pattern of inheritance, any sex-linked mutations occurring in a male should show up immediately in his progeny. Thus all sex-linked visible mutations occurring in the male parent should be identifiable, and can be expressed as a fraction of the total male offspring obtained.

DETECTION OF A SOMATIC LETHAL   For the study of somatic lethals, one can use a modification of the Star-Dichaete method of localizing genes, which was taken up in chapter 11. Assume that second chromosome lethals are under study. As a test stock, flies heterozygous for Star (S) and Curly (Cy) may be used. These are both second chromosome dominants which are lethal when homozygous. Thus all Star-Curly flies $\left(\dfrac{S\,+}{+\,Cy}, \text{ not } \dfrac{S\,Cy}{+\,+}\right)$ must be heterozygous. This is called a *balanced lethal* combination. Let us say that one wishes to test for the occurrence of second chromosome lethal mutations in a stock of flies which has been subjected to an experimental procedure. The treated flies may be mated to S/Cy flies in individual vials. All of the progeny should carry one second chromosome from the marker stock and one from the stock being tested. The $S/+$ flies are now mated *inter se*. The offspring of any pair heterozygous for a new lethal must include four types: S/S, which is lethal; $S+/+l$; $+l/S+$; and $+l/+l$, which is lethal. Thus, no wild type offspring should occur in the progeny of flies with a new lethal mutant. But in the absence of such a mutant, one third of the progeny should be wild type. A similar sequence can be completed with the Curly flies.

The methods reported above may be sufficient to give some idea of the methods necessary for the quantitative study of mutation. Additional methods will be reported below in connection with experimental mutation and inheritance in man.

MUTATION IN A SERIES OF MULTIPLE ALLELES   The existence of multiple alleles is itself evidence of the mutation process, for there is no conceivable way by which such series could have been formed other than by mutation from an original wild type to the various mutant forms of the same gene. But the phenotypes based upon such a series commonly vary from one another in a simple, quantitative way. Thus the white eye color series of *Drosophila* may be regarded as a dilution sequence, starting with red and passing through such colors as cherry, eosin, and honey to white. *A priori*, one might suspect that the mutation process also would have to go through the sequence from higher to lower alleles. But this is not the case. Any allele may mutate directly to any other; although some do occur more frequently than others. In general, mutation from the dominant member of the series to a recessive form is most common, but *reverse* mutation, from a recessive member of the series to its wild type allele, has also been reported.

MUTATION IN RELATION TO THE CHROMOSOMAL CYCLE   Mutation can occur at any point in the life cycle, and in somatic cells as well as in sex cells. If a recessive mutation occurs in a sex cell, it will not show until recombination makes it homozygous. Special methods are necessary to detect the occurrence, as discussed above. But if a dominant mutation occurs in a sex cell, there is a possibility that it will be fertilized and so will show up in the first generation after its occurrence. In a general way, the earlier in the sex chromosome cycle that such a mutation occurs, the more affected offspring there should be. Thus a dominant mutation occurring in a single sperm cell could only affect one zygote, but a mutation occurring in a primary spermatocyte could show up in two zygotes (not four, because simultaneous mutation in both members of a pair of chromosomes is unknown, if not impossible). On the other hand, a mutation in an early spermatogonium would affect hundreds of sperm and possibly many offspring.

Identification of a somatic mutation is much more difficult, at least in animals. At the outset, a recessive mutation could not be identified at all, unless it were in the simplex condition, or unless the organism were at first heterozygous, with the dominant allele then mutating to the recessive form. A dominant mutation could potentially show up at once. In either case, the organism would be a mosaic of tissue with mutant and non-mutant genotypes. If the mutation should occur in one of the first two blastomeres, then a half-and-half mosaic would result. If it should occur in one of the first four blastomeres, then one fourth of the organism would have the mutant genotype. The later it occurs, the smaller the mutant segment. Some characters cannot be expressed in small segments of the body, while others can be. What appear to be mutants of only a single facet of the eye of *Drosophila* have been detected.

In addition to the above difficulties, there is the problem of distinguishing a somatic mutation from environmentally induced modifications. It has been suggested that those characters which are maintained in tissue culture are true mutants, while those which disappear in tissue culture are merely modifications. But there is no assurance that this hypothesis is correct. Incidentally, it is partly upon this basis that it has been claimed that cancer depends upon somatic mutation. The crux of the problem is that the identification of true mutations depends primarily upon their behavior in sexual reproduction, and this is not a property of somatic tissues.

In plants, the situation is simpler, because so many plants can be propagated successfully from cuttings, or by other asexual methods. A suspected mutant branch may be so propagated, and it may then flower, permitting a direct test of whether the variant is a genuine mutation, or simply an environmental modification. The search for such *bud mutants* (fig. 92) is a standard method of plant breeding. When a valuable mutant is found, it is ordinarily propagated asexually in order to prevent segregation from breaking up a fortunate combination of genes. Most of the commercial varieties of apples, and many other fruits, have arisen in this way. The phenomenon has been known a long time, for Darwin described the origin of the nectarine from the peach in this way.

39. EXPERIMENTAL MUTATION

In the scientific study of any subject, its experimental control is a basic goal. The first progress in this direction in the case of mutation was made by H. J. Muller, who found in 1927 that irradiation of *Drosophila* would increase the mutation rate enormously. During the intervening years, Muller and others have exploited the method exhaustively, and

Fig. 92. *A bud mutant in* Narcissus. *The larger flower is growing from a bulb which was budded off from the smaller one. Actually, the smaller one is diploid and the larger one tetraploid. See the following chapter for a discussion of this phenomenon. (From de Mol, in Cytologia, Fujii Memorial volume.)*

thus have greatly increased our knowledge of mutation. For this work, Muller received the Nobel prize in medicine in 1946.

THE *ClB* METHOD Muller's success depended not only upon the selection of an efficient mutagenic (mutation-producing) agent, but also on the invention of a suitable method for quantitative determination of the rate of formation of a specific class of mutations. To do this, he restricted his study to sex-linked lethals, as these can be easily and unequivocally identified, whereas identification of visible mutations depends upon the degree of refinement of observation. To identify the sex-linked lethals, he used a marker stock called the *ClB* stock. *C* stands for a crossover inhibitor in the *X* chromosome, and is now (but not in 1927) known to be an inversion. The *l* symbolizes a re-

cessive lethal, and is probably actually identical with *C*. *B* is the bar eye gene, and is used to make visible which flies carry the marked chromosome. *ClB* females, then, have one *ClB* chromosome and one normal *X* chromosome.

In practice, males are irradiated to produce mutations in the sperm, then they are mated to *ClB* females, one pair to a vial. All of the female offspring must have an *X* chromosome from each parent. Half of these will have the *ClB* chromosome from their mother, and only these flies are studied further, by mating them, one pair to the vial, to normal males. If such a female received a normal sperm (no sex-linked lethal mutations) from her father, then she will produce two females to one male (because *l* of the *ClB* complex is lethal when simplex).

But if she received a mutated *X* chromosome from her father, she could have *only daughters*, because both of her *X* chromosomes would carry genes which are lethal when simplex. Why is such a female viable herself? Because the new mutant is very unlikely to be an allele of the *l* of the *ClB* complex. Hence each chromosome carries the normal allele of the lethal gene in the other chromosome. Thus the proportion of females which produce only daughters indicates the proportion of sperm of the irradiated male in which sex-linked lethal mutations occurred. The *ClB* test is summarized in figure 93.

A correction factor is necessary, because about 0.2 per cent of the flies will show new sex-linked lethals in the absence of irradiation. Hence only the increase above this spontaneous mutation rate can be considered to be caused by the treatment. But the increase is striking: with 1000 r units of radiation, the rate increases to about 3 per cent; with 2000 r, it increases to 6 per cent; with 4000 r, it increases to 12 per cent. The curve of relation of dosage to mutation rate is a straight line curve.

RESULTS FROM EXPERIMENTAL MUTATION A massive literature has emerged from the work of Muller and his collaborators. This cannot be summarized here, but a few generalizations are possible. The first of these is that the mutation rate appears to be directly proportional to the dosage of radiation administered to an organism, *irrespective of the rate of administration*. It was suggested soon after Muller's first publication that there must be a minimum effective rate of administration of radiation. Muller tested this by varying the rate from a minimum of one one-hundredth of an r unit per minute up to 200 r per minute or greater. Over the entire range, any particular total dosage still produced the same amount of mutation, and the straight line curve was maintained. Subse-

quently, the rate of dosage was reduced still further, but the results were still concordant with Muller's. Mutation was interpreted as the end result of a direct hit of an ionizing particle upon a sensitive molecule.

A second generalization is that the mutation rate is independent of the wave length of the *X*-rays. This was established by irradiating flies with many different wave lengths. The result was that similar dosage produced similar results irrespective of wave length. Hence it appeared that a direct hit of an ionizing particle upon a sensitive molecule was responsible for the mutagenic effect, rather than the absorption of a specific wave length.

Finally, it should be noted that radiation causes an increase of visible mutations as well as of lethals, but quantitative studies are much more difficult to make, and much less reliable.

RADIATION AS A BIOLOGICAL HAZARD Before leaving the subject of induction of mutations by radiation, a word of warning should be added. It has long been known that exposure of organisms, including man, to heavy doses of radiation causes *radiation sickness*, which may even be fatal. In the clinical, industrial, and experimental usage of the many forms of high energy radiation, care is always taken that the personnel do not receive dosages approaching the minimum for the production of radiation sickness. On this basis, responsible physicians and administrators have expressed the opinion that there is *no danger* in carefully regulated exposure to radiation. However, *there is no minimum dose known for the production of mutations*. And, as mutation is a random phenomenon, the great majority of those produced are harmful. For this reason, the increasing use of radiation is a public health problem of growing importance, even though evidence of damage may not appear for several generations. Radiation has be-

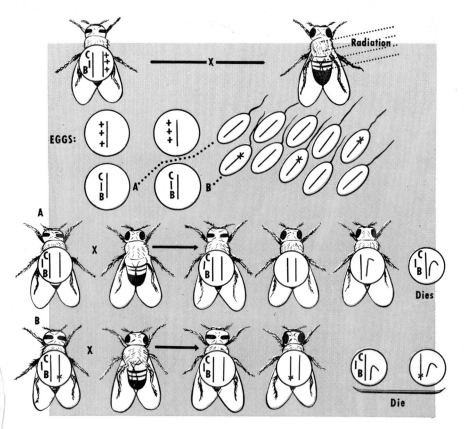

Fig. 93. *The ClB test for sex-linked lethal mutations. An "x" on a chromosome in a sperm indicates such a lethal mutation. If a ClB egg is fertilized by a sperm with an unmutated X chromosome, then the offspring of the resulting female will show a sex ratio of 2 females: 1 male (line A). But fertilization by a sperm with the mutated X chromosome leads to a female whose progeny are all daughters (line B).*

come so important a tool in medicine, industry, research, and military development that there can be no general curtailment of its use. But it is not too much to suggest that precautions be taken to shield the gonads from radiation whenever possible. Unlike radiation sickness, genetic damage does not have the benefit of a minimum threshold of dosage. Any radiation whatever may do irreparable damage.

OTHER MUTAGENIC AGENTS Following Muller's successful induction of mutations by x-rays, an intensive search was made for other effective agents. Many types of radiation were tested, and it turned out that any high energy radiation will cause a similar increase in the mutation rate. These include such diverse radiations as ultraviolet light, cosmic rays, gamma rays, and neutron bombardment. It was also found that temperatures near the limits of viability, whether hot or cold, would increase the mutation rate more than could be accounted for by the thermal coefficients of chemical activity.

Many chemicals were tested for mutagenic activity. Poisons like alcohol and lead salts were thoroughly investigated, as were metabolites such as the nucleic acids. But all gave negative results until 1947, when Charlotte Auerbach found that mustard gas

was a highly effective mutagen. Since then, several other chemicals have been demonstrated to have some mutagenic activity, but none has approached the activity of the nitrogen mustards. Formaldehyde is perhaps the closest runner-up. It is particularly convenient for experiments upon bacteria, for it can easily be included in the culture medium.

WHAT MUTANTS ARE PRODUCED? One final word of caution should be added regarding experimental mutation, and that is that only the *rates* of mutation have been influenced by experimental techniques. It would be a matter of extraordinary interest if one could select a specific target gene and cause it to mutate in a specific way. But not only has this not been accomplished, but it is doubtful that it ever will be done.

RÉSUMÉ While the permanence of the gene is one of its most striking properties, yet genes are occasionally inexactly reproduced, and the resulting mutants are then perpetuated with the same regularity as the parent genes. Mutation rates are sufficiently high to be measured, a fair average being one in 100,000 gametes. However, the rate varies for different genes of the same organism, for different races of a species, and for different species of a genus. Some specific genes mutate with great rapidity, indicating that the genes concerned must have an unstable physicochemical structure. While mutation may occur anywhere in the chromosomal cycle, it is difficult to get conclusive evidence of the event, especially in animals, unless it occurs in germinal tissue. The mutation rate can be greatly accelerated by high energy radiation and by various chemicals, such as mustard gas. Special methods, such as the ClB method, have been devised to measure the induced mutation rates. Although the rate of mutation can be increased easily, this is an undirected increase in the sense that the experimenter cannot determine which mutations shall be produced.

Questions and Problems

1. Define:

Aberration	Mutagen
Attached-X	Mutation
Balanced lethals	Sport
Bud mutant	Unstable gene
ClB method	

2. Discuss the significance of the problem of mutation for genetics in general.

3. Most of the experimentally produced mutations are obviously detrimental to the organism. Why should studies of this sort be conducted?

4. Can studies of such abnormalities be of significance for the understanding of nature? Enlarge upon your answer.

5. Which of the explanations of unstable genes seems most probable to you? Why?

6. Several male *Drosophila* were given about 1000 r units of x-radiation, and then were mated to ClB females. 247 female offspring were obtained, and, of these, 125 carried the ClB chromosome as shown by their bar eyes. These were then mated to normal males, one pair to the vial. Most had offspring in a ratio of two females to one male, but four flies had only female offspring. Explain the results, and calculate the rate of mutation represented.

7. In a second experiment, 20 males were subjected to 2000 r units of x-radiation, and then crossed to ClB females. 750 ClB females were obtained in the progeny, and these were tested as in problem 6. Of these, 706 had both sons and daughters, while 44 had only daughters. What was the mutation rate?

8. In a third experiment, 30 males were given 4000 units of radiation, and the experiment carried out as above. 1130 ClB females were obtained, and of these 134 had only daughters. Calculate the rate of mutation.

9. Now plot a curve of relation of dosage to mutation rate, using the data of the preceding problems.

10. From your curve, read the rates of mutation to be expected with dosages of 3000 r and 5000 r.

References

Auerbach, Charlotte, 1949. Chemical mutagenesis. Biological Reviews of the Cambridge Philosophical Society, 24:355-391.

———————— 1951. Problems in chemical mutagenesis. Cold Spring Harbor Symposia on Quantitative Biology, 16:199-213.

Demerec, M., 1935. Unstable genes. Botanical Reviews, 1:233–248.

Morgan, L. V., 1922. Non-criss-cross inheritance in *Drosophila melanogaster*. Biological Bulletin, 42:267–274. This is the original paper on attached-*X* chromosomes.

Muller, H. J., 1941. Induced Mutations in *Drosophila*. Cold Spring Harbor Symposia on Quantitative Biology, 9:151–167.

——————— 1947. The production of mutations. Journal of Heredity, 38:259–270. This is the address which Muller gave when awarded the Nobel Prize in Medicine in 1946.

Muller, H. J., 1955. Genetic damage produced by radiation. Science, 121:837–840. In this short paper, Muller discusses social and political problems arising out of genetics in the atomic age, including those based upon radiation from A-bomb and H-bomb fallout.

Spencer, W. P., 1947. Mutations in wild populations of *Drosophila*. Advances in Genetics, 1:359–402.

Stadler, L. J., 1942. Some Observations on Gene Variability and Spontaneous Mutation. Spragg Memorial Lectures, third series, 3–15. Michigan State College.

CHAPTER 14

Chromosomal Mutation

The possibility that changes in the architecture of the chromosomes might have a mutational effect was raised in chapter 12. Hence, when a method for rapid production of mutations by radiation became available, it became necessary to check the irradiated chromosomes for visible changes as well as for genetically detectable mutations. Whenever it turned out that a new mutation could not be separated by crossing over from a new chromosomal rearrangement, it could be concluded that the mutation was actually a position effect. But, if no change in the structure of the chromosome could be detected, it was necessary to conclude that the mutation was based upon a change in a single gene, a *gene mutation* or *point mutation*.

Both chromosomal mutations and point mutations occur both in nature and in experiments. But not all experimental mutagens produce the two in the same proportions. X-rays and most other types of radiation produce a preponderance of chromosomal mutations, while ultraviolet light and neutron bombardment produce mainly point mutations and extremely small rearrangements. Production of point mutations is proportional to the number of induced ionizations, but production of chromosomal rearrangements is proportional more nearly

to the square of the number of induced ionizations. Originally, it was thought that this meant that a single direct hit on a chromosome produced a point mutation, while two such hits produced a rearrangement. But it now appears that direct hits on the chromosomes are not likely to be involved, and even the cytoplasm may be necessary as an intermediary. A more complete examination of chromosomal mutations may now be in order.

40. CHANGES INVOLVING ENTIRE CHROMOSOMES

In addition to the chromosomal rearrangements which were discussed in chapter 12, there are several kinds of chromosomal mutations which involve changes in whole chromosomes, or even in whole sets of chromosomes. These will be described below.

TRISOMICS An organism which has an extra chromosome is called a *trisomic*. The general formula is 2n + 1, as one of the chromosomes is present in triplicate. Such an organism is mutant in phenotype, presumably because the genes of the trisomic are out of balance with those of the rest of the chromosomes. In *Drosophila*, for example, flies in which the fourth chromosome is trisomic, called Triplo-IV, are somewhat larger than normal diploids, have coarser bristles, and show many other minor differences. Triplo-II and III are not obtainable because of lethality, and Triplo-X shows greatly reduced viability.

Trisomics are transmitted only through the female parent, as an extra chromosome in the pollen or sperm acts as a gamete lethal. When eggs are formed, half should be normal haploid eggs and half should be n + 1 eggs which, upon fertilization, would yield trisomic progeny. Thus the trisomic condition should be transmitted in a ratio of 1 : 1 with normal diploids. Actually however, less than 50 per cent transmission is generally obtained, as the extra chromosome tends to lag behind the others in meiosis, and so fails to be included in either daughter nucleus.

The trisomic condition also causes abnormal ratios of transmission of the genes. An example is afforded by a cross between a Triplo-IV fly with normal eyes and a fly homozygous for the gene *ey,* which results in eyeless flies when homozygous. This experiment is best described by figure 94. In summary, when a female ++*ey* is crossed to a male *eyey,* half of the progeny are Triplo-IV, but only one in six is eyeless, and this one will be diploid. But when a female *eyey*+ is crossed to a male *eyey,* a 1 : 1 ratio is obtained for both traits.

Trisomics are much more common among plants than among animals, and they have been studied particularly intensively in the genus *Datura,* the Jimson weed, by Blakeslee and his collaborators. In this genus there are twelve pairs of chromosomes, and Blakeslee has found natural races characterized by all twelve of the possible trisomic types. Each of these shows a recognizable phenotype, with many deviations from the standard diploid in all parts of the plant. Variations

in the shape of the seed capsules are outstanding, and the various trisomic types have been named on this basis, with such names as "sugarloaf," "rolled," "polycarpic," and "echinus."

But the *Datura* case does not end with the abundance of such *primary* trisomics, in which a normal chromosome is present in triplicate. Blakeslee has also discovered *sec-*

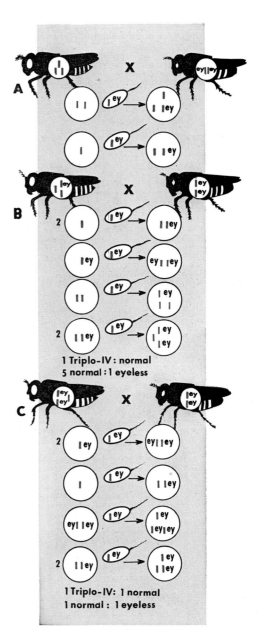

Fig. 94. *Triplo-IV inheritance. Parts A, B, and C represent three kinds of crosses involving Triplo-IV females and the gene for eyeless, as discussed in the text.*

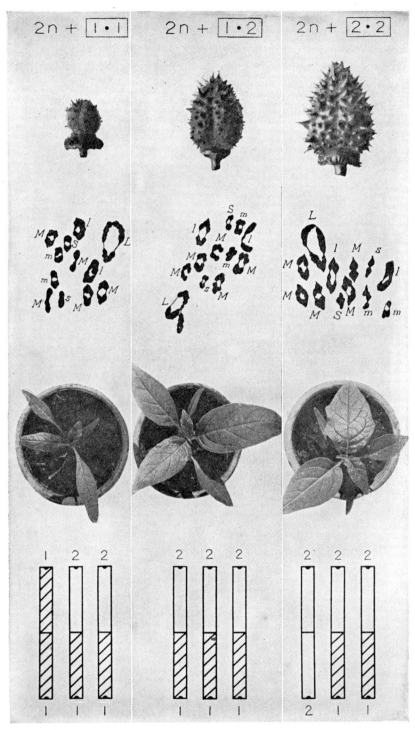

Fig. 95. *Trisomics in Datura. The center column shows seed capsule, chromosomes, and plant for the primary trisomic 2n + 1·2, called "Rolled." The left hand column shows one of the secondary trisomics, 2n + 1·1, or "Polycarpic." The right hand column shows its other secondary, 2n + 2·2, or "Sugarloaf." (From Blakeslee, in the Journal of Heredity, vol. 25.)*

ondary and *tertiary* trisomics. A secondary trisomic is one in which the extra chromosome represents only one half of a normal chromosome, but this half is duplicated to form a chromosome with two identical arms. Twenty-four secondary trisomics are thus possible, but by no means all of them have been found. Each again has a characteristic phenotype. Figure 95 shows a primary trisomic and its two secondaries.

The tertiary trisomics are still more complicated, for in these the extra chromosome is a translocation product, and so is made up of halves of two non-homologous chromosomes. Of the great number of possible tertiary trisomics, only a few have been found. Again, each has a characteristic phenotype by which it is recognizable even without examination of the chromosomes. At meiosis, the extra chromosome forms a link between the two tetrads with which it shares homology thus forming a rather striking figure.

In all types of trisomics, the n + 1 condition is a pollen lethal, and so the trisomics are transmitted only by the ovule parent.

MONOSOMICS Just as there may be an extra chromosome, so there may be a chromosome missing. These have the general formula 2n - 1, and are called monosomics. The phenotype of a monosomic generally differs from the diploid in many ways which may be complementary to the corresponding trisomic. Thus Haplo-IV in *Drosophila* (fig. 96) is characterized by slower embryonic development, smaller bristles, and smaller, roughened eyes. Like trisomics, the meiotic

mechanism should lead to 50 per cent transmission of monosomics, because half of the gametes of a monosomic individual should contain n chromosomes and the other half n - 1. Ordinarily such a monosomic will be crossed to a normal diploid, so that a 1 : 1 ratio should be obtained. But actually, a transmission rate of more than 50 per cent is commonly obtained, because the unpaired chromosome tends to behave irregularly in meiosis, and frequently is not included in either daughter nucleus.

Haplo-IV in *Drosophila* is again a good example of the influence of the chromosomal mutant upon the ratios of gene transmission. If a homozygous normal fly is crossed to an eyeless fly, all of the progeny should be normal, although heterozygous. But if the parental fly with normal eyes is also Haplo-IV, then half of the progeny are normal and half are eyeless ($+X$ *eyey* $\longrightarrow$ 1 $+ey$: 1 *ey*). Of course, the eyeless progeny are also Haplo-IV.

Because a recessive gene will show up at once in the progeny from such a cross, monosomics may be a useful tool for the determination of the chromosome upon which a gene is located. This has proved to be the case, for example, in tobacco, *Nicotiana tabacum*. This species has twenty-four pairs of chromosomes, and so it would be very difficult to localize genes by the meth-

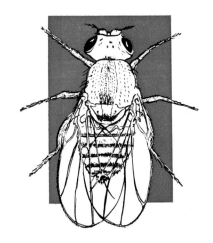

Fig. 96. *A Haplo-IV fly. Almost every part of the fly shows minor deviations from the normal.*

ods developed for *Drosophila*. But all twenty-four monosomics are available. When a new recessive gene is under study, a strain homozygous for it can be crossed to each of the monosomic strains. The progeny from most of these crosses should be all normal. But one of the crosses will yield normal and mutant progeny in a ratio of 1 : 1. The particular chromosome which is monosomic in this cross, then, is the chromosome on which the new gene is located.

Sex-differential chromosomes of the *XO* type are a very widespread example of monosomics. But aside from this rather specialized example, monosomics do not appear to be of general importance in nature. They do not characterize whole races, as do trisomics.

POLYPLOIDY Not only may mutants differ from the wild type by a whole chromosome, but in many cases they differ by whole *sets* of chromosomes. Thus instead of the usual diploid constitution, an organism may have three sets of chromosomes (triploidy) or four sets (tetraploidy), or even higher multiples of the basic haploid chromosome set. This phenomenon of *polyploidy* (Greek, many times) is very common among plants, although it is rather rare among animals. A polyploid plant differs from the corresponding diploid in many characters throughout the plant. While one cannot predict from the appearance of a diploid plant what the phenotype of its tetraploid (the commonest kind of polyploid) will be, still certain kinds of phenotypic variations are very common among tetraploids. In the course of the studies which led to the rediscovery of Mendelism, Hugo DeVries was investigating the evening primrose, *Oenothera lamarckiana*. A mutant appeared in his stock which was so different from the rest that he described it as a new species under the name of *O. gigas,* because of its large size (Greek, *gigas,* giant). This "species" has since proved to be a spontaneously produced tetraploid, and, as it shows a complex of characters very generally found among tetraploid plants, the character complex itself is referred to as the "gigas habitus." This includes such characters as thicker stems; leaves which are shorter, broader, and thicker than those of the diploid; larger size of the plant as a whole; and slower growth rate (fig. 97).

AUTOPOLYPLOIDY AND ALLOPOLYPLOIDY It may seem self-evident that the four genomes of a tetraploid should be identical, or at least that they should differ no more than do the two genomes of an ordinary diploid. This condition is well known, and is referred to as autotetraploidy (or, in more general terms, autopolyploidy). If each set of like chromosomes be designated by the letter *A*, then the formula for an autotetraploid would be *AAAA*. But there is another possibility: two (or more) different sets of chromosomes could enter into the make-up

Fig. 97. *Diploid (right) and tetraploid (left) specimens of* Aster novae-angliae. (*Courtesy of Dr. Albert L. Delisle.*)

of the tetraploid, as described by the formula *AABB*. This condition is also well known, and is called allotetraploidy (or allopolyploidy, for the more general case).

While at first glance allotetraploidy seems improbable, yet it has proven to have much more general importance in the Plant Kingdom than autotetraploidy. There are several ways that an allotetraploid might be formed in nature. Perhaps the most obvious is by the crossing of two different autotetraploids, *AAAA* and *BBBB*, to yield the hybrid *AABB*. Yet this does not appear to be an important method, because a cross between different autotetraploids is generally more difficult to make than is a cross between the corresponding diploids. Hence the most usual method of formation of an allotetraploid is probably by means of an interspecific cross followed by doubling of the chromosome compliment. The latter would happen if the hybrid, *AB*, would form unreduced gametes. This is common in interspecific hybrids, because the chromosomes generally cannot synapse properly.

Many naturally occurring species have been demonstrated to be allotetraploids (or higher polyploids). This was first demonstrated for a species of *Drosera* (the sundew, an insectivorous plant), which has twenty pairs of chromosomes, while other species have only ten pairs. Upon crossing this species to either of the most similar ten chromosome species, sterile hybrids were obtained with thirty chromosomes (not pairs). At meiosis, such hybrids showed ten synapsed pairs and ten singletons. Hence it was concluded that the chromosomes of each ten chromosome species had their homologues in the twenty chromosome species, and that the latter must be a natural allotetraploid.

About the same has been proven for many natural species, including such commercially important ones as tobacco, which is an allotetraploid and wheat, which may be either diploid (not commercially important), allotetraploid, or allohexaploid. In a still more complex case, it has been demonstrated that different species of the range grass *Bromus* (fig. 98) may be hexaploid, octaploid, or duodecaploid (12-ploid). Hence it may be concluded that the formation of allopolyploid series has been a regular feature of plant evolution.

EXPERIMENTAL INDUCTION OF POLYPLOIDY
Many methods have been employed to increase the rate of production of polyploids. These include selection of bud mutants, administration of temperature shocks to the

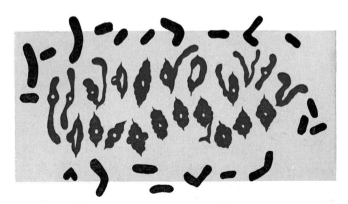

Fig. 98. *Synapsis in a hybrid between an octoploid and a 12-ploid species of range grass,* Bromus. *Synapsed pairs are shown in color, while unmated chromosomes are black. (Modified from Stebbins, Tobgy, and Harlan in Proceedings of the California Academy of Science, vol. 25.)*

seed, irradiation of seed, and selection of re-generating shoots. But all of these were made obsolete in 1937, when it was learned that the drug *colchicine* acts as a mitotic poison. Because colchicine blocks the formation of a functional spindle, all of the daughter chromosomes are included in a single resti-tution nucleus, which is then tetraploid. If the untreated plant is an interspecific hybrid, then the treatment results in an allotetra-ploid. Yields of 50 to 100 per cent are easily obtainable with this drug.

One of the most interesting results of the artificial production of polyploids has been the artificial production of new species. Actually this was first accomplished long before the colchicine method was intro-duced. In the early 1920's, G. D. Karpe-chenko experimented in Russia with crosses between the radish (*Raphanus*) and the cabbage (*Brassica*). Each of these has $n = 9$. The hybrid had 18 chromosomes which did not pair off at all in meiosis. Out of many hybrids raised, a few were fertile. Cytologi-cal examination showed that these had 18 *pairs* of chromosomes, which synapsed per-fectly. Thus it was evident that the allo-polyploid had been formed spontaneously. As it bred true, had unique morphological characters, and was reproductively isolated from both parental species, Karpechenko described it as a new, artificially produced genus, under the name *Raphanobrassica*.

By a similar method, new species of to-bacco have been synthesized. Such species synthesis is now a standard method of wheat breeding. Furthermore, it has been possible to duplicate in the laboratory the synthesis of some existing natural species. Thus the hemp nettle (fig. 99), *Galeopsis tetrahit*, has 16 pairs of chromosomes, while other species of the genus have 8 pairs. Müntzing selected two 8 chromosome species, *G. pubescens* and *G. speciosa*, which on morphological grounds he thought most likely to be the parent species of *G. tetrahit*. An allotetraploid was formed from these "suspected parents," and it proved to be morphologically indistin-guishable from naturally occurring *G. tetra-hit*. Furthermore, this artificial *G. tetrahit* was fertile in crosses with itself and with natural *G. tetrahit*, but sterile in crosses with the two parental species. Thus Müntzing could justly claim to have duplicated the feat of nature in synthesizing this species.

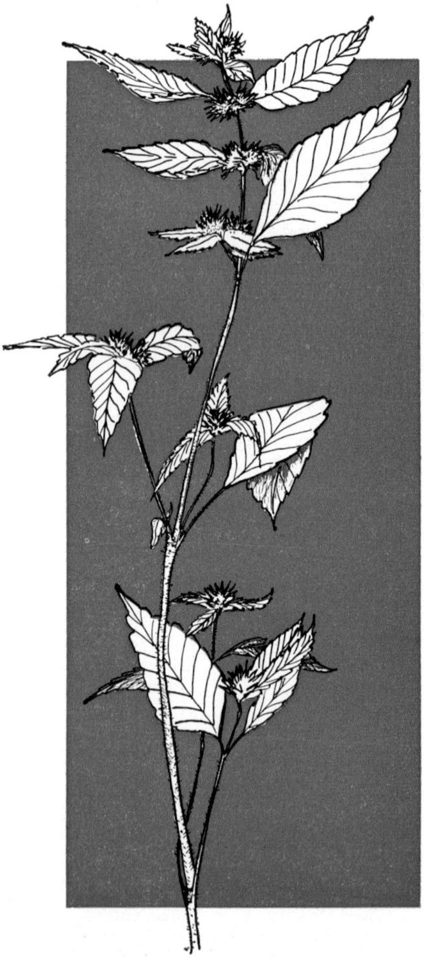

Fig. 99.   *The hemp nettle,* Galeopsis tetrahit. (*Drawn from a specimen in the Nieuwland Herbarium of the University of Notre Dame.*)

41. CHROMOSOMAL REARRANGEMENTS AS MUTANTS

The several types of rearrangements of the chromosomes were introduced in chapter 12. But there the interest was focused upon their nature as visible features of the chromosome which could be correlated with genetic loci in order to compare the crossover map with the real chromosome. It was mentioned in passing that all types of architectural rearrangement were known to behave as mutations in some instances. For the present discussion, this will be the leading feature of the chromosomal rearrangements.

EXAMPLES A few additional examples will suffice to reemphasize the fact that chromosomal rearrangements may act as mutants. When one of the breaks for an inversion or a translocation occurs near a known gene locus, it (the rearrangement) generally behaves as a multiple allele of that locus. Examples include genes from all of the chromosomes of *Drosophila*, such as: yellow (*y*), cut (*ct*), and bar (*B*) in the X chromosome; brown (*bw*), star (*S*), and held out (*ho*) in chromosome II; stubble (*Sb*) and ebony (*e*) in chromosome III; and eyeless (*ey*) in chromosome IV. In some cases, no gene locus is known which is independent of the rearrangement, as in the case of the Curly (*Cy*) and Moiré (*Me*) inversions. Bar (*B*) is much the best known example of a mutant based upon a duplication, and other known cases seem to behave as modifiers rather than as major genes. The notch deficiency has already been discussed. Here again, a deficiency may act as a modifier. The genotype *vg+*/deficiency should lead to normal wings. In a male fly, the simplex *vg+* is perfectly normal. But the same gene opposite a deficiency in a female leads to scalloped wings, that is, to a low grade vestigial. Again, a small deficiency near the yellow locus (but not including *y*) makes this gene, which is usually recessive to its normal allele, behave as a dominant.

All of these examples have been taken from *Drosophila*. Actually, very few are known in other organisms. Some geneticists have concluded that this phenomenon must be a special aspect of *Drosophila* genetics without general applicability to other organisms. Others believe that, just as other aspects of *Drosophila* genetics have proven to be generally applicable, so will this when adequate data are available. They point out that such rearrangement effects were quite obscure in *Drosophila* until the discovery of the salivary gland chromosomes made possible a much more intensive study of the chromosomes than had ever been attempted before. Until comparable methods are available for other organisms, negative data may not be at all conclusive.

POSITION EFFECTS The discovery that such rearrangement effects existed was one for which geneticists generally were unprepared. The gene was discovered without relation to the chromosomes, and the earliest studies in genetics emphasized the independence of the various genes. The discovery of linkage groups led to crossover studies and the localization of genes, but still with no hint of interdependence of the various genes. Thus Babcock and Clausen were able to state that ".... for development the important desideratum is the presence of the factors; their position in the genetic system appears to be of little consequence."[*]

Nonetheless, here was a large class of mutants which seemed to be based not upon any changes in the individual genes, but rather upon a changed spatial relationship among the genes. To this type of mutation the name *position effect* was given by its discoverer, Sturtevant. Let us examine his original case, bar eyes in *Drosophila*. The eyes of normal flies are broadly oval, but this gene, which is dominant, reduces the number of facets so that the eyes are much

[*] Genetics in Relation to Agriculture, 1927, McGraw-Hill Book Co., New York.

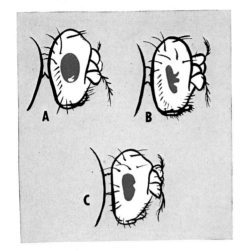

Fig. 100. *The bar eye series in* Drosophila. *Upper left, normal; below, bar; and upper right, double bar.*

narrower. Because crossover tests gave an inexact location for the bar gene at about 57 in the X chromosome, it was suspected that a duplication might be involved. It was found that homozygous bar stocks (B/B) produced about one normal fly in 1500 and about an equal number of the more extreme double-bar type (fig. 100). It was suspected that this was based upon *unequal crossing over* between the two X chromosomes, with one of the X chromosomes getting both bar genes (to give double-bar progeny) and the other having no bar gene at all (to give normal progeny). In order to test this hypothesis, Sturtevant and Morgan tried this experiment with a stock of flies which was also heterozygous for fused (fu) and forked (f), genes which lie on either side of the bar

locus and very close to it. All of the double-bar and normal progeny also showed crossing over between fused and forked. Hence they concluded that the unequal crossing-over theory was actually correct, and that the double-bar flies must have the constitution $BB/+$. It was evident, then, that two bar genes in tandem in one chromosome had a different, more extreme effect than did two bar genes located one in each of a pair of chromosomes. To describe this unprecedented datum, Sturtevant and Morgan introduced the term *position effect*.

When the salivary gland chromosome technique was introduced, the analysis of bar was finally completed. It was then proved that a section of the X chromosome which is present only once in normal flies is present twice in bar and three times in double-bar flies (fig. 101).

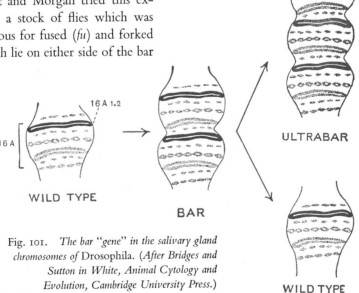

Fig. 101. *The bar "gene" in the salivary gland chromosomes of* Drosophila. *(After Bridges and Sutton in White,* Animal Cytology and Evolution, *Cambridge University Press.)*

When the phenomenon of position effect was first discovered, many geneticists suspected that it was not genuine, that actually the same force which caused the breaks in the chromosomes caused mutations at nearby loci, and thus point mutations were the only genuine genetic variants. Geneticists who have studied position effects extensively are agreed that this cannot explain the phenomenon generally, even though it may explain some specific examples. But the most exquisite proof of the genuineness of position effects was obtained by a Russian geneticist, N. P. Dubinin. Hairy (h) (fig. 102) is a recessive gene, located on chromosome III of *Drosophila*, which causes supernumerary bristles when homozygous. If a hairy fly is crossed to a normal with a translocation break near this locus, the progeny are heterozygous and normal for this character. But, if a crossover should now interchange the h and h^+ genes so that h is adjacent to the translocation break, then h becomes dominant. As no evidence has ever suggested the possibility that crossing over might cause mutation, it seems certain that the change of dominance observed by Dubinin is a genuine position effect. He also found a similar case involving cubitus interruptus (ci) a fourth chromosome gene which causes incomplete development of the wing veins when homozygous.

Further consequences of the chromosomal mutations will be considered in chapter 17, on the theory of the gene. But first let us consider the determination of sex and the physiology of the gene, two subjects which have contributed much to our understanding of the gene.

RÉSUMÉ In addition to gene mutations, mutational effects may be obtained by larger scale changes in the chromosomes. Some of these involve changes in whole chromosomes. In trisomics, there is an extra chromosome, while in monosomics there is a chromosome missing. In either case, there is an associated mutant phenotype and predictable irregularities of meiosis. Both types are unstable, but trisomics do characterize some races of plants. Further, whole sets of chromosomes may be duplicated to form polyploids of various degrees, tetraploids being much the most common. These, too, are characterized each by a typical phenotype, with many individual traits being affected. A polyploid may be an autopolyploid, with all of the genomes coming from the same source, or it may be an allopolyploid, having genomes from two or more different species. The latter play a very important role in plant evolution.

Chromosomal rearrangements—the inversions, deletions, duplications, and translocations which were discussed in chapter 12—also have mutational effects. In some cases the "position effects" of these rearrangements behave as alleles of nearby loci, while in other cases no "gene" is known in-

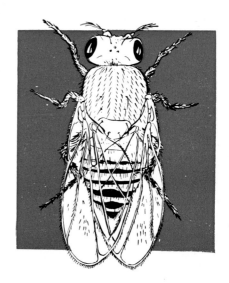

Fig. 102.   *The hairy phenotype in* Drosophila.

dependent of the rearrangement. While such position effects are well known only in *Drosophila*, it must be remembered that the salivary gland chromosomes make it far easier to recognize such effects in *Drosophila* than in other organisms.

Questions and Problems

1. Define:

Allotetraploid	Position effect
Autotetraploid	Primary trisomic
Chromosomal mutation	Secondary trisomic
Colchicine	Species synthesis
Gene mutation	Tertiary trisomic
Monosomic	Trisomic
Polyploidy	

2. Evaluate the proposition that all position effects result from gene mutations at or near the points of breakage.

3. Now evaluate the proposition that all mutations are actually position effects, with point mutations simply being rearrangements too small to be seen.

4. Explain how monosomics could be used to assign a gene to the correct chromosome.

5. What will be the outcome of the cross $++ci \times cici$?

6. What will be the outcome of the cross $+cici \times cici$?

7. It has been emphasized that crossing over does not occur in inversion loops. Draw a diagram of a pair of synapsed chromosomes heterozygous for an inversion. Include the centromere (not in the inversion) and a chiasma (in the inversion). Now see if you can figure out why the above statement is true. Or is it strictly true?

8. How could you distinguish gene mutations from chromosomal mutations?

9. Returning to the material of problem 7, would you expect any inhibition of *double* crossing over in inversion heterozygotes?

10. In the Jimson weed (*Datura stramonium*), there are 12 pairs of chromosomes, and all possible primary trisomics are known. How many is this?

11. Not quite all of the secondary trisomics of the Jimson weed are known. How many would be possible?

12. Only a small portion of the possible tertiary trisomics are known. Can you calculate the total number possible?

References

Blakeslee, A. F., 1934. New Jimson weeds from old chromosomes. Journal of Heredity, 25:80–108. An interesting and well illustrated summary of the chromosomal mutants of *Datura*, by their principal investigator.

Darlington, C. D., 1937. Recent Advances in Cytology. Second edition. Blakiston Co., New York. A thorough, though sometimes controversial, review of the subjects discussed in this chapter.

Dobzhansky, T., 1936. Position effects on genes. Biological Reviews of the Cambridge Philosophical Society, 11:364–384. An old paper, but still a valuable one.

Goodspeed, T. H. and M. V. Bradley, 1942. Amphidiploidy. The Botanical Review, 8:271–316. A comprehensive review on allopolyploidy.

Karpechenko, G. D., 1928. Polyploid hybrids of *Raphanus sativus* L. × *Brassica oleracea* L. Zeitschrift für inductive Abstammungs- und Vererbungslehre, 48:1–83. An early report of artificial species synthesis by means of allopolyploidy.

Lewis, E. B., 1950. The phenomenon of position effect. In Advances in Genetics, 3:73–115. An up-to-date viewpoint on the subject.

Müntzing, A., 1932. Cyto-genetic investigations on synthetic *Galeopsis Tetrahit*. Hereditas, 16:105–154. This paper reports the first successful re-synthesis of a natural species.

Sturtevant, A. H., 1925. The effect of unequal crossing over at the Bar locus of *Drosophila*. Genetics, 10:117–147.

CHAPTER 15

The Determination of Sex

In chapter 6, the elementary facts of sex determination by the *XX–XY* and *XX–XO* mechanisms were reviewed. These facts, which are included in every elementary course in botany and zoology, are adequate to explain the ordinary cases in which only normal sexuality is involved, but they give little insight into *how* sex determination works. There are, however, some cases of normal sex determination which do not readily fit into the picture of sex-differential chromosomes, and there are some cases of abnormal sexuality which afford more insight into the mode of gene action in sex determination. These cases will be the subject of the present chapter.

42. INTERSEXUALITY AND SEX DETERMINATION

Two types of atypical sex constitution, hermaphroditism and gynandrism, have already been discussed above. Here a third kind, the intersex, must be introduced. The three are easily confused, but they are all different. An hermaphrodite is a normal organism which has complete, functional reproductive systems of both sexes. The earthworm is a good example which most students have dissected. A gynander, as explained in chapter 6, is a sex mosaic, in which different parts of the organism have different primary and secondary sex characters because they have different genetic constitutions. A gynander is, therefore, essentially a spatial mosaic of different sex genotypes. An intersex, like a gynander, is an abnormal organism and a mosaic, but it is essentially a mosaic in time. The entire organism has one unified genotype, but those characters which differentiate earliest in ontogeny agree with the genetic sex of the individual, while those which differentiate later agree with the opposite sex. A very early switch-over may result in complete or nearly complete sex reversal, while a late switch-over results in a low-grade intersex which has most of the characters of the genetic sex. Both of these are fully fertile, but the intermediate grades of intersexuality are generally sterile because neither reproductive system is sufficiently complete to function.

Intersexes are widely known in nature. They have been found in many groups of invertebrates and in all classes of vertebrates. The human "hermaphrodites" of the side shows are actually intersexes. Two cases of intersexuality have been thoroughly analyzed genetically, and these will be reported below.

INTERSEXUALITY IN DROSOPHILA By special methods and great care, it is possible to raise triploid *Drosophila* females. These may be represented by the formula *AAAXXX*, where each *A* represents a complete haploid set of autosomes and each *X* represents a single *X* chromosome. When crossed to a normal diploid male, the progeny of such a female regularly includes some intersexes. Meiosis in such a female is highly irregular, and most of the gametes formed are inviable. But those which contain complete sets of chromosomes (*AAXX, AAX, AXX,* and *AX*) are viable, and upon fertilization they produce an array of zygotes which is summarized in table 14 (modified from Bridges, who did the original work now being reported).

Several noteworthy facts stand out from the array of karyotypes (chromosomal constitutions) and sex phenotypes summarized in table 14. First, it may be mentioned that the haploid type, *AX*, could not survive as an independent organism, but patches of haploid tissue may survive in a generally diploid organism. Second, Bridges found that all of the data could be adequately expressed in terms of the ratio *X/A*, irrespective of the presence or absence of the *Y* chromosome. That is, organisms with the same ratio of *X* chromosomes to autosomes have the same sex phenotype, regardless of the actual numbers of chromosomes involved. Thus *AAXX*, *AAXXY*, *AX*, and *AAAXXX* all lead to a female sex phenotype. The normal ratios are 1.0 for femaleness and 0.5 for maleness.

But other ratios also occur, and they are of considerable interest. Karyotypes AAAXX and AAAXXY have a ratio of 0.67, roughly midway between the two normal ratios. Such flies are always intersexes. Karyotypes AAXXX and AAAXY have ratios which are, respectively, greater than that for femaleness and less than that for maleness. These show the appropriate sex phenotypes,

but the secondary sex characters are all strongly exaggerated. Hence Bridges called them superfemales (*AAXXX*) and supermales (*AAAXY*). There is just one disappointing feature of these glamour boys and girls of the fly world: they are completely sterile.

Bridges' interpretation of the data is straightforward and simple. At the outset, it is clear that the *Y* chromosome does not influence the sex phenotype at all. This is not to say that the *Y* chromosome plays no role at all in the biology of sex, for *AAX* males, although morphologically normal, are sterile. But it evidently plays no role in sex determination. When *X* chromosomes are present in greater than normal proportion, female characters are exaggerated, while an excess of autosomes results in exaggerated male characters. Hence the genetic factors for sex must be present in all of the chromosomes, with those for femaleness predominating in the *X* chromosomes and those for maleness predominating in the autosomes. Normal development results from the *balance* between the two, and disturbances of the balance result in the various abnormal sex phenotypes. Because there are normally two sets of autosomes in a zygote, the presence of one or two *X* chromosomes determines which way the balance goes, and hence the simple story of sex determination in chapter 6 is adequate for all normal cases.

Table 14. Triploid Intersexes in Drosophila

(Modified from Bridges, 1939)

P *AAAXXX* × AAXY

F₁ Karyotype	No. of X	No. of A	Ratio X/A	Sex
AAXX / *AAXXY*	2	2	1	♀
AX	1	1	1	♀
AAXY	1	2	0.5	♂
AAAXX / *AAAXXY*	2	3	0.67	Intersex
AAXXX	3	2	1.5	Superfemale
AAAXY	1	3	0.33	Supermale
AAAXXX	3	3	1	♀

An interesting question based upon the above data is that of whether there is a single gene for femaleness on the X chromosome and a single gene for maleness on an autosome, or whether there is a whole series of each, with the individual genes having only minor effects. Bridges investigated this by crossing triploid females to diploid males with duplications for parts of the X chromosomes, and in some cases, with autosomal duplications. If there is a single gene for femaleness, then the appropriate duplication should make an AAAXX fly predominantly a female. Similarly, an autosomal duplication containing the gene for maleness should make a male or near-male of such a fly. In fact, small duplications were not effective, but large X chromosome duplications did make the intersexes more nearly female, and some were even functional females. Hence Bridges concluded that there must be many minor sex-determining genes. Since then, many autosomal duplications have been tested, including almost all sections of the set, without finding any with a male-producing effect. Hence the results may be used

in support of Bridges' conclusions. An alternative explanation is that the X chromosome *as a whole* is responsible for the production of femaleness, while one or more of the autosomes as a whole is responsible for the production of maleness.

INTERSEXUALITY IN LYMANTRIA An even more complicated case of intersexuality has been worked out by Goldschmidt in the gypsy moth, *Lymantria dispar*. This is a very widespread species, originally distributed across the entire Eurasian continent, from England to Japan. Because of introduction by man, it is now found in the New World as well. Across this great expanse, the species is broken up into a considerable number of local subspecies. Crosses *within* any subspecies lead to perfectly normal Mendelian inheritance, including normal sex determination, according to the XX–XY pattern, with female heterogamety. But when crosses are made between different races, then intersexes often result.

The basic phenomena involved may be illustrated by the reciprocal crosses between a European race and a Japanese race, as

Table 15.   Intersexuality in Lymantria, the Basic Crosses. Let E Stand for a European Moth and J for a Japanese Moth

Cross 1

P   J♀ × E♂

F₁ all normal

F₂   ♀ ♀ all normal
     ♂ ♂ 1/2 normal
          1/2 intersexes

Cross 2

E♀ × J♂

♀ ♀ all intersexes
♂ ♂ normal

♀ ♀ 1/2 normal
     1/2 intersexes
♂ ♂ all normal

The same crosses in genetic symbols. Let (F) equal a factor for femaleness in the cytoplasm of the egg, M a factor for maleness in the X chromosome, and subscripts st and w strong and weak respectively.

Cross 1

P   J♀ $(F_{st})M_{st}$ × E ♂ $(F_w)M_wM_w$

F₁   ♀ ♀ $(F_{st})M_w$ ♂ ♂ $(F_{st})M_{st}M_w$
          All normal

F₂   ♀ ♀ $(F_{st})M_{st}$ or $(F_{st})M_w$

     ♂ ♂ $(F_{st})M_{st}M_w$ or $(F_{st})M_wM_w$
          normal   intersex

Cross 2

E ♀ $(F_w)M_w$ × J♂ $(F_{st})M_{st}M_{st}$

♀ ♀ $(F_w)M_{st}$ ♂ ♂ $(F_w)M_wM_{st}$
     Intersex   Normal

♀ ♀ $(F_w)M_w$ or $(F_w)M_{st}$
     normal   intersex

♂ ♂ $(F_w)M_wM_{st}$ or $(F_w)M_{st}M_{st}$
          all normal

summarized in table 15. If the female parent is from the Japanese race, the F_1 is entirely normal, as are the F_2 females. But only half of the F_2 males are normal, the other half being intersexes. In the reciprocal cross, in which the original female parent is from the European race, the F_1 males are all normal, while the F_1 females are all intersexes. In the F_2, the males are again all normal, half of the females are normal and half are intersexes.

Goldschmidt saw that these data required that the factors for maleness segregate in ordinary Mendelian fashion, and that the factor for femaleness be passed alike, without segregation, to all offspring. In accordance with the data presented, the female factor could be cytoplasmic, or it could be a Y chromosome factor, taking its effect upon the egg before the maturation divisions. The latter possibility has been eliminated, so that inheritance of femaleness in *Lymantria* can be attributed to the cytoplasm of the egg.

But why should interracial crosses lead to intersexuality? In order to answer this question, Goldschmidt found it necessary to assume that the sex-determining factors have different relative strengths in different races. Within any single race, these are so balanced that again the presence of one or two X chromosomes determines whether the ontogenetic pattern shall be that of a male or of a female. But when sex factors of different relative strengths are brought together by means of interracial crosses, then the usual balance cannot be struck, and intersexuality results. The Japanese race discussed above is a strong race, while the European race is a weak one. Hence any zygote of genotype (F_{st}) $M_w M_w$ will be a male intersex (one which begins development according to the male pattern then switches to the female pattern), while any zygote of genotype (F_w) M_{st} will be a female intersex.

The degree of intersexuality depends upon the relative strengths of the races crossed. Where the difference is very great, complete sex reversal may occur. Where the difference

is slight, low grade intersexes, which show only a few traits of the non-genetic sex, occur. Both of these are fully fertile, and hence such were used to obtain breeding data. But moderate differences may lead to intermediates which are hopeless from a reproductive viewpoint.

The analysis of this very complicated case comprises a genetic study of exceptional brilliance. But it should be noted that Goldschmidt's analysis has not been accorded universal acceptance among geneticists. However none has repeated the work and brought forward a simpler or more plausible hypothesis, and until this is done, the work reported above may be provisionally accepted at face value.

THE THEORY OF SEX DETERMINATION On the basis of his own studies and those of Bridges, Goldschmidt arrived at a general theory of sex determination, which may be briefly summarized here. In normal development, genetic factors for both sexes are active, but the influence of one or the other predominates throughout development, and so leads to a unified sex phenotype. But when the genetic control of sex differentiation is disturbed, as in the cases described above, then development begins under the predominant control of the factors for the genetic sex of the zygote, but at some definite time there is a switch-over to the pattern of differentiation of the non-genetic sex. Goldschmidt thinks of the switch-over as being caused by changes in the velocities of specific but unidentified reactions in the embryo which have the sex phenotype as an end product, and he concludes that the data demonstrate a coordination between quantity of genetic factors (ratio of X to A in *Drosophila*, or relative strengths of sex factors in *Lymantria*) and speed of morphogenetic reactions. Again, it is necessary to point out that this ingenious theory has not achieved complete acceptance, and the critical reactions have not been identified nor their rates measured.

The only known biological process which might fit the requirements of this theory is the production of sex hormones. The facts, as demonstrated among the vertebrates, and discussed in chapter 6, pages 76–77, are easily harmonized with the theory. But the best analyzed cases of intersexuality are in invertebrates, and sex hormones, while they probably exist, are yet to be proven in invertebrates. Thus the status of the problem remains unsatisfactory.

43. SOME PROBLEMS OF SEX IN FLOWERING PLANTS

In the great majority of the higher plants, no sex differential chromosome mechanism is possible, because both sexes are combined in a single individual. Such a plant is said to be *monoecious* (Greek—*mono-*, one + *oikos*, house). Typically, each flower (fig. 103) contains one or more *pistils*, in which the ovules are produced, and a number of *stamens*, in which the pollen is produced. In some plants, however, separate *staminate* and *pistillate* flowers are borne on the same plant, so that the sexes are separated flower for flower but not plant for plant. As all of the flowers of a single plant must have the same genotype, it is clear that some nongenetic factor must be responsible for the formation of the two kinds of flowers. Finally, there are relatively few species in which staminate and pistillate flowers are borne upon different plants. That is, the sexes are completely separate. For these, sex differential chromosomes and typical sex-linked inheritance have been demonstrated. Such plants are said to be *dioecious* (Greek—two houses).

SELF-STERILITY GENES OF MONOECIOUS PLANTS An interesting feature of the biology of sex in monoecious plants is the occurrence in many of them of specific mechanisms for the prevention of self-fertilization. Such mechanisms may be partially morphological, as in the case of plants with gross differences in the lengths of pistils and stamens. Or the mechanism may be entirely physiological. The genetic basis of self-sterility has been analyzed in a great many plants, beginning with a study by Correns in the first years of modern genetics. Several genetic systems have come to light, but the most widespread by far is based upon the occurrence of an extensive series of multiple alleles of so-called S genes, designated as S_1, S_2, S_3, ... S_n. In general, a pollen grain will grow satisfactorily only on a style which does not include its own S allele. This not only insures self-sterility, but it also insures intersterility of members of the same clone (a clone includes all of the vegetatively produced, and therefore genetically identical, descendants of a single individual). This has considerable practical importance, as many of the standard varieties of fruits are ordi-

Fig. 103. *A tulip, with two petals pulled down to expose the sexual parts of the flower. The female parts are: O, the ovary, at the base of St, the style; and S, the stigma. The male parts are Sm, a stamen; and A, an anther.*

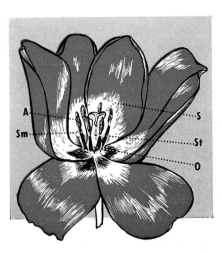

narily propagated by grafting cuttings onto a hardy rootstock. Hence, intervarietal pollination is necessary in order to set fruit. Further, this will prevent crossing even of unrelated plants if they chance to carry the same S genes.

One consequence of this phenomenon of S genes has been selection pressure in favor of the production of very extensive series of multiple alleles at the S locus. A population including only a few such alleles would probably have a very poor seed set. In *Nicotiana sanderae*, a species of tobacco, fifteen S alleles have been found. A snapdragon and a plum species have each yielded eight. A primrose, *Oenothera organensis*, has no less than forty-five S alleles, while in some cases there appear to be more than a hundred!

In concluding this discussion, it should be mentioned that self-sterility is by no means universal among monoecious plants. Indeed, self-fertilization is the norm among many, such as peas and beans, and it is readily obtained in others, such as corn, which are normally cross-fertilized.

TRANSITION FROM THE MONOECIOUS TO THE DIOECIOUS STATE In many families of plants, both monoecious and dioecious species exist; indeed, this may be the case even within a single genus. Hence it seems probable that one has been derived from the other. One pathway by which this might have occurred has been demonstrated in maize by D. F. Jones. This plant is a monoecious one in which the male and female flowers are separate. The tassel is the staminate or male inflorescence, while the ears are the pistillate inflorescences. There is a recessive gene, *sk*, which, when homozygous, prevents the formation of silks (styles), and hence such a plant is female sterile, and functions as a male. A second recessive gene, *ts* (tassel seed), converts the tassels into ears, and so a *tsts* plant functions only as a female. Jones tried crossing strains homozygous for these genes. The F$_1$ plants, *Sksk Tsts*, were all normal, monoecious plants because of dominance. In the F$_2$, there was a ratio of 9 monoecious plants (*Sk?Ts?*) to 3 males (*sksk Ts?*) to 4 females (3 *Sk?tsts* and 1 *sksktsts*). By backcrossing, it was possible to select out the homozygous females. Crossing these to the males now produced a regular 1 : 1 sex ratio, as follows: sksk tsts ♀ × sksk Tsts ♂ ⟶ 1 *sksktsts* : 1 *sksk Tsts*. For all practical purposes, an *XX–XY* sex determining mechanism has been established, with the chromosome with the *ts* locus being the sex differential pair.

No one would wish to claim that recombination of two pairs of genes under experimental conditions to separate the sexes proves that the natural separation of sexes would proceed along such simple lines. Yet there are some data which indicate that a very similar process has occurred in some natural species. Thus asparagus is normally dioecious, but rudimentary pistils occur on the staminate flowers and rudimentary stamens occur on the pistillate flowers. Occasionally, the rudimentary pistils may set seed, and the progeny of such have been investigated. A ratio of 3 males to 1 female was found. Upon crossing the male progeny to normal females, one third of the males proved to be homozygous, giving only male progeny (using the corn symbols, *TsTs* × *tsts* ⟶ *Tsts*); while two thirds gave a 1 : 1 ratio (*Tsts* × *tsts* ⟶ 1 *Tsts* : 1 *tsts*). Thus the data proved that sex determination in asparagus is based upon the segregation of a single pair of alleles.

Note that the Y chromosome of these plants, if the *Ts* chromosomes be so regarded, plays an active role in sex determination, unlike those of *Drosophila* and *Lymantria*. This was established at the turn of the century by Correns, whose studies on *Bryonia*, a genus of cucurbits, indicated a single factor segregation for sex. *B. dioica* is dioecious, while *B. alba* is monoecious. If a female of *B. dioica* is pollinated by *B. alba*, the progeny are all female. But if *B. alba* is pollinated by a male of *B. dioica*, then a ratio of 1 : 1 is obtained. Hence Correns concluded that the eggs of *B. dioica* must be all alike in sex determining capacity, while the sperm are two kinds. In other words, it amounts to an *XX–XY* sex determining mechanism.

A similar sex-determining mechanism has been found in a pink, *Melandrium*. But here tetraploids have been produced with varying numbers of *X's* and *Y's*. These prove that the *Y* chromosome has a male-producing effect, unlike that of *Drosophila*.

44. ATYPICAL SEX DETERMINATION AMONG INVERTEBRATES

In addition to the well-known mechanisms of sex determination which have been discussed above, there are some more unusual ones, involving little understood factors in the distribution of the chromosomes, or environmental factors, or factors which cannot be specified at all at present. Some of these will now be discussed.

SEX DETERMINATION IN BEES AND OTHER HYMENOPTERA It was discovered by Dzierzon and confirmed by Mendel that male bees are derived from *unfertilized eggs*, while females are derived from fertilized eggs. Thus the males are parthenogenetic and haploid, while the females are biparental and diploid. Little additional light was thrown upon this subject until recent years, when P. W. Whiting and his collaborators studied the genetics of a parasitic wasp, *Habrobracon juglandis* (fig. 104). The haploid chromosome number in this species is 10, and this is also the somatic number for males, while the females have 20 chromosomes. But occasionally, especially in inbred stocks, diploid males occur. These diploid males have a very low viability. Whiting has demonstrated that there is a series of multiple alleles for sex, *Xa, Xb, Xc*, etc. Any heterozygous genotype (as *XaXb*, or *XcXf*) results in a female phenotype. But any haploid or homozygous constitution (as *XdXd*) results in a male phenotype. This situation is reminiscent of the self-sterility alleles of plants. Like the latter, it is a selective advantage for a breeding population to include many different alleles.

It has been proven that much the same sex determining mechanism occurs in the honey bee and many other Hymenoptera.

THE SEX CYCLE OF THE APHIDS The plant lice, or aphids have a life cycle characterized by parthenogenetic reproduction throughout the spring and summer, with only the final generation in the fall repro-

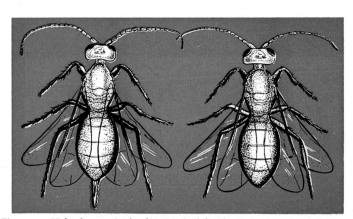

Fig. 104. Habrobracon juglandis. *On the left a female, and on the right a male.*

ducing biparentally. The fertilized eggs then remain dormant throughout the winter, only to hatch as females in the spring and start the cycle all over again.

The main facts were discovered by Boveri and the details were worked out by Morgan. Morgan worked on the genus *Phylloxera*, and this case will be detailed, as the species has only three pairs of chromosomes. The winter eggs, which hatch in the spring, all have six chromosomes, and all hatch as females. These then reproduce parthenogenetically, and their progeny likewise all summer long, with only females being produced. Study of oogenesis revealed that no reduction divisions occurred, and hence all eggs and adults too have six chromosomes. But in a late fall generation, there is an atypical maturation division, in which one chromosome lags on the metaphase plate, so that one daughter nucleus has the usual six chromosomes, but the other has only five (fig. 105). If the egg gets six chromosomes, it develops as a female, as expected. But if the polar body gets six and the egg only five, then the egg develops as a male. Thus there is actually an *XX–XO* sex-determining mechanism, with male heterogamety.

This bisexual generation is the last of the year, and it reproduces in the typical biparental fashion. The fertilized eggs which result are dormant throughout the winter, and emerge as females in the spring. But why only as females, when the parents have a sex-differential mechanism? The female parent can produce only one kind of egg, with two autosomes and an *X* chromosome. The males should produce two kinds of sperm, all with two autosomes, but only half including an *X* chromosome. This should lead to *XX* and *XO* zygotes, yet only the former appear in the progeny. Study of spermatogenesis showed that the first maturation division is unequal. A large daughter cell receives three chromosomes, but the smaller cell receives only two. The latter degenerate without producing sperm, so that all zygotes must be of the *XX* type.

Thus this complex cycle is fully described, but it is noteworthy that the *causes* of the unusual features of aphid reproduction are still to be learned by future research.

ALTERNATION OF GENERATIONS IN A NEMATODE   Somewhat similar to the Aphid case is that of the nematode worm, *Angiostomum nigrovenosum*. This worm alternates between a free living generation and a generation parasitic upon a frog. The parasitic generation is hermaphroditic, and all somatic cells have twenty-four chromosomes. In the free living generation, the sexes are separate, with the females having twenty-four chromosomes and the males twenty-three.

This cycle shares some features with the aphid cycle. Oogenesis in the hermaphrodite is perfectly normal. But in spermatogenesis, one chromosome again lags, so that some sperm have twelve chromosomes and others have eleven. Fertilization of these eggs by the two classes of sperm leads to free living worms of two classes, females with twenty-four chromosomes and males with only twenty-three. Again, oogenesis is normal in the free living females, but of the

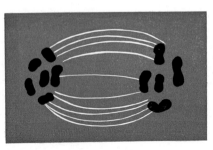

Fig. 105.   *Telophase of the first division in an oocyte of* Phylloxera, *showing five chromosomes at one pole and six at the other. The lagging chromosome was missed in this section. (Modified from Morgan.)*

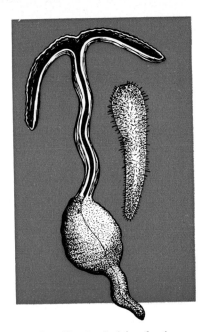

Fig. 106. Bonellia. *On the left, a female; on the right, a male, drawn on a very much larger scale.*

two classes of sperm produced by the males those with only eleven chromosomes degenerate. Thus all zygotes must have twenty-four chromosomes, and they develop into hermaphroditic parasites.

ENVIRONMENTAL DETERMINATION OF SEX In some instances, the chromosomes seem to determine only general potentialities of sex development, for environmental factors control the differentiation of the sex phenotype irrespective of genotype. The best known example is that of an echiuroid worm, *Bonellia viridis*. (The Echiuroidea are a small group of aberrant marine worms usually lumped with the Annelida, but perhaps best treated as a separate phylum). This species is characterized by an extreme sexual di-

morphism, the females being about an inch long and having a complex anatomical organization. But the males are very small, on the size order of large ciliates, and their organ systems are rudimentary (fig. 106). They live as parasites upon the female.

The eggs of *Bonellia* develop into indifferent larvae which soon settle down onto the substrate to become adults. It has been shown that those which settle onto the ocean bottom become females, while those which settle on the proboscis of an established female develop as males. Intersexes can be produced by removing the incompletely differentiated males from the controlling female. It is assumed that the females must produce a substance comparable to a hormone which causes male differentiation on the part of larvae contacting the proboscis. But the identification of such a substance is still in the future.

A second example of environmental determination of sex involves the interesting phenomenon of *protandry*. A protandrous animal is one which first develops as a male, then later is transformed into a female. As this is a normal sequence for every individual of the protandrous species, sex-differential chromosomes are out of the question. The marine mollusc *Crepidula*, the slipper shell (fig. 107), has such a life cycle. An environmental factor controls the rate of change from male to female. A mated male remains as such for a long time, but a male which is unable to secure a mate changes into a female very quickly.

Fig. 107. *The slipper shell,* Crepidula.

Protandry seems to be rather common among the molluscs, for Coe has described it among oysters and ship worms (genus *Teredo*, comprising a number of species of wood-boring molluscs, despite their common name). The Western oyster of the Pacific coast showed regular protandry, with only occasional individuals which were permanent males or females. In the Virginia oyster protandry was also found, but the permanent males and females were much more common. The interesting problem of the genetic relationship of the latter to the protandric individuals has not been investigated. Coe found that the change from male to female occurs so early in the life cycle of *Teredo* that about 90 per cent of a typical population is made up of females. But the small number of very young and prolific males present is sufficient to fertilize the enormous number of eggs produced by this large female population.

Protandry is also known in the tunicates, and a related phenomenon occurs in so high a group as the Amphibia. Anterior to the testes of the toad is a pair of small organs, the potential ovaries (some times called Bidder's organs). If the testes are removed either by parasitism or by experiment, then the potential ovaries enlarge and the toad becomes a functional female.

There is a very interesting case of environmentally conditioned sex determination in a nematode worm, *Mermis subnigrescens*. The eggs of this worm are laid upon low foliage, and are eaten along with the latter by grasshoppers. The larvae emerge in the intestine of the grasshopper and penetrate the intestinal wall to reach the body cavity, where they complete their development. The mature worms then leave their host to live free in the soil. The sex of the worms depends upon the number of parasites infecting one host. With one to three parasites, all develop as females, and it has been demonstrated that these can reproduce parthenogenetically. Four to twenty-three parasites result in production of both sexes, and some intersexes as well. Finally, when twenty-four or more worms parasitize a single grasshopper, all develop as males.

ALTERNATION OF GENERATIONS IN THE COELENTERATES As is well known, coelenterates are characterized by alternating sessile, polyp and free-swimming, medusa generations. The polyps reproduce asexually by budding off medusae, and the medusae reproduce sexually, the larvae settling on the substrate to become polyps. The chromosomal situation here has been inadequately studied, but it is noteworthy that in some instances, such as *Tubularia*, male-producing and female-producing polyps can be distinguished by somatic characters. In this case, there is a minor color difference.

45. PROBLEMS OF SEX IN MICROORGANISMS

Although unexpected at first, sexual reproduction has proved to be very widespread among microorganisms. There is genetic evidence (recombination of characters) that sexual reproduction occurs in at least one species of bacteria. While sexual reproduction may or may not be of general significance for the bacteria, it certainly is for algae, fungi, and protozoans. As these primitive organisms are close to those in which sex first originated, it is to be expected that they show some unusual features, remnants of the first experiments of nature toward biparental reproduction. Some of these will be discussed below.

SEX DETERMINATION IN CHLAMYDOMONAS The green alga *Chlamydomonas* (fig. 108) presents several very interesting features from the viewpoint of the present chapter. The ordinary, vegetative individuals are haploid, and they may reproduce by simple,

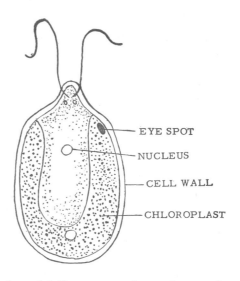

Fig. 108. Chlamydomonas. (*Redrawn from Weatherwax, Plant Biology, via Dodson, Textbook of Evolution.*)

EYE SPOT

NUCLEUS

CELL WALL

CHLOROPLAST

mitotic division for many generations. But occasionally gametes may be formed by a series of rapid mitotic divisions. There is no morphological difference between the sexes. Excepting for their much smaller size the gametes look much like the vegetative cells. Gametes from different parent cells then unite to form zygotes. The zygote may be encysted before resuming active life, but when it does become active it immediately undergoes the two meiotic divisions to produce four haploid zoospores which become adult algae and again reproduce asexually. Thus the zygote is the only diploid cell in the entire life cycle. This is probably the primitive condition, for before the evolution of sexual reproduction, haploidy must have been the norm, as it still is for many asexual organisms. Diploidy is the inevitable consequence of the union of two haploid cells, and meiosis appears to have been introduced not as a means of producing gametes but as a means of restoring the normal, haploid chromosome number. But diploidy, once introduced, has become progressively more and more predominant in life cycles because it makes possible the accumulation of variability in the heterozygous condition, and probably also because of the physiological advantage of increased production of nuclear enzymes.

In *Chlamydomonas eugametos*, the most thoroughly investigated species, the gametes are morphologically all alike, a condition called *isogamy*. Yet there must be a physio-

logical differentiation of sexes, because fertilization occurs only between members of different clones. F. Moewus of Heidelberg believes that he has identified the physiological factor concerned, for the organisms secrete the cis- and trans-isomeres of dimethyl crocetin in varying concentrations, varying from 95 per cent cis- and 5 per cent trans- to about 5 per cent cis- and 95 per cent trans-. Those strains with more than 50 per cent of the cis- isomere are designated as "plus" strains, and those with less as "minus" strains. This is genetically controlled by an identified series of multiple alleles. In general, plus strains mate with minus strains, but extremely different members of either group can mate. The result is that there are eight different mating types. This condition is sometimes called *relative sexuality*, but it can also be considered as *multiple* sexuality. While Moewus' work has been disputed, still no one has produced evidence against his explanation in terms of the isomeres of dimethyl crocetin (a rather simple compound, which is chemically similar to isoprene), and there is no doubt whatever that the eight mating types are valid.

Not all species of *Chlamydomonas* are

isogamous. In some there are macrogametes (egg-like) and microgametes (sperm-like), both of which are flagellate and motile (heterogamy). In some species, fertilization can occur only between a macrogamete and a microgamete, but in others, all possible types of fertilization (large—large, large—small, and small—small) occur. Finally, there are species in which the macrogamete is non-motile (an egg) and must be sought by the flagellate microgamete (sperm), so that one may speak of oogamy, as in higher organisms.

MATING TYPES IN PARAMECIUM The ciliates have developed a unique type of sexual reproduction called *conjugation*. The details are quite complex, and, as the subject is thoroughly treated in textbooks on general zoology, only a brief summary need be given here. *Paramecium* is the most thoroughly studied example, and so will be used as the basis of this discussion. Each cell includes *two* nuclei, the genetically active, diploid micronucleus, and the vegetative, probably polyploid macronucleus which is derived from the micronucleus. The organism may reproduce indefinitely asexually with the micronucleus dividing mitotically and the macronucleus dividing amitotically. Thus large clones of genetically identical individuals may be built up. Within such a clone, conjugation does not occur.

But when members of different clones are brought together, they may pair off quite rapidly (fig. 109). The macronuclei of the conjugants degenerate, while the micronuclei undergo the usual two meiotic divisions. Three of the daughter nuclei degenerate, but the fourth divides mitotically to form a stationary nucleus and a wandering nucleus in each conjugant. The wandering nucleus of each migrates into the other conjugant, so that a mutual cross-fertilization is accomplished. The conjugants now separate, and their new diploid nuclei divide to reestablish the two types of nuclei.

The sexual behavior of *Paramecium* has been studied especially by H. S. Jennings and T. M. Sonneborn. They found as many as eight different mating types in one variety of *P. bursaria*; four in another variety; and only two in the third variety. Conjugation can occur between any two mating types, but not within a mating type. Thus it amounts to a system of multiple sexuality. Much the same has been found in *Euplotes*, another genus of ciliates, and it seems probable that the same system prevails throughout the class Ciliata, and very probably also in the class Suctoria, a minor class of Protozoa which has been derived from the Ciliata. While the genetic control of the mating types is complex, it is definitely controlled by the micronucleus, and follows a regular pattern. It may be added that numerous generations may be produced by simple fission between conjugations, thus building

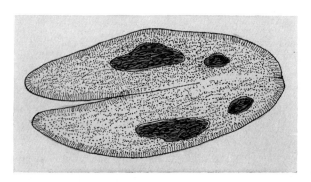

Fig. 109. *Conjugating* Paramecia. *The macronuclei are breaking up, and the micronuclei are dividing meiotically.*

up large clones of genetically identical organisms.

MEIOSIS IN OXYMONAS   The occurrence of reduction by the formation of tetrads followed by two divisions has been found almost universally, in groups so widely separated as the green algae and the mammals, the ciliates and the flowering plants. But cytologists at the end of the nineteenth century speculated upon the possibility that this nearly universal type of meiosis might have been derived from a simpler, "primary type," with no tetrad formation and only a single division. They looked for this in many primitive organisms, but failed to find it. Recently, however, L. R. Cleveland of Harvard has reported just such a simple meiosis in *Oxymonas*, a flagellate which is parasitic in the gut of a roach, *Cryptocercus*. The chromosomes pair very loosely, but they do not divide, and so no tetrads are formed. Hence when the homologues separate in the anaphase of the only meiotic division, reduction is complete. Unfortunately, there are no genetic data available for *Oxymonas*. This work remains to be corroborated, and many zoologists are gravely skeptical of it. The work has considerable theoretical interest, however, and so further independent observations should be made. The near universality of the two-division type of meiosis, however, attests that it must have been favored by enormous selective value.

From this brief survey it is clear that nature has experimented with the most diverse mechanisms for biparental reproduction. In all probability, there have in the past been many such experiments, no remnants of which have survived to the present. But the near universality of the system characterized by oogamy, diploidy, and two-division meiosis indicates that this system has had a great competitive advantage over other systems.

RÉSUMÉ   The usual description of sex determination as a backcross is adequate on an elementary level, but it affords little insight. The analysis of intersexuality is more instructive, and leads to the conclusion that the *X* chromosome carries factors for femaleness and the autosomes (or the cytoplasm in some cases) carry factors for maleness. The sex phenotype results from the balance between the two, with the sex-differential chromosomes determining the way the balance tips. Abnormal sexuality results if the usual balance is disturbed (as by an extra *X* chromosome). In typical cases, the *Y* chromosome does not play an active role in sex determination, but in some plants it has been shown to have a male-determining effect.

Self-sterility genes are an interesting feature of many monoecious plants. These are generally extensive series of multiple alleles. A pollen grain cannot grow on the style of a plant which has its own *S* allele. Other self-sterility mechanisms are also known.

Many atypical sex-determining mechanisms occur. In the Hymenoptera, males are typically haploid and females diploid. But there is a series of multiple alleles for sex determination. Any heterozygote develops as a female, but homozygotes, even though diploid, become males. In some species, there is a regular sequence of parthenogenetic and bisexual generations, or an alternation of hermaphroditic and dioecious generations. Descriptively, these cycles are clear, but the causal factors are obscure. Protandry is a curious kind of cycle in which each individual begins life as a male, but is subsequently transformed into a female. If unmated, this change is more rapid than if mated. In *Bonellia*, environmental control of sex is complete. Microorganisms show a wide variety of sexual mechanisms, including relative sexuality, multiple sexuality, conjugation, and possible one-division meiosis.

Questions and Problems

1. Define:

Alternation of genera-	Multiple sexuality
tions	
Conjugation	Pistillate flower
Dioecious	Primary type
	meiosis
Dimethyl crocetin	Protandry
Gynandrism	Relative sexuality
Hermaphroditism	S-genes
Intersexuality	Staminate flower
Isogamy	Superfemale
Monoecious	Supermale

2. What is the sex of each of the following organisms:

a. AAAXXX	f. XaXb
b. AAAXXY	g. Xa
c. AAXXX	h. XbXb
d. AAX	i. $(F_{st})M_w M_w$
e. AAXY	j. $(F_w)M_{st}$

3. How can an abnormal thing like intersexuality afford insight into normal processes?

4. Evaluate the problem of whether there are one or many sex determining genes.

5. Summarize the evidence for sex determination through a balance between male and female determiners.

6. Why should intermediate grade intersexes be sterile when more extreme intersexes are fertile?

7. Many varieties of apples and of some other fruits comprise a single clone. They are ordinarily propagated vegetatively by cuttings to avoid breaking up favorable character combinations. In view of the present chapter, can you cite another reason for vegetative propagation rather than growing the trees from seed?

8. Explain the origin of the dioecious condition in corn or asparagus.

9. Explain the chromosomal cycle in aphids. What type of sex determination is found in this group?

10. Explain the alternation of generations in the nematode, *Angiostomum nigrovenosum*.

11. Discuss fully any case of protandry.

12. What are the potential ovaries of toads?

13. How is sex determined in *Chlamydomonas*?

14. In *Chlamydomonas*, what does the function of meiosis appear to be?

15. Are the mating types of *Paramecium* sexes?

References

Allen, C. E., 1940. The genotypic basis of sex-expression in angiosperms. The Botanical Review, 6:227–300. A comprehensive review of sex determination in the higher plants.

Bridges, C. B., 1939. Cytological and Genetic Basis of Sex. In Sex and Internal Secretions, Edgar Allen, editor. Williams and Wilkins Co., Baltimore, pp. 15–63. A general review of the subject of sex determination by one of the principal investigators in the field.

Cleveland, L. R., 1950. Hormone-induced sexual cycles of flagellates. II. Gametogenesis, fertilization, and one division meiosis in *Oxymonas*. Journal of Morphology, 86:185–200. The original report of a most unusual phenomenon.

Coe, W. R., 1933. Sexual phases in *Teredo*. Biological Bulletin, 65:283–303. A readable study of a case of protandry.

Goldschmidt, R. B., 1923. The Mechanism and Physiology of Sex Determination. London. An old review, but still a valuable one.

Jones, D. F., 1934. Unisexual maize plants and their bearing on sex differentiation in other plants and in animals. Genetics, 19:552–567. A report of the experimental separation of the sexes in corn.

Kuhn, Richard, 1951. The Problem of Self-Sterility. Reilly Lectures, 4:1–14. University of Notre Dame Press. A Nobel Prize winner summarizes the work of his collaborator, Moewus, on *Chlamydomonas*, and extends it to higher plants. This paper includes references to Moewus' own publications, all of which are in German.

Lewis, D., 1949. Incompatibility in flowering plants. Biological Reviews of the Cambridge Philosophical Society, 24:472–496. A general review of the problem of self-sterility.

Sonneborn, T. M., 1947. Recent advances in the genetics of *Paramecium* and *Euplotes*. In Advances in Genetics, 1:263–358. Includes a treatment of multiple sexuality in ciliates.

Whiting, P. W., 1945. The evolution of male haploidy. Quarterly Review of Biology, 20:231–260. A thorough review, not only of sex determination in the Hymenoptera, but also in other groups with male haploidy.

CHAPTER 16

The Physiology of the Gene

The preceding chapters have dealt principally with numerical relationships between various phenotypes and the genotypes upon which they are based. The genotype is expressed as a characteristic of the zygote, while the phenotype is generally conceived in terms of the traits of the adult, fully differentiated organism. Between the two there are causal sequences which act through ordinary physiological agencies, in which the gene is simply the primary causal factor.

This viewpoint has not always been self-evident. The earliest studies in heredity were directed entirely toward the problems of the mechanisms of transmission, the understanding of the genetic ratios, the "statics of genetics," as Goldschmidt has put it. The problems of dynamic genetics, or how genic effects are obtained, was seldom touched upon. As a result, heredity was commonly regarded as more or less magical in its operation. The studies of Goldschmidt and Bridges upon the determination of sex comprised the first major effort to understand the dynamics of gene action. But progress has been slower in this more difficult field. As late as 1938, one geneticist wrote that "it is as if heredity was represented by a long underground tunnel. We are in the light at either end. . . . but we are still largely in darkness throughout the passageway itself."[*] And in 1945,

Sewall Wright, one of the leading physiological geneticists, wrote that "even physiologists sometimes attribute a character partly to physiological factors, partly to heredity, as if heredity could operate by some sort of sympathetic magic independently of physiological channels. The attitude of physiological genetics is that characters are determined 100 per cent by physiological processes, but that genes are the ultimate internal physiological agents." It will be the purpose of the present chapter to consider some of the evidence bearing upon physiological channels through which genes obtain their effects.

46. GENES AND EMBRYONIC DIFFERENTIATION

An obvious problem is posed by the fact that diversified tissues and organs develop from a single zygote, and that all parts of the organism should have the same genotype because of the regularities of the mitotic mechanism. Weismann tried to solve this problem by postulating qualitatively unequal mitoses, so that only the potential germ cells would retain the entire genome, and all other tissues would lack certain parts of it. Thus all tissues would have different genotypes. The theory had to be dropped because studies of mitosis failed to give any indication of qualitative differences between the chromosomes of daughter cells. Quite the contrary, the regular duplication of chromosome sets appeared to be the most striking feature of the mitotic process. But the *coup de grâce* was added only recently, when a technique was developed for removing the nucleus from a frog egg and replacing it with a nucleus from a differentiated tissue, such as

[*] Walter, H. E. 1938. Genetics. Fourth Edition. The Macmillan Co., New York.

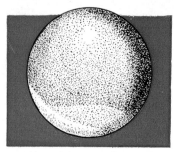

Fig. 110. *An amphibian egg, showing the gray crescent at the lower right. (Redrawn from Huettner.)*

a neural plate cell, or a notochord cell of a gastrula. Had the differentiation of these tissues depended upon any permanent differentiation of their nuclei, then such eggs should have failed to develop, or they should have developed abnormally. Actually, normal development occurred, and so it is clear that no such irreversible differentiation as Weismann and others postulated could have occurred.

CYTOPLASMIC DIFFERENCES AS A BASIS OF EMBRYONIC DIFFERENTIATION But though the cleavage divisions should parcel out identical chromosome complements to all daughter cells, these divisions are plainly *unequal* as regards the cytoplasm. There may be visible differences between various regions of an undivided egg. Thus there is the very widespread distinction between a yolky vegetal pole and less yolky animal pole of the egg. These are often differently pigmented. Between the two lies the much investigated gray crescent in amphibian eggs, while the same area is occupied by a yellow crescent in the eggs of tunicates. The cleavage divisions parcel out these different sorts of cytoplasm into many separate cells, and while the nuclei of these cells are all alike, they are working in collaboration with several different sorts of cytoplasm. Thus the nuclear constitution which is capable of subserving all types of tissue differentiation actually induces one type or another according to the type of cytoplasm in which it

works. As soon as one realizes that the cytoplasm has an active role to play in differentiation, it seems obvious that the yolky vegetal pole cells and the yolk-free animal pole cells must have different prospective fates in the organism.

EMBRYONIC ORGANIZERS But it is not only that an identical genotype behaves differently in different cytoplasms: developing tissues influence one another also. The classical example is that of the amphibian organizer, originally investigated by Hans Spemann. In the late blastula of an amphibian egg, the gray crescent material is located in a band of cells just below the equator of the cell (fig. 110). When gastrulation begins, the blastopore forms below the gray crescent. The cells of the gray crescent are carried inward as the archenteron forms, and they come to lie in the roof of the archenteron, in contact with the overlying ectoderm. From that ectoderm the central nervous system is formed, while the roof of the archenteron forms the notochord and the mesoderm. The important thing for the present discussion is that it can be demonstrated that

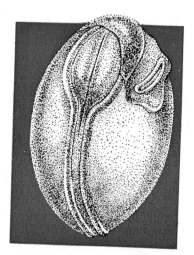

Fig. 111. *An amphibian embryo at the neurula stage, with a secondary embryo which was induced by implantation of the gray crescent from another embryo. (Redrawn from Holtfreter.)*

contact between the gray crescent material and the prospective neural tissues (or diffusion of a substance from the gray crescent) is necessary for the differentiation of the latter. Such contact may be prevented by injecting gelatin into the blastula cavity, and the result is a grossly defective embryo with no nervous system. Or one may dissect out the gray crescent from one blastula and insert it into the side of another. The host embryo will then develop *two* nervous systems, one induced by its own gray crescent, the second induced by the transplant (fig. 111). This may lead finally to Siamese twin embryos.

Such embryonic inductions suggest that a specific substance diffuses from the organizer into the target tissue in order to produce the effect. The amphibian organizer has been thoroughly studied in an effort to identify such a substance, but conflicting results have been obtained, one school considering it to be a simple organic acid, while another finds it to be a sterol.

If this primary organizer were kept out of contact with the ectoderm until after the usual time of formation of the neural plate and normal contact then again permitted, no neural plate would form. And so it is

clear that the target tissue is not entirely passive in embryonic induction: it must be *competent* to respond. In the example mentioned, competence is lost fairly soon. Frequently, competence for a specific induction is distributed over a very wide field which becomes progressively more restricted with advancing age. Thus the optic cup of vertebrates induces lens formation by the contiguous ectoderm. Transplantation experiments have demonstrated that the field of ectoderm capable of responding to contact with the optic cup may be very broad. In the frog, *Rana esculenta*, the entire ectoderm shows lens competence in the early neurula stage. But soon competence is lost by most of the ectoderm, and only that over the head region remains competent. And a little later, only a small area including the usual lens-forming ectoderm retains competence. Details differ from species to species.

Organizer actions have been demonstrated in all major groups of vertebrates, and certainly they are a major factor in the emergence of differentiation and pattern from the "homogeneous" zygote. The exposition of these phenomena has been a major achievement of experimental embryology. The experimental embryologists have demon-

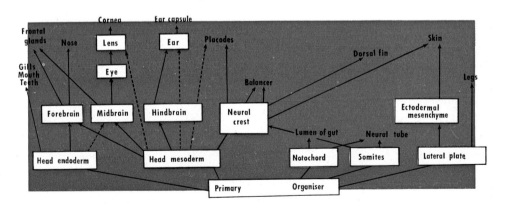

Fig. 112. *A chart of the amphibian organizers, showing their interrelations and sequence of action. (After Waddington, Genes and Organizers, Cambridge University Press.)*

strated a sequence of organizer effects controlling important embryonic processes from gastrulation to the formation of adult structures. How varied these are may be learned from inspection of figure 112, which is based upon a diagram which sought to summarize the knowledge of amphibian organizers as it stood in 1938. While this phenomenon has been more thoroughly studied in amphibians than in any other group, there is little doubt that the control of embryonic differentiation by such organizers is very general.

Both the inductive capacity of an organizer and the competence of the target tissues are under genetic control, as one would expect. The processes concerned are essential to the life of the organism, and so it is not surprising that mutations affecting them are often lethals. But some non–lethal examples are available. It is very probable that the control of direction of coiling in snails belongs in this category, as well as the other cases of maternal inheritance, which were discussed in chapter 6. An interesting and well-analyzed example is provided by the phenomenon of *homeosis*, the production of the "wrong" member of a series of serial homologues on a particular segment. Thus the head of *Drosophila* bears antennae, while the thoracic segments bear legs. But the mutant aristapedia, *ar*, causes part of the antenna to develop as a tarsus (fig. 113).

Embryological study has clarified the action of this gene. The appendages make their first appearance as a series of *imaginal discs*, thickenings of the epidermis. These differentiate in a regular sequence with the leg discs far ahead of the antennal discs. A "leg organizer," or evocator, causes any disc which is competent to react to develop according to the pattern called forth by the specific organizer substance which is then diffusing through the organism. Normally, the antennal disc is not yet competent to react at this time, but the gene *ar* shifts the timing of its competence to coincide with that of the leg discs.

Another very good example concerns the gene for short tail, *Sd*, in the mouse. This is a recessive lethal with the shortening or absence of the tail appearing as a phenotypic effect in the heterozygous condition. Other effects of the gene include defects of the kidneys and ureters. The effects vary considerably from individual to individual and even between the two sides of the same individual. But it is noteworthy that no kidney ever develops unless the ureter is long enough to reach the normal site of the kidney. Embryologically, the kidney has a dual origin. The ureter forms as a bud growing dorsally and anteriorly from the mesonephros. This normally comes into contact with a mass of unsegmented mesoderm at the posterior end of the nephrogenic ridge and the latter then forms the secretory portion of the kidney. It is evident, then, that

Fig. 113. *Aristapedia. Above, a normal antenna; below, the aristapedia, or leg-like, mutant of* Drosophila. *(Redrawn from Balkaschina.)*

the ureter acts as a kidney organizer, and that the *Sd* gene prevents its action in some of the mice of genotype *Sd*/+. In mice homozygous for this gene, development of the endodermal and mesodermal structures at the posterior end of the body is grossly deficient, and lethality always results. It is probable that a defect of the primary organizer is responsible.

PHENOCOPIES AND THE RATE CONCEPT As long ago as 1896, a thorough study of the color patterns of butterflies was published in which it was demonstrated that environmental factors may so modify a butterfly that it will mimic related races or species. For example, if pupae of butterflies of the central European race of *Vanessa* were treated with low temperatures, the adults which emerged from the pupae resembled the race from Lapland, while pupae treated with high temperatures were indistinguishable from the race found on the island of Sardinia. This phenomenon, by which organisms of one genotype mimic the phenotype appropriate to a different genotype, has been studied systematically by Goldschmidt, and he calls such organisms *phenocopies*. Using *Drosophila*, Goldschmidt has produced phenocopies of a great many mutants, affecting all parts of the organism. He concluded that, if the appropriate experimental agency were used, a phenocopy could be obtained of any mutant whatever. It should be emphasized that a phenocopy is *not* a mutation: if returned to a normal environment, the phenocopies breed true to the original type, showing that there has been no mutation, but only a phenotypic copy of a mutation.

Goldschmidt experimented with only one method of producing phenocopies, namely heat shocks. While he obtained phenocopies of many mutants, he found that for any particular mutant there is a sensitive period during larval life when its phenocopy can be produced. Thus, if larvae four and a half to five and a half days old were subjected to a temperature of 35° centigrade for twelve to twenty-four hours, about 70 per cent emerged with scalloped wings. And if seven day old larvae were subjected to a temperature of 37° for a similar time, about 40 per cent had miniature wings.

Embryological studies showed that the phenocopies were produced by speeding up or slowing down specific embryological processes, and Goldschmidt drew the conclusion that the mutant genes must act in much the same way that the phenocopies are produced. And from this the further inference was made that the normal gene also acts as a regulator of rates of reactions in the organism.

Numerous examples are available in which it can be demonstrated that particular genes actually do control rates of developmental reactions. The original example was afforded by Goldschmidt's analysis of the determination of sex in *Lymantria*, reported in the preceding chapter. In the crustacean *Gammarus*, the eyes are at first red, but they darken progressively until they are black. In the red-eyed mutant, pigmentation begins later and proceeds more slowly so that the adult stage is reached while the eyes are still dark red, and pigmentation is stopped. In rabbits, it has been shown that large and small races differ principally in the rate of cell division, with hybrids having an intermediate rate.

While it seems highly probably that the work on phenocopies has lead to a correct insight into the nature of genic action through control of rates of embryological processes, it is noteworthy that this leaves largely unsolved another very basic problem: namely, why does one process occur rather than another, irrespective of rates? Some light may be shed upon this question below in the section on the type of reactions controlled by the mutant gene.

197

47. DOMINANCE AND THE THRESHOLD CONCEPT

When De Vries first did experiments in Mendelian genetics, he found that one member of a pair of alternative characters was always expressed to the exclusion of the other in heterozygotes. He believed this to be a universal condition, and so he spoke of the "law of dominance." Dominance was regarded as an integral property of the gene. For Bateson, a dominant gene was a real entity, while a recessive was only the absence of the corresponding dominant.

CONDITIONS INFLUENCING DOMINANCE Gradually, however, geneticists came to realize that dominance is not actually a fundamental property of the gene, but only a characteristic of the phenotype. Dominance is a thing capable of being shifted. A gene which behaves as a dominant at one stage in a life cycle may behave as a recessive at another stage. Or a gene which is dominant in one environment may be recessive in another. Again, the *genetic* environment may influence dominance, that is, other genes may act as *dominance modifiers*. Finally, a pleiotropic gene may be dominant for some of its effects and recessive for others.

Many examples of these phenomena have been discussed for other reasons in the preceding chapters, and some of these may be reviewed now. First let us consider a new example of change of dominance during the life cycle. In the flour beetle, *Tenebrio mollitor*, there is a pair of genes which controls color, whether orange or brown, and the homozygotes are colored the same throughout the life cycle. But the heterozygotes are orange in the larval and pupal stages, but brown in the adult, or imago, stage. Dominance, then, has changed, most probably because of the differences in the physiological state of the organism during the different phases of the life cycle.

Shifting of dominance by environmental conditions has already been illustrated with the example of the Himalayan rabbits. These, it may be recalled, are generally white, but the tail, nose, ears, and paws are black. Animals of genotype C^h/C are all black if raised in severe cold, but they are all white if raised under hot, humid conditions. A. H. Hersh has studied thoroughly the reactions of the heterozygotes between bar, double bar, and normal eye ($+/B$, $BB/+$, BB/B) over the temperature range from $15°$ to $30°$ centigrade. The details of his study are rather complex and do not belong here, but the general conclusions are very much à propos. He found that for any genotype, the number of facets of the eye varied progressively with the temperature. For some genotypes, the relationship is direct, for others inverse. Hence the degree of dominance for a particular allele actually varied with the temperature, and it was possible to calculate a coefficient of dominance.

The residual genotype, that is, the rest of the genotype in addition to the gene pair under study, also influences dominance. The examples of sex-influenced inheritance discussed in chapter 6 apply here, with the sex-determining genes determining also which allele of a given pair shall be dominant. Many other examples, not associated with sex determination, are also known. Thus *Drosophila* of genotype $vg/+$ are ordinarily wild type. But Goldschmidt found three dominance modifiers which tend to shift dominance in favor of vg. Individually, they cause low-grade vestigial effects in a small percentage of the flies heterozygous for vg. But when all three dominance modifiers are present, their effects are additive, and all of the flies show dominance of vg over its usually dominant allele. Again, the gene for truncate, T, affects both the wings and the bristles. The allele T^o is dominant for the wing trait and recessive for the bristle trait, while the reverse is true of the allele T^{vo}. Their compound, T^o/T^{vo}, is actually wild type. Obviously, dominance cannot be a fundamental property of *this* gene.

THE PROBLEM OF THE NATURE OF DOMINANCE The many examples above demonstrate that dominance is not a fundamental characteristic of the gene, but simply an aspect of the phenotype which is subject to many internal and external influences. Nonetheless, it is an extraordinarily widespread and striking phenomenon, and it must be explained. The first theory advanced in explanation was the presence or absence theory of Bateson and Punnett. This was actually disproved even before it was proposed, for it was inconsistent with the discovery of Correns in 1899 that endosperm characters of maize might show relative dominance, the gene which is present twice being expressed over the one present only once (see chapter 9).

A second suggestion is that various alleles of a gene have different potencies, which may mean that they produce varying quantities of an enzyme or other substance essential for the production of a particular phenotype. Then, if there is a minimum *threshold* quantity of this substance which must be present in order to produce its effect, any gene of high enough potency to reach or surpass this threshold when heterozygous will behave as a dominant. As there might be any degree of potency above the threshold, this concept carries with it the inference that there may be different wild type alleles. There is some evidence that this may be true. The idea of genes of different potencies was derived originally from the work on the sex-determining alleles of different races of *Lymantria*, but it is supported by work on other characters as well. For example, Stern has studied the effects of the gene for bobbed bristles, a sex-linked re-

cessive in *Drosophila*. A single gene in the male, or two in the female, results in underdeveloped bristles. By the use of duplications, it was possible to get females with three or four bobbed alleles. These had normal bristles, showing that the product of the bobbed gene is of the same sort as that of its normal allele, but that product does not reach the minimum threshold for formation of normal bristles when only two bobbed alleles are present.

A third theory of dominance was proposed by R. A. Fisher on the basis of studies of inheritance of dominant genes in fowl. He found that, if domestic birds with dominant mutations were repeatedly backcrossed to the wild fowl of Malay, specific genes of the domestic birds could be studied in relation to the residual genotype of the wild birds. One striking result was the loss of dominance by the mutant genes. Hence Fisher concluded that dominance in the domestic fowl must have resulted from a complex of modifiers. In terms of the threshold concept, this would mean that the modifiers had reduced the threshold of action of the gene. This theory has assumed considerable importance in evolutionary studies. As was mentioned in chapter 13, the same mutations tend to occur over and over again, and there is no doubt that this has always been so, as long as there have been mutable organisms. Now if any favorable mutation should occur, any other mutation which might lower its threshold of action would also be favored by natural selection. Hence the dominant genes which we now study are presumed to be dominant because of long continued natural selection of modifying genes which lower the thresholds of action of the major genes.

GENE DOSAGE AND THE BALANCE CONCEPT Stern's experiment discussed above leads immediately to the question of whether the dosage of a gene—the number of times it is represented in the genotype—is important for genic action. The obvious conclusion from Stern's study of the bobbed gene is that the phenotype depends upon the quantity of some gene product which is in turn dependent upon the quantity of the gene. Much the same idea had already been derived from the study of intersexes, as developed in the preceding chapter. But an additional conclusion may be drawn from the studies on intersexuality: the phenotype depends not only upon the dosage of a single gene (or complex of genes, if one considers that there are many sex-determining alleles), but it depends upon the proportions between the various members of the genotype. Two X chromosomes in the usual genotype leads to a female, but two X chromosomes in a genotype including three sets of autosomes leads to an intersex. Three X chromosomes will ordinarily determine a superfemale, which is sterile, but three X chromosomes with three sets of autosomes results in a fertile, triploid female.

Studies on monosomics, trisomics, and duplications all reinforce the above data. In all of these, with no mutants whatever present, the phenotype differs from the wild type. In all, the proportions of the different kinds of genes are disturbed. Hence it may be considered that, in general, gene action is proportional to gene quantity, and that the balance between different genes is as important as their absolute quantities. Here also belong the considerations relative to collaboration of genes which were taken up in chapter 9.

48. THE REACTIONS CONTROLLED BY GENES

In one sense, every paragraph of this chapter has been concerned with the reactions controlled by genes. The production of differentiated cytoplasms and of organizers, the action of intracellular enzymes and extracellular hormones, the control of developmental rates and thresholds—all of these *are* reactions controlled by genes. But their visible evidence is most commonly found in morphological traits which are obviously the end points of long reaction chains which began with the genes. The primary action of the gene must be a chemical one, most probably catalytic, and hence an especial interest attaches to the demonstration of chemical variations which are genetically controlled. There is a hope that such cases may lead to direct knowledge of the primary products of the gene. A few of these will be reviewed below.

BIOCHEMICAL MUTANTS OF NEUROSPORA Much the most extensively explored series of genetically controlled chemical traits is that of the nutritional mutants of the bread mold, *Neurospora crassa*, which has been investigated by Beadle and his collaborators. As this work was discussed in chapter 9, it need not be repeated here. But it may be mentioned that mutants are available which block specific steps in the synthesis of nearly all of the amino acids and vitamins required for the nutrition of the organism. In most cases, the mutant appears to block only one specific reaction in the synthesis of a particular compound. From this, the inference has been drawn that the normal allele must produce the enzyme, or at least cause the final specificity of the enzyme which normally promotes the blocked reaction. In the preceding sections of this chapter, evidence was presented to show that genes control the rates of morphogenetic reactions. Now, for the first time, we have some insight into the primary reaction itself.

PRODUCTION OF PIGMENTS Colors and patterns are among the most obvious characters of many plants and animals, and so were among the first to be analyzed genetically. Some of the resulting information was summarized in chapter 9. It was found that melanin pigments of many animals depended upon the presence of two components, a chromagen (tyrosine) and an oxidase. Chemical studies were soon made and correlated with the genetic studies. From the skins of black, gray, and brown rabbits an enzyme (peroxidase) was extracted which would catalyze the oxidation of the tyrosine to melanin in the presence of hydrogen peroxide. Attempts to extract the enzyme from the skins of recessive white rabbits failed. When a dominant white rabbit was tested, the enzyme was found, but it was accompanied by an inhibitor. There is a similar situation in the guinea pig, but here there are two genetically controlled oxidases, with one lowering the threshold of the other.

Plant pigments have been very extensively studied. Of these, chlorophyll (green) and carotin (yellow) are contained in the plastids, while the sap contains an extensive series of pigments, the anthoxanthins and the anthocyanins. The anthoxanthins range from ivory to yellow, while the anthocyanins range from red through purple to blue. All of these are rather similar substances which may be treated as derivatives of flavone (fig. 114), a three-ringed heterocyclic compound (see books on organic chemistry or biochemistry for details). The phenotype is determined by a considerable number of factors which are under genetic control. These include such specific things as the number of carbons on which an hydroxyl group or methyl group is substituted, whether the molecule is or is not conjugated with a sugar molecule, presence or absence of co-pigments, and pH.

BLOOD GROUPS The blood groups were introduced in chapter 8 as an unusually thoroughly studied example of multiple alleles. While the chemical constitution of the antigens and antibodies is not known, still it is certain that they are specific proteins (with the exception of some carbohydrates which have been shown to have antigenic activity), and hence they belong in the present discussion. As each gene seems to determine a single antigen without any evidence of collaboration of genes, the inference has been drawn that the antigens must be very close to the primary products of the genes concerned. This is not a necessary inference, but it may be correct.

SOME GENE-CONTROLLED METABOLIC DEFECTS IN MAN Many examples of genetic control of specific biochemical traits are known in man, and a few of these may be mentioned. Alcaptonuria is a condition with arthritic symptoms, hardening and blackening of the cartilage of the patient, and blackening of the urine upon exposure to the air. These symptoms result from an abnormally high concentration of homogentisic acid in the blood. This acid is a normal metabolic waste, but it is broken down to acetoacetic acid in normal persons, who have an enzyme for the purpose. Absence of the enzyme is ordinarily caused by a single pair of recessive genes.

Fig. 114. *The structural formula of flavone, upon which many plant pigments are based.*

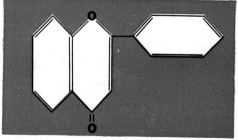

Gout is another disease with well-known genetic and biochemical bases. Genetically, it is based upon a dominant gene. Biochemically, it results from a defect of nucleic acid metabolism. This results in accumulation of uric acid (a degradation product of nucleic acid) in the blood. If the blood level of uric acid exceeds six milligrams per cent, gouty arthritis may occur because of uric acid crystals forming in the joints. However, although a single dominant gene will always cause a high level of uric acid in the blood, it does not always result in clinical gout.

Diabetes mellitus is an important disease, which was highly fatal before insulin was isolated and made available for replacement therapy. As is well known, the diagnostic symptom of the disease is sugar in the urine, which is turn results from elevation of the blood sugar level above 180 milligrams per cent. This is caused by a blockage of carbohydrate metabolism because of a deficiency of insulin, the hormone of the pancreatic islets. Analysis of pedigrees has shown that the defect is inherited as a recessive in most families, but a dominant form is also known. Incidentally, the pancreatic defect may not be the direct effect of the gene, for it has been shown that injection of a product of the anterior lobe of the pituitary gland, alloxan, will cause degeneration of the pancreatic islets in normal animals.

49. CONCLUSIONS

Much evidence has been presented to show that genes obtain their effects through ordinary physiological channels. We have seen that the nature of the processes by which the gene produces the phenotype are known in part, although this field is only scantily explored. Yet it is clear that such basic morphogenetic processes as the actions of embryonic organizers, of hormones, and of enzyme systems are under genetic control, which is to say that genes act through these media. In many instances, the relationship between specific enzymes and specific genes has caused speculation as to whether the enzyme may actually be the primary product of the gene. Yet there is no single instance in which the primary product of genic action can be identified with assurance and so this most fundamental problem of the physiology of the gene remains in an unsatisfactory state. Finally, there is a great body of evidence which proves that genes control the rates at which developmental and other processes occur.

In the middle 1920's, W. J. Crozier of Harvard directed some very interesting experiments on tropisms of animals. Young rats, whose eyes had not yet opened, were placed on an inclined plane. Being negatively geotropic, the rats always crawled up the plane. But the angle between the path of the

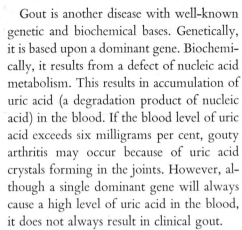

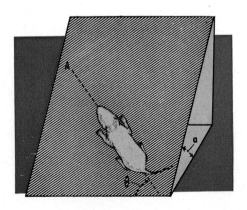

Fig. 115. *Crozier's experiment on inherited response to gravity. (Redrawn from Crozier and Pincus in the Journal of General Physiology, vol. 10.)*

rat and the base of the plane (θ, the angle of orientation) was not random: as the angle of inclination of the plane (α) increased, so did the angle of orientation (fig. 115). The correspondence was so close that it was possible to express it with an equation, $\theta = K \log \sin \alpha$, where θ and α are the angles of orientation and inclination as described above, and K is a constant *which varies in different genetic strains of rats*. For any individual rat, there is of course a certain limited amount of variation, but the regularity of the response to gravity is indeed striking. And because the constant K varies from one inbred line to another, it is clear that this is an inherited behavior pattern.

A few years ago, a distinguished biologist reviewed Crozier's work before his class in general physiology. He described with enthusiasm the regularity of the response to gravity. He acknowledged with some perplexity the evidence for the inheritance of quantitative differences in response, then concluded with evident disbelief and sarcasm, "How in the world can an animal inherit a constant in an equation?" That class, of which the present author was a member, was much impressed. We agreed that the data had led to an absurd conclusion. However, professor and students had fallen into the error, against which Wright had warned, of attributing "a character partly to physiological factors, partly to heredity, as if heredity could operate by some sort of sympathetic magic independently of physiological channels." As constants in equations play an important role in other physiological processes, such as enzyme action, it should be expected that they would play an important role in the functions of genes. Indeed, the abundant data on inheritance of variations in rates of processes may well indicate that a constant in an equation is a major part of the burden of every gene.

Questions and Problems

1. Define:

Alcaptonuria	Induction
Competence	Inhibitor
Dominance	Organizer
Dominance modifier	Phenocopy
Gray crescent	Threshold
Homeosis	

2. Many years ago, Boveri demonstrated the process of "chromatin diminution" in *Ascaris*. During the early cleavage divisions, the chromosomes are fragmented in all prospective somatic cells, with about two thirds of the chromosome complement being destroyed. Only in the prospective germ cells is the entire chromosome complement retained. This was generally interpreted as supporting Weismann's theory of unequal mitoses as the basis of differentiation. How could you investigate whether this inference is correct or incorrect?

3. What is the basis for the action of embryonic organizers?

4. Discuss an example of a mutation which modifies the action of an organizer.

5. What is the difference between a phenocopy and a mutation?

6. What insight do phenocopies afford into the physiology of the gene?

7. Discuss the pigmentation of the eyes of *Gammarus*, showing how this demonstrates the control of the *rate* of a process by the genotype.

8. Cite evidence that dominance is not an integral property of the gene.

9. Which of the theories of dominance seems most probable to you? Defend your answer.

10. What evidence can you advance in favor of the importance of the *balance* among the genes?

11. Have any experiments afforded evidence as to the nature of the primary products of the genes? Discuss fully.

12. Explain Crozier's experiments on geotropism in rats.

References

Beadle, G. W., 1945. Genetics and metabolism in *Neurospora*. Physiological Reviews, 25:643–663. A readable summary by the founder of this important field.

Crozier, W. J. and G. Pincus, 1926. The geotropic conduct of young rats. Journal of General Physiology, 10:257–269. This paper presents some of the quantitative work on geotropisms of rats.

Fisher, R. A., 1935. Dominance in poultry. Philosophical Transactions of the Royal Society of London, Series B, 225:195–226.

Goldschmidt, R. B., 1938. Physiological Genetics. McGraw-Hill, New York. The only available systematic treatment of the subject. It is badly in need of revision, but is still the most valuable reference on work up to 1938.

Haldane, J. B. S., 1954. The Biochemistry of Genetics. The Macmillan Co., London. This book has appeared too recently for evaluation, but it is the only book yet to attempt a comprehensive survey of this field.

Hersh, A. H., 1930. The facet-temperature relation in the bar series of Drosophila. Journal of Experimental Zoology, 57:283–306. This paper establishes different coefficients of dominance at different temperatures.

Horowitz, N. H., 1950. Biochemical genetics of Neurospora. In Advances in Genetics, 3:33–72.

Spemann, Hans, 1938. Embryonic Development and Induction. Yale University Press, New Haven. A general review by the discoverer of the amphibian organizer.

Stern, Curt, 1929. Über die additive Wirkung multipler Allele. Biologisches Zentralblatt, 49:261–290. For those who read German well, this paper presents the evidence that the gene for bobbed bristles and its normal allele do the same thing qualitatively but not quantitatively.

Villee, C. A., 1942. The phenomenon of homeosis. American Naturalist, 76:494–506. A concise and readable review by a leading student of this interesting phenomenon.

Waddington, C. H., 1940. Organizers and Genes. Cambridge University Press. A concise treatment of the relations between genetics and experimental embryology.

Wagner, R. P. and H. K. Mitchell, 1955. Genetics and Metabolism. John Wiley and Sons, New York. This book, written by two biochemical geneticists, was published after the above chapter was written. A cursory examination indicates that it will be a very useful book.

Wright, Sewall, 1945. Genes as physiological agents. American Naturalist, 79:289–303. A short summary of some of the main aspects of the subject as seen by one of the leaders in the field.

CHAPTER 17

The Theory of the Gene

In the preceding chapters, we have reviewed the statics of gene transmission and the dynamics of gene physiology. Repeatedly, the data have raised questions regarding the nature of the gene, and these questions have been evaded for the most part. Now evasion is no longer possible. In the present chapter, we shall review data and theories on the nature of the gene, and try to reach some understanding.

In considering the nature of the gene, it is first necessary to take stock of the available knowledge of the chemistry of the chromosomes. As the location of the genes in the chromosomes is beyond doubt, any valid theory of the gene must be consistent with the properties of the chromosomes. One of the fundamental properties of the gene is self-duplication. This process—whatever it is—is repeated at least once in every cell generation, and the transmission of the duplicated genes via the germ cells is the basis of Mendelian inheritance. A second property is the occasional inexactness of gene reproduction, so that a mutant gene results. The mutant is then reproduced with the same regularity as was the parent gene. Finally, the gene functions as a physiological agent, as discussed in the preceding chapter. All of these diverse requirements must be synthesized in the present chapter.

50. THE CHEMISTRY OF THE CHROMOSOMES

The chemistry of the chromosomes is an extremely difficult field to investigate, not only because of the complexity of the compounds, but because of the extremely small quantities with which one must work. That some progress has been made is a tribute indeed to the ingenuity and the persistence of those biochemists and cytologists who have studied the chemistry of the chromosomes.

THE STRUCTURAL MATERIALS OF THE CHROMOSOME Two principal types of compounds have been identified in the chromosomes, proteins and nucleic acids, and these may be combined to form nucleoproteins. The building stones of proteins are amino acids, organic acids in which an amino group ($-NH_2$) has been substituted on one of the carbons, always the α carbon in natural amino acids. In all, about thirty amino acids are known in nature. The carboxyl radical ($-COOH$) dissociates as an acid, while the amino radical adds on a molecule of water and dissociates as a base. Thus the net reaction of the molecule is neutral. Some of the larger amino acids, however, have an excess of carboxyls, leading to an acid reaction, or of amino groups, leading to a basic reaction. The basic amino acids are important in the chromosomes. The most strongly basic of the amino acids is arginine (fig. 116), which has two amino groups and two other nitrogenous radicals.

The most important reaction of the amino acids is the *peptide linkage*, which is essentially a salt-forming reaction between two amino acid molecules. It may be illustrated by the reaction between two mole-

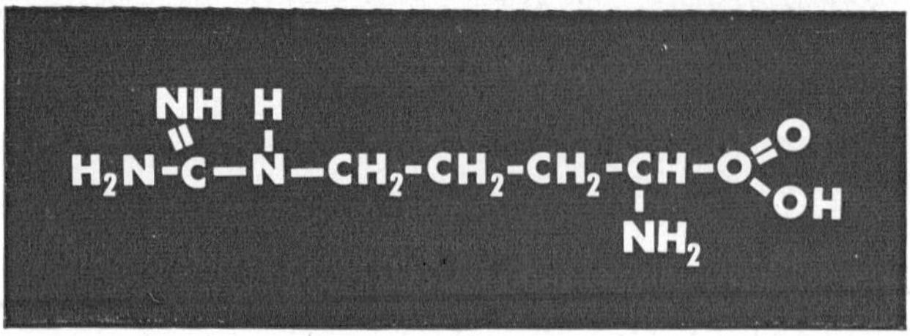

Fig. 116.   *The structural formula of arginine, the most strongly basic of the amino acids, and an important constituent of the chromosomes.*

cules of glycine, the simplest of the amino acids as shown at the bottom of this page. Perhaps the most significant feature of this reaction is that it always leaves a free acid radical at one end and a free amino radical at the other end of the resulting *dipeptide.* Thus the reaction can be repeated to form polypeptides of any degree. Proteins are very large molecules built in this way. While this is a surprisingly simple structure for such a varied and specific array of compounds, still it may be remembered that the number of amino acids is about equal to the number of letters in the alphabet, and so the number of compounds obtainable by combining them in different proportions and orders is potentially as great as the number of words which can be spelled out with the letters of the alphabet.

Proteins may be basic (the basic amino acids predominate), acidic (the acidic amino acids predominate), or neutral. The basic proteins are readily studied because they combine with nucleic acid to form nucleoproteins, the chromatin of cytology. They have been extensively studied and have been regarded as the most probable substance of the gene. Recently, however, neutral and acidic proteins have been found in the chromosomes in considerable quantities, and they may be more important than formerly supposed.

NUCLEIC ACIDS   The nucleic acids are composed of pentose (five-carbon sugars), purine and pyrimidine bases, and phosphoric acid. There are two principal types, desoxyribonucleic acid (DNA), which is found only in the chromosomes, and ribonucleic acid (RNA), which may be present in traces in the chromosomes, but which is found principally in the nucleoli and in the cytoplasm. DNA is more highly oxidized, and it is polymerized into large complexes by a phosphate—sugar—phosphate—sugar bonding. The bases are side chains on the sugars. Two such structures are joined together by hydrogen bonds (very weak) between the bases. Thus a ladder-like structure is formed, with the phosphate—sugar bands forming the uprights and the pairs of bases forming the cross-bars. Finally, the whole structure is spiralled about a central axis to form a structure something like a spiral staircase (fig. 117). The base pairs occur only in four specific ways, but these may occur in any sequence or relative abundance, thus permitting an enormous number of stereoisomers of DNA. Using this structure, a very

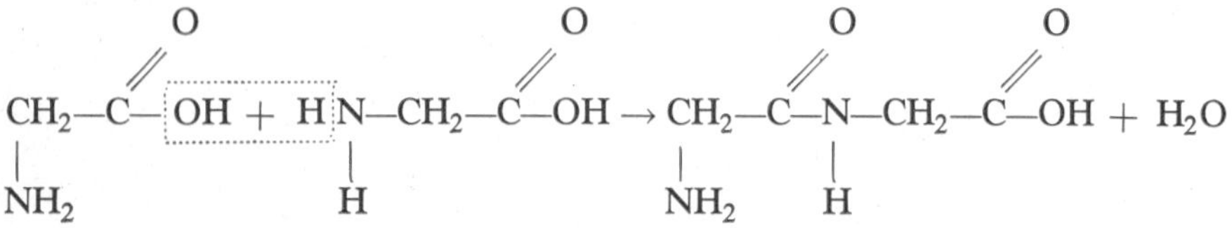

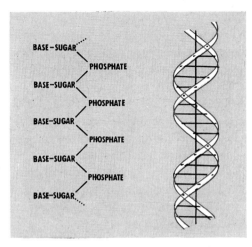

Fig. 117. *The structure of DNA as visualized by Crick and Watson. (Redrawn from Nature, vol. 171.)*

BASE–SUGAR
PHOSPHATE
BASE–SUGAR
PHOSPHATE
BASE–SUGAR
PHOSPHATE
BASE–SUGAR
PHOSPHATE
BASE–SUGAR
PHOSPHATE
BASE–SUGAR

clever possible scheme of reproduction of the DNA molecule has also been worked out.

It has generally been assumed that genetic diversity must depend upon the protein component of the chromosomes, but some recent developments have focused attention upon DNA. As mentioned above, it now appears that the number of DNA stereoisomers may be great enough to account for the diversity of genes. A second important fact is that of bacterial *transformation*. If purified DNA be extracted from certain strains of bacteria and then be added to a culture of genetically different bacteria of the same species, it may induce mutation to the type of the culture from which the DNA was extracted. Thus *Pneumococcus* occurs in many serologically different types, and mutation from, let us say, type *r* to type *s* can be induced by adding DNA from a type *s* culture to a type *r* culture. These mutant cultures then breed true. This is nothing less than *directed* mutation, and as such it has enormous theoretical significance for the study and control of mutation. With respect to the present problem, it indicates that the specificity of genes may reside in the DNA. Finally, it may be mentioned that there is very strong evidence that virus reproduction is associated primarily with the DNA rather than the protein of the virus.

CHEMISTRY AND GENE FUNCTION The two most obvious functions of genes are self-reproduction and the production of substances—most probably enzymes—which initiate the chain of reactions terminating in the visible phenotype. Actually, no data are available which permit a direct insight into either of these problems. Many geneticists feel that these two functions may be only different aspects of the same type of reaction. It has been suggested that in either case the primary product of the gene is a copy of the gene. In chromosome duplication, these copies remain in contact with the parent chromosome and become linked together to form a sister chromatid. Otherwise, the copies diffuse away to react with each other and with other substances to carry out the genetically controlled reactions of the cell.

The mode of formation of these copies is not known. Most probably, the genes act as an autocatalytic system to organize precursor substances which are present in the nucleus. The whole problem is a major challenge for future research.

51. THEORIES OF THE GENE

Mendel spoke of the units of inheritance as "factors" or "elements," but ventured no guess as to their nature. His terminology was accepted by the early students of heredity, but the need was soon felt for a more specific name. The term "gene" was proposed by Johannsen, because it is the root of the Greek verb *to become*. It was his intention that this term should be just a convenient word to designate the units of heredity, with no theoretical implications regarding the nature of the unit. Subsequently, however, the term "gene" has become heavily charged with such meaning. As emphasized above repeatedly, a gene can be identified only if it has mutated, so that a pair of alternative genes can be followed through a succession of generations. Because of this, most theories of the gene have been based upon some aspects of the mutation problem, and have sought to explain these.

THOMAS HUNT MORGAN AND THE THEORY OF THE PARTICULATE GENE The first quarter century of genetic research produced a good many theories of the nature of the gene. Most of these, like the *one gene—one character* hypothesis of DeVries and the *presence* or *absence* theory of Bateson and Punnett, served a useful purpose in promoting the understanding of the most elementary facts of genetics, but they had to be discarded as soon as more complex data proved incompatible. Perhaps no one has contributed

more to the development of genetics than has Thomas Hunt Morgan (fig. 118), whose researches culminated in the publication of a fully developed theory of the gene in 1926. The phrase "gene theory," unqualified, generally refers to Morgan's conception of the gene. Morgan used three principal categories of data: the fact of mutation; the fact that the order of genes in the chromosomes can be ascertained by crossover tests; and the fact that this order, once established, can be reshuffled, with difficulty, by chromosomal rearrangements. From the first, the inference was drawn that in the unmutated chromosome there must be a real unit, the normal gene. From the second and third, it was concluded that the genes must be circumscribed corpuscles of some kind, each with a definite normal locus in the chromosome. Hence the genes were conceived to be corpuscles on the chromosomes, arranged in linear order like beads on a string, each different in substance from all of the others, and separated from all of the others by an indifferent substance.

The gene theory, thus defined, is an admirable synthesis and simplification of much of the genetic research of the first quarter of the present century. For it, Morgan received the Nobel Prize in Medicine in 1933, the first to be awarded to a geneticist. The theory earned wide acceptance, and it is still the starting point for most considerations of the nature of the gene. Most subsequent proposals on this problem may be regarded as footnotes to Morgan's theory.

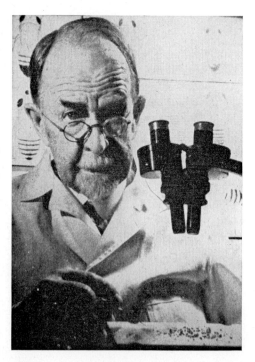

Fig. 118. *Thomas Hunt Morgan. (From Genetics, vol. 32.)*

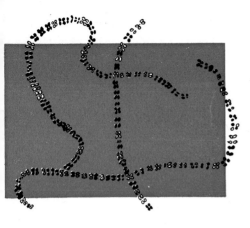

Fig. 119. *The ultimate chromomeres of Lilium. (Redrawn from Belling, in University of California Publications in Botany, vol. 14.)*

GENE NUMBER AND SIZE   The concept of the gene as a discrete particle of course raised questions about gene number and size. Some regarded the leptotene chromomeres as visible genes (fig. 119), and on this basis the number of genes in *Lilium* was estimated at 2200. However, the number of leptotene chromomeres in *Drosophila* is only about 150, while the number of known gene loci is greatly in excess of this. The number of genes in man has been estimated as not less than 5000 nor more than 120,000, with 24,000 as a fairly probable intermediate figure. Of course, it is not possible to make a direct count of the genes of any species.

J. W. Gowen and E. H. Gay have made an unusually thorough study of gene number and size in *Drosophila*. They arrived at a figure of about 15,000 loci in the entire chromosome set. Using this figure and the total volume of the chromosomes, they calculated the volume of the gene as averaging 1×10^{-18} cubic centimeters. It is interesting to note that photographs of sections of the salivary gland chromosomes have shown small, leaf-shaped bodies (fig. 120) with an average size of 1×10^{-17}. These have been thought to be genes. While they are ten times the size estimated by Gowen and Gay, still the salivary gland chromosomes are giant chromosomes, so there is no real inconsistency here. On the other hand, there is no proof that the objects photographed actually are genes.

Some geneticists define the gene simply as the smallest segment of the chromosome within which crossing over does not occur. This has been identified with a single band in the salivary gland chromosomes; however, as no evidence of crossing over can be seen in the salivary gland chromosomes, this is insecure.

THE ONE GENE—ONE ENZYME THEORY Beadle and his group of *Neurospora* geneticists have taken a new approach, and have defined the gene in terms of its function. As described in chapters 9 and 16, they have studied the biosynthesis of essential amino acids and vitamins by means of x-ray induced mutations which block specific steps in these syntheses. While many different

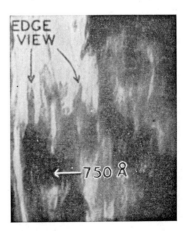

Fig. 120. *The genes? This is an electron micrograph of a portion of a salivary gland chromosome. The leaf-shaped bodies may be genes. (From Pease and Baker, in Science, vol. 109.)*

mutants may block the synthesis of any given compound, non-allelic mutants always block the synthesis at different stages in the chain of reactions leading to the final compound. The simplest interpretation of the data is that a single mutation interferes with a single enzyme which is essential for the blocked reaction. The further inference is then drawn that in the unmutated organism the normal allele is responsible for the specificity of the enzyme. While Beadle and his group do not claim that all genic reactions must have a one-to-one relationship with specific enzymes, they do think that this is probably true for gene-controlled syntheses. And, as all genic reactions may (and may not) depend upon production of specific enzymes, the theory potentially has very broad significance.

This one gene—one enzyme theory is one of the most productive and exciting developments in genetic theory in recent years, but unfortunately it has some defects. The most serious criticism is that the method of identification of the mutants is selective for such mutations as fit the theory. An earlier acting mutant, blocking several essential syntheses, would be lethal under the conditions of the experiment and would be missed. Also, the evidence upon which the theory is based has no direct bearing upon morphological traits, nor upon any traits which cannot be defined in biochemical terms.

POSITION EFFECT AND THE THEORY OF THE GENE While position effects have been known since 1925, they were regarded as more or less exceptional until the discovery of the salivary gland chromosomes made possible their intensive study. Then many supposed point mutations turned out to be position effects of small rearrangements, and it was shown that all types of mutation can occur as position effects as well as point mutations. Further, the same experimental agencies which produce point mutations also produce rearrangements in abundance. These facts led many geneticists to question whether there is actually a difference between the two kinds of mutation, or whether the gene might not be better interpreted as a pattern of organization in the chromosome rather than as a discrete corpuscle.

Most geneticists who have considered this problem have tried to harmonize the data of position effect with the theory of the corpuscular gene. Thus Dobzhansky has suggested that the two may be reconciled on "a higher level" of gene physiology, but gives no specific details, while Muller has suggested that the gene may be regarded as a restricted corpuscle with a broad field of action, perhaps without a definite boundary. A few have taken a more radical viewpoint, abandoning the concept of the corpuscular gene altogether. Thus Libbie Hyman has stated that "all particulate theories are intellectually unsatisfactory since the very matters for which an explanation is sought are attributed without explanation to imaginary particles."[*] As Goldschmidt has been the principal spokesman for this group, the argument may best be summarized in his own words:[†]

"It is our considered opinion that a single explanation must embrace position effect and point-mutation, an explanation which must take care of all the basic facts of both phenomena, viz.:

"(1) The fact that the production of chromosome rearrangements by radiation follows the same dosage law as the production of point-mutation.

"(2) The fact that in such experiments with x-rays (not neutrons) the seriation is found: two hits (or more) give large rearrangements with at least two distant breaks; one hit may produce small rearrange-

[*] Hyman, L. H., 1940. The Invertebrates. McGraw-Hill Book Co., New York.
[†] Experientia, 2:22–24, 1946.

ments or point-mutations. Ultraviolet radiation produces almost exclusively point-mutation though it also produces breaks (only the former radiations are supposed to act via ionization).

"(3) The fact that the phenotype of a position effect is the same or nearly the same (multiple allele) as that of one or more point-mutants in a nearby region of the chromosome.

"(4) The fact that position effects and point-mutants of the same region act as alleles.

"(5) The fact that all types of mutant action are known also as position effect, i.e. dominance, recessiveness, homozygous lethality, modifier action, dominance modification, multiple allelism and subjection to selection in the case of invisible effect.

"(6) The fact that in certain regions position effect may be overlapping between two loci of point-mutation.

"(7) The fact that, in properly studied cases, a point-mutant is located in a small chromosome segment within which rearrangement breaks give the position effect, though in some cases it is claimed that only one definite interval between two bands can produce the effect.

"(8) The fact that sometimes breaks within a proper region do not produce position effects.

"(9) The fact that sometimes the position effect is found with breaks very distant from the locus.

"(10) The fact that the last feature seems characteristic for those rearrangements with a second break in the heterochromatin, and that other special effects of heterochromatic neighborhood (mottling) are known.

"It is obvious that the simplest and most logical interpretation of points 1 to 5 is the assumption that point-mutants are also position effects, i.e., invisible rearrangements within the so-called locus, the smallest visible size of which is a single band in a salivary chromosome. Actually, Muller and Prokovieva had considered this interpretation but had rejected it because they thought that evolution needs the old concept of the gene. . . . The present author has since repeatedly tried to show that such an interpretation of mutation is unavoidable. The facts mentioned as points 6 to 10 require, in addition, the assumption that the properties attributed to a corpuscular gene or gene molecule are actually those of small chromosome segments which function differently when the order of their architecture is changed, i.e., visible change of order = position effect, invisible change of order = point-mutation. Furthermore, the existence of such an architectural mutant effect neither presupposes nor proves the existence of a not mutated gene in the same segment. (Most geneticists speak loosely of a gene, when only a mutant locus has been found).

"Let us discuss briefly these points. . . . There is, of course, no doubt that the chromosome has a serial structure and that localized changes of this structure, the mutant loci, can be located by the cross-over method. There is no doubt either that these localized conditions of change can be handled descriptively as separate units, the mutant locus or gene, and that for all descriptive purposes the extrapolation can be made that at the normal locus a normal gene exists. Further, there can be no doubt that almost all genetical facts can be described in terms of corpuscular genes, and that a geneticist who is not interested in the question of what a gene is may work successfully all his life long without questioning the theory of the corpuscular gene. In the same way . . . a chemist can describe and handle almost all the content of chemistry with valences represented as one or more dashes between atoms. But when he wants to know what valence is, he has to use the tool of quantum mechanics which the ordinary chemist does not need in his work. Similarly, the concept of the corpuscular gene comes under scrutiny only when the problem of the nature of the gene and the explanation of mutation and position effect is attacked."

Thus Goldschmidt envisions the chromosome as a chemical continuum, in which the genes are not separate particles but simply functional regions of varying sizes. For one function, a chromosomal segment on the order of size estimated for the corpuscular genes might be the effective unit; for another, a segment equivalent to a leptotene chromomere might be the effective unit; or it might be a segment of the size order of the alternating blocks of euchromatin and heterochromatin; or, finally, the chromosome as a whole might function as a unit, as may be the case in sex determination.

A few additional data which favor Goldschmidt's viewpoint may be mentioned. At the Brookhaven National Laboratory, there has been large scale research on the production of mutations in corn by gamma rays. A non-linear relationship was found between dosage of radiation and mutation frequency. This was interpreted to mean that at least two hits may be required to produce a mutation. While this is difficult to understand in the framework of the theory of the corpuscular gene, it is to be expected if mutations be interpreted as pattern changes in a continuum.

There is also some cytological evidence which favors the viewpoint that the chromosome is more highly integrated than indicated by the theory of the corpuscular gene. During the growth period of the primary oocytes of many vertebrates, while yolk and formative substances are being deposited, the chromosomes are modified as *lampbrush* or *lateral loop* chromosomes. The very small ultimate chromomeres of the synapsed chromosomes give rise to lateral loops which may extend for considerable distances on all sides of the main axis of the chromosome (fig. 121). Groups of four to eight such loops, together with the parent chromomeres, form rosette-like whorls. That such complex structures are functionless is possible, but it seems more likely that so complex a structure, involving segments of the chromosome that are very large from the viewpoint of the gene theory, has an important role in the physiology of the nucleus. A similar structure appears to be latent in the salivary gland chromosomes, and can be demonstrated by appropriate chemical treatment.

52. PROSPECT

The theory of the gene, then, is still highly speculative, in spite of more than fifty years of research. On the one hand, crossover experiments and allied data point toward a corpuscular theory of the gene, while the data of position effects favor a theory of the gene as a unit of organization in a highly integrated chromosome. The problem will probably remain speculative and controversial until microchemical methods are developed which will permit far more exacting analyses than have so far been possible.

Fig. 121. *Lampbrush chromosomes in a primary oocyte of a salamander,* Amphiuma.

What is required is not only more specific information on the nucleoproteins which make up the chromosome, but information on the regional differences within a single chromosome. This still appears to be far in the future.

Meanwhile, we can reassess the data which are now available. The diversity of hereditary characters and the data on crossing over leave no doubt that the chromosome must be highly differentiated longitudinally, and that alternative pairs can be localized at definite points, the mutant loci. On the other hand, the data of position effect and the lampbrush structure of oocyte and salivary gland chromosomes show that functional regions of the chromosome may be too large (i.e., visible) to be harmonized with the theory of the particulate gene.

One of the suggestions cited above for the reconciliation of position effects and the corpuscular gene was that the gene might be a restricted point with a broad field of action. Any data which will permit such an interpretation of the gene will also permit the definition to be inverted, so that the gene is defined as a broad field of action with a restricted point focus, modeled upon the concept of physical centers of gravity. Crossover experiments, and other data supporting the corpuscular theory, would then deal primarily with these point foci, while position effects would deal with the broader fields. In such a concept, there is no reason why such functional areas should not vary in size from molecular dimensions up to the entire chromosome. Nor is there any reason why different genic fields should not overlap, so long as their foci are separate, as required by the crossover data.

If chromosomal rearrangements were arranged in a spectrum from the largest possible to the smallest possible, they would blend into stereochemical changes at the lower end, and these would be the point mutations of classical genetics. It should be expected that

this whole range of possibilities would take part in the mutation process, and also that qualitative chemical changes might be involved.

Thus the old and the new data can be harmonized by thinking of the gene as a more or less broad field of action with a restricted point focus. The upper limit of this genic field is the whole chromosome (as possibly in sex determination), while the lower limit is the individual chemical radical. Morphologically, these genic fields are indefinite, and they may overlap, so long as their point foci remain separate. This combines the essential features of the position effects and of the gene theory of Morgan, except that it rejects the beads-on-a-string aspect of the latter.

In concluding this discussion, it is important to reemphasize the fact that all theories of the gene must remain speculative and provisional until much more specific biochemical data upon the chromosomes become available.

Questions and Problems

1. Define:

Amino acid	Lateral loop chromosome
Basic protein	One gene—one character
DNA	hypothesis
Gene	One gene—one enzyme
Genomere	theory
Globulin	Peptide linkage
Histone	Presence or absence theory
	RNA
	Transformation

2. What are the principal properties of the gene?

3. Discuss the probable chemical organization of the chromosomes.

4. Why is not more detailed information on the chemical structure of the chromosomes available?

5. What evidence is there that DNA plays an active role in the mutation process?

6. What has synapsis to do with gene action?

7. Who coined the term *gene*, and what did he mean by it?

213

8. With whose name is the "gene theory" most intimately associated?

9. What are the bases of the gene theory?

10. How are estimates of gene size made?

11. Explain the one gene—one enzyme theory.

12. What are the defects of the one gene—one enzyme theory?

13. What is the bearing of position effects upon the theory of the gene?

14. Do you believe that position effects and the theory of the gene can be harmonized?

15. If your answer to question 14 is affirmative, explain how they might be harmonized. If negative, explain why not.

References

Beadle, G. W., 1955. The Gene. Nieuwland Lectures. University of Notre Dame Press. A leading biochemical geneticist states his views simply and effectively.

Bonner, David, 1946. Biochemical mutations in *Neurospora*. Cold Spring Harbor Symposia on Quantitative Biology, 11:14–24. An effective presentation of the one gene—one enzyme theory, together with a brief rebuttal by Max Delbrück.

Dobzhansky, Th., 1936. Position effects of genes. Biological Reviews of the Cambridge Philosophical Society, 11:364–384. A leading student of position effects shows how he harmonizes them with the theory of the corpuscular gene.

Goldschmidt, R. B., 1951. Chromosomes and genes. Cold Spring Harbor Symposia on Quantitative Biology, 16:1–11. The principal opponent of the corpuscular gene here summarizes his views.

Gowen, J. W. and E. H. Gay, 1933. Gene number. kind, and size in *Drosophila*. Genetics, 18:1–31. Difficult reading, but an unusually thorough approach to the problems concerned.

Johannsen, W., 1911. The genotype conception of heredity. American Naturalist, 45:129–159. The man who coined the word "gene" states his viewpoint.

Kavanau, J. L., 1949. On correlation of the phenomena associated with chromosomes, foreign proteins, and viruses. American Naturalist, 83:95–138. A thought-provoking consideration of problems of synapsis, gene reproduction, and chromosome reproduction.

Morgan, T. H., 1926. The Theory of the Gene. Yale University Press, New Haven. A classic by the author of the theory of the corpuscular gene.

Muller, H. J., 1951. The Development of the Gene Theory. In "Genetics in the 20th Century," pp. 77–99. The Macmillan Co., New York. An historical résumé.

CHAPTER 18

Cytoplasmic Inheritance

During the last half of the nineteenth century, Weismann prepared the way for the chromosomal theory of heredity. Nonetheless, when Mendelian inheritance was rediscovered, many biologists thought that it was a more or less exceptional phenomenon, and that the more important aspects of heredity were still to be discovered, most probably in the cytoplasm. As the experimental basis of the chromosomal theory grew broader, the conviction grew that this was an adequate explanation for all of the facts of heredity. Actually, some of the classic experiments of Boveri, which were recounted in chapter 3, were planned to test whether a cytoplasmic element in heredity could be demonstrated. At first, the results seemed to be positive, and Boveri suggested that the characters of higher taxonomic groups might be determined by the cytoplasm, while varietal and specific characters were determined by the chromosomes. As Jacques Loeb aptly put it, the cytoplasm determines "the embryo in the rough," while the chromosomes add the finishing details. Boveri's experiments finally, however, seemed to support the chromosomes as the sole bearers of heredity, and for many years most biologists took that position. In recent years, however, evidence has accumulated that genuine cytoplasmic inheritance does

occur, and its importance probably extends far beyond the substantiated cases. The sum total of the self-reproducing, hereditary material of the cytoplasm is referred to as the *plasmon*, in contrast to the genome, the hereditary content of the chromosomes.

53. RELATED BUT DISTINCT PHENOMENA

Cytoplasmic inheritance is fundamentally much more difficult to study than nuclear inheritance. The regularities of behavior of the chromosomes in mitosis, meiosis, and fertilization make it easy to determine whether a parallel regularity characterizes the inheritance of any particular pair of alternative phenotypes. For the cytoplasm, no such obvious rules of behavior have been established. One striking feature of the behavior of the cytoplasm in reproduction, however, is the unequal size of the gametes: while egg and sperm nuclei are equivalent, the egg carries a large amount of cytoplasm, while the sperm carries only a trace. Therefore, one might expect that reciprocal crosses would give different results for cytoplasmically determined characters, and that such characters would be transmitted unilaterally through the female parent. Such findings are usually sought in studies of cytoplasmic inheritance, but Ephrussi has pointed out this is not valid, because even the small quantities of cytoplasm carried by the sperm might include the essential material for some inherited traits. Specifically he points out that the middle piece of the sperm carries a mass of mitochondria, and he thinks it probable that mitochondria may play an active role in heredity. Thus this is a field subject to an unusual degree of potential confusion, and one should be especially wary in it. We may now consider some specific problems which have led to confusion in studies on cytoplasmic inheritance.

MATERNAL INHERITANCE The phenomenon of maternal inheritance was discussed in detail in chapter 6. It will be recalled that this is a genotypically determined type of inheritance in which the phenotype of the offspring corresponds to the genotype of the mother. In order to demonstrate the Mendelian character of the inheritance, it is necessary to breed an F_3, and if this is not practical, then the results might well appear to be influenced only by the mother. Yet the complete analysis of such cases as direction of spiraling of snail shells and inheritance of tendency to gynandrism in moths proves that ordinary Mendelian inheritance is involved, with the qualification that the character is already determined in the egg before fertilization. Hence all expected Mendelian ratios are delayed by one generation. It is probable that many embryonic characters especially are inherited in this way. While the role of the chromosomes is clear when the analysis is complete, yet maternal inheritance has often been regarded as cytoplasmic inheritance. And if only an F_1 be available, the two might very well be indistinguishable.

DAUERMODIFICATION About forty years ago, Jollos tried treating protozoans with various poisons (in sublethal doses) and with heat shocks. He found that the treatments induced morphological abnormalities in the treated animals, and that these abnormalities were transmitted to the offspring and maintained for a number of generations in the absence of the original stimulus (poison or heat). But the degree of abnormality became progressively less in successive generations and finally it disappeared altogether. This cytoplasmic modification, transmitted only through the maternal parent, is called *dauer-modification* (German—lasting modification). Here the case for cytoplasmic inheritance is a little stronger, but there is a fatal weakness, the gradual return to normalcy. Surely a plasmon character should depend upon a self-reproducing part of the cytoplasm, not upon something which must be renewed from the outside every few generations.

THE MILK FACTOR AND VIRUS INFECTION There is a very interesting type of "inherited" mammary tumor in mice. The tendency to produce tumors is passed from mother to daughter. Sons of tumorous mothers, if crossed to normal females, have only normal progeny, whereas tumorous females have tumorous daughters whether crossed to males of the same strain or of a normal strain. Such matroclinous inheritance (resembling the mother, irrespective of cause) is regarded as the hallmark of cytoplasmic inheritance. But it has been shown that the tumor-causing agent is transmitted via the milk. If daughters are foster-nursed by a normal female, they are normal and so are all of their progeny. On the other hand, daughters of normal mice, when foster-nursed by mice of the tumorous strain, become tumorous and subsequently pass the tendency to develop mammary tumors on to their offspring.

It is clear that some tumor-producing agent is transmitted by the milk from mother to daughter in these mice. Present evidence favors the viewpoint that the infective agent is a virus. But it simulates cytoplasmic inheritance very closely.

When it is possible to transmit such an infective agent artificially, evidence for its virus nature is convincing. But if no such experimental transmission is possible, then one assumes true cytoplasmic inheritance. However, it may merely indicate inadequate experimental technique. This raises the broader question of the relationship between viruses, genes, and cytoplasmic particles.

Viruses show some of the important properties of genes. They are nucleoproteins; they are self-reproducing (or do they induce their host to synthesize more virus? This question cannot be answered conclusively either for viruses or for chromosomes at present); they are relatively stable; and they are capable of mutating, the mutants then being as stable as the original. Some investigators regard viruses as "escaped genes." In view of these facts, it may be that no sharp line should be drawn between virus infection and cytoplasmic inheritance.

ENZYMATIC ADAPTATION IN MICROORGANISMS Inherited biochemical systems are often most readily studied in microorganisms. Specific enzymes are necessary for each of the reactions carried out. These are produced under genetic control, but instances are known in which colonies with the genotype for a particular enzyme produce it or fail to produce it according to whether the substrate of the enzyme (the substance upon which it acts) is present in the medium or not. This phenomenon is called *enzymatic adaptation*. It has been particularly well studied in brewer's yeast, *Saccharomyces cerevisiae*, and this example will be discussed. Yeast grown on a medium lacking the sugar galactose fails to produce galactozymase, the galactose-splitting enzyme. But if a portion of such a colony is transferred to a medium containing this sugar, galactozymase is soon produced, and the sugar is fermented. Upon removal to the galactose-free medium, the ability to form the enzyme is again lost in a matter of six or seven cell generations. Perhaps this should be regarded as a case of dauermodification, but it usually is not so considered because of the short duration of each generation.

Enzymatic adaptation is also known in bacteria. Thus in *Escherichia coli*, galactosidase cannot be demonstrated in cultures grown in media not containing galactoside.

But addition of this compound is soon followed by appearance of the active enzyme. Much the same is true in this species for the lactose-lactase and maltose-maltase combinations. In *Bacillus cereus*, a similar relationship has been demonstrated between penicillin and an enzyme which attacks it. But in this instance, unlike other bacterial examples, there appears to be some dauermodification: the enzyme is produced for a considerable time after removal to a penicillin-free medium.

Present opinion of students of enzymatic adaptation is that the genotype determines formation of the adaptive enzymes, but that they are produced in an inactive form when the appropriate substrate is not present. Addition of this substrate results in modification of the enzyme molecules to the active form, and these are then maintained autocatalytically, which thus establishes a possible connection of the phenomenon with cytoplasmic inheritance.

It is important to note that cytoplasmic inheritance can be identified only when the limits of nuclear inheritance are defined. The latter depends upon the regularities of sexual reproduction. For yeasts, this is no problem, for sexual reproduction is well known. But among bacteria, sexual reproduction has been demonstrated only for a single species, *Escherichia coli*. And even here, the evidence is purely genetic—recombination was shown to occur—and none of the cytological "facts" have been observed (but the science of bacterial cytology is getting under way). Hence inferences regarding nuclear heredity, and in consequence extranuclear heredity, are not on the same secure footing that characterizes our knowledge of heredity in sexual organisms. That some progress has been made in recent years in the study of genetics in this difficult field is indeed a tribute to those pioneers who have been bold enough to work in this field. But unusual caution and reserve of judgment are needed in interpreting their results.

54. EXAMPLES OF CYTOPLASMIC INHERITANCE

With so many possible sources of confusion, one may well ask whether he could ever have assurance that a character is cytoplasmically determined. Ernst Caspari has stated the criteria which must be met rather succinctly as follows: "Only when a certain character proves to be more or less constant in a series of backcrosses to the paternal strain, or when genic transmission is excluded by substitution of all chromosomes in a species, and dauermodifications are unlikely since no decrease in action of the cytoplasm appears in successive generations, evidence for cytoplasmic inheritance seems to be good, unless another interpretation of the facts can be found."[*] A fairly good number of cases are known which fit these criteria, and a few of these will be recounted below.

GYNODIOECY In *Cirsium*, a genus of thistles (fig. 122), most plants are monoecious, but purely female plants also exist, and these, of course must be pollinated by the monoecious plants, as there are no pure males. Such female plants for which corresponding males do not exist are said to be gynodioecious (Greek, *gynē*, female + sexes separate). Such females, pollinated by the monoecious plants, have only female offspring. In order to test whether genes for femaleness might be involved, Correns crossed the gynodioecious females to another species of *Cirsium* in which only monoecious plants exist, and which therefore seemed unlikely to carry any sex-differential genes. The offspring were still all females. They were then backcrossed to the male parental type for six successive generations, in the course of which all or most of the maternal chromosomes must have been replaced by those of the paternal species. But still, only female offspring were produced. Hence it is difficult to avoid the conclusion that femaleness must have been determined by the

[*] Advances in Genetics, vol. 2, p. 7, Academic Press, Inc., New York.

Fig. 122. *A thistle of the genus* Cirsium. (*Drawn from a specimen in the Greene Herbarium of the University of Notre Dame.*)

cytoplasm of the female parent, without any chromosomal influence whatever. It may be recalled that it is the cytoplasm which carries the female factor in *Lymantria* also.

INHIBITION OF POLLEN FERTILITY IN EPILOBIUM An interesting case in which reciprocal crosses between species give quite different results has been investigated in *Epilobium*, a genus of the evening primrose family. The principal species used were *E. hirsutum* and *E. luteum*. If *E. hirsutum* be used as the ovule parent and *E. luteum* as the pollen parent, then the F_1 is ovule fertile but pollen sterile. Such plants can be backcrossed to *E. luteum* as the pollen parent, but the offspring are more severely defective than were the F_1 plants. A repetition of the backcross yields plants which die in the seedling stage. It appears that *luteum* chromosomes and *hirsutum* cytoplasm form an unworkable combination, and the more *luteum* chromosomes there are present, the more severe the defect.

The reciprocal cross, *E. luteum* female $\times$ *E. hirsutum* male, can also be made. Such plants are fertile in both ovules and pollen, but pollen fertility is reduced as compared to that of either parent species. These hybrid plants (fig. 123), with *luteum* cytoplasm and chromosomes from each species, were then

Fig. 123. *Pollen sterility in* Epilobium F_1's. *Left, a flower with small stamens and high sterility; right, the reciprocal hybrid with normal stamens and normal fertility.*
(*From Michaelis, Acta Biotheoretica, vol. 11.*)

repeatedly backcrossed to *hirsutum*, so that the end product should be plants with only *hirsutum* chromosomes in *luteum* cytoplasm. As this series of backcrosses was made, the degree of pollen sterility gradually increased to a maximum of about 70 per cent. The first backcross generations showed typical Mendelian segregation of morphological characters, but after the eighth generation, the plants were practically identical with pure *hirsutum*, except for the pollen inhibition and a few physiological characters such as resistance to mildew. These characters in which the plants resembled *luteum* must have depended upon the cytoplasm, while the rest depended upon the chromosomes.

PLASTID CHARACTERS The plastids of plant cells are obviously self-reproducing units, and so it might be expected that they would show autonomous inheritance, independent of the nucleus. While many gene mutations are known which affect the plastids, still plastid inheritance was among the first cases of non-Mendelian inheritance to be demonstrated. For example, Correns studied a type of variegation which he called the *albomaculatus* type. In albomaculatus plants, the normal green foliage is splotched with white (or light green) as in figure 124. Entire leaves or even entire branches may be white or green. But the breeding behavior is the important feature for the present. Flowers on normal or on all white branches set seed true to the maternal type. But flowers on variegated branches set seed which may develop into any of three types: white, green, or variegated. The inheritance appears to be entirely matroclinal, as the pollen has no influence on the phenotype.

The most obvious hypothesis to explain these data is that the variegated flowers have two types of plastids, the normal greens and a deficient type which must have arisen by mutation. If both types are included in an ovule, a variegated plant results, whereas segregation of the two kinds into separate ovules results in all green or all white plants. Correns did not accept this explanation, as he thought that the rest of the cytoplasm caused the defect in the plastids, and there is some positive evidence for his theory. But closely similar cases are known in which the simpler explanation appears to be most

Fig. 124. *Albomaculatus phenotype in the nasturtium,* Tropaeolum majus. *(From Correns, Hb. der Vererbungswiss., II H.)*

probable. These are found in such diverse genera as *Pelargonium*, *Antirrhinum* (snapdragons), *Zea* (corn), and *Primula* (primrose). Correns' original material was the four o'clock, *Mirabilis jalapa*.

CO₂ SENSITIVITY IN DROSOPHILA A strain of *Drosophila* has been studied which is characterized by an unusually high degree of sensitivity to CO_2. All of the offspring of a sensitive female are sensitive, even if the father is resistant. Backcrossing sensitive females to resistant males yields only sensitive offspring, for however many generations the backcross may be repeated. That none of the chromosomes of the original sensitive female remain can be proven by the use of markers on the chromosomes of the male parental strain. As sensitivity is still maintained when only paternal strain chromosomes are present, there can be no doubt that the character depends upon the cytoplasm.

This case shows one outstanding difference from those described above: when a resistant female is crossed to a sensitive male, both resistant and sensitive offspring are produced, in varying proportions. It appears that the trace of cytoplasm brought in by the sperm can be sufficient to cause sensitivity, but often it is not. The substance which causes sensitivity has been separated from the cytoplasm. It is inactivated by high temperatures, and can be inoculated into resistant eggs to make them sensitive. Thus it seems to be a virus.

KILLER AND THE PLASMAGENES Perhaps the best known example of cytoplasmic inheritance is the "killer" characteristic of *Paramecium aurelia*, which has been investigated by T. M. Sonneborn and his collaborators. Some clones, called "killers," produce a substance called paramecin which, when released into the water, kills the members of other strains of the same species. Crosses between killer and sensitive strains show that the killer trait depends upon a single, dominant gene, *K*. The cross *KK* × *kk* yields heterozygous individuals, *Kk*, and clones derived from both exconjugants should show the killer character. The cross between two such heterozygous strains, *Kk* × *Kk*, should yield three killer clones to one sensitive.

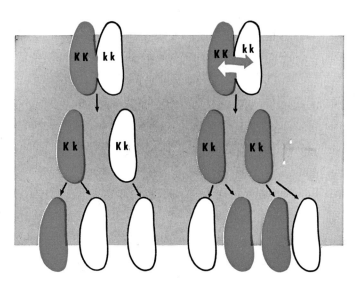

Fig. 125. *Inheritance of the killer characteristic of* Paramecium aurelia. *On the left is a cross* KK *x* kk *with brief conjugation. Descendants of the* kk *parent, although themselves* Kk, *are all sensitive, while both sensitives and killers are derived from the* KK *parent. On the right is shown a similar cross with prolonged conjugation and exchange of cytoplasm. All resulting progeny are killers, but sensitives segregate out in latter generations. (Modified from Sonneborn, in the American Scientist, vol. 37.)*

Up to this point, the applicability to cytoplasmic inheritance is not apparent. But let us return to the cross $KK \times kk$. All of the progeny should be killers. If conjugation is brief, however, the clone derived from the kk parent will be sensitive in spite of having the genotype Kk. On the other hand, prolonged conjugation leads only to killer strains. As the nuclear content of the exconjugants must be identical in both cases, the difference must depend upon the greater probability of exchange of cytoplasm during prolonged conjugation (fig. 125). The cytoplasmic factor necessary for the killer trait has been called *kappa*. Kappa can be maintained only in the presence of K. This can be demonstrated by studying kk clones produced from the cross $Kk \times kk$. If conjugation is prolonged, such clones at first have kappa and behave as killers. But they soon lose kappa and become sensitive. Nor can kappa be produced by K, as shown by the failure of production in one clone derived from the cross $KK \times kk$ after brief conjugation. Thus kappa is a self-reproducing particle which is, however, dependent upon a specific nuclear gene, K. Such cytoplasmic entities are called *plasmagenes*, and some geneticists broaden the term to include all self-reproducing bodies in the cytoplasm. Kappa has been shown to be particulate and to include DNA.

55. CONCLUDING REMARKS

The brilliant successes of Mendelian genetics for many years tended to direct attention away from the role of the cytoplasm in heredity. At first, the albomaculatus phenomenon and others which could not be interpreted except in terms of cytoplasmic heredity were regarded as rare exceptions, something of an embarrassment to the new science of genetics. The total number of verified examples still is not large (though much larger than the series reviewed in this chapter), but it is drawn from many taxonomic groups and concerns highly diversified phenotypes. In view of this, it seems probable that the phenomenon of cytoplasmic inheritance is one of general significance. It is not better known simply because investigation in this field is especially difficult, and numerous sources of error may be difficult to eliminate.

Cytoplasmic inheritance no longer appears isolated from the main body of genetic knowledge. On the contrary, current studies tend to emphasize the relationships between the nuclear genes and the plasmagenes (or other cytoplasmic factors, if one does not wish to use the term plasmagenes broadly). The relationship between K and kappa is especially illustrative here, with kappa depending upon K for its maintenance and K expressing its phenotype only through kappa. While some plasmagenes appear to be entirely independent of nuclear genes (sigma, the plasmagene for CO_2 sensitivity, for example), yet some degree of interrelationship is more usual. Such interrelationships have become a basic concept of physiological genetics, and even the orderly progress of embryonic differentiation has been interpreted on the basis of successive activation of different plasmagenes. For some geneticists, the plasmagenes are replicas of the nuclear genes, which are released into the cytoplasm, where they function as self-reproducing physiological agents. Thus the problem of the relationships between nuclear and cytoplasmic elements in heredity must be an important field for future research.

Questions and Problems

1. Define:

Albomaculatus	Maternal inheritance
Cytoplasmic inheritance	Paramecin
Dauermodification	Plasmagene
Enzymatic adaptation	Plastid
Gynodioecy	

2. Why has progress been so slow in the field of cytoplasmic inheritance?

3. How could one distinguish cytoplasmic inheritance from dauermodification?

4. How could it be proven that maternal inheritance is not cytoplasmically determined?

5. Explain the milk factor in mammary tumors of mice.

6. Could a permanent virus infection, transmitted via the eggs, be distinguished from cytoplasmic inheritance?

7. What properties do genes and viruses share?

8. Discuss in detail a well-verified example of cytoplasmic inheritance.

9. Discuss the killer factor and its inheritance in *Paramecium*.

10. Discuss the relationship between cytoplasmic inheritance and physiological genetics.

References

Braun, Werner, 1953. Bacterial Genetics. W. B. Saunders Co., Philadelphia. The first textual treatment of this new field.

Caspari, Ernst, 1948. Cytoplasmic inheritance. Advances in Genetics, 2:1–66. A clear and authoritative summary.

Correns, Carl, 1937. Nicht mendelnde Vererbung. Handbuch der Vererbungswissenschaft, 2 H:1–159. One of the codiscoverers of Mendelism recounts his long experience with cytoplasmic inheritance.

Ephrussi, Boris, 1951. Remarks on Cell Heredity. In Genetics in the 20th Century, pp. 241–262.

———, 1953. Nucleo-Cytoplasmic Relations in Micro-organisms. Oxford University Press, New York and London. A very helpful, brief treatise by an outstanding student of the genetics of yeasts.

Michaelis, P., 1954. Cytoplasmic inheritance in *Epilobium* and its theoretical significance. Advances in Genetics, 6:288–401. A long-time student of cytoplasmic inheritance reviews his work.

Rhoades, M. M., 1946. Plastid mutations. Cold Spring Harbor Symposia, 11:202–207. A brief report summarizing some of the author's research in relation to older literature on this subject.

Sonneborn, Tracy M., 1949. Beyond the gene. American Scientist, 37:33–59.

———, 1951. The Role of the Genes in Cytoplasmic Inheritance. In Genetics in the 20th Century, pp. 291–314. These two papers review the subject from the viewpoint of a leading student of protozoan genetics.

CHAPTER 19

Genetics
and Evolution

Man has always sought explanations for the enormous diversity among natural species of plants and animals, and for the fact that the million-odd species are not chaotic, but show varying degrees of similarity and difference to form systematic categories. The suggestion that these resemblances might depend upon descent from common ancestors has been made repeatedly since the time of the Greek philosophers. But scientific men remained unconvinced up to the middle of the nineteenth century, because no one had been able to suggest a sound, plausible mechanism by which evolution of diverse species from a common ancestor could be accomplished. Then in 1859 Charles Darwin published the "Origin of Species." In it he proposed a plausible theoretical basis for evolution, and he adduced a great mass of factual evidence in favor of his hypothesis. As a result, the great majority of competent scientists were soon convinced of the basic correctness of his hypothesis.

56. INTRODUCTORY CONCEPTS

As every course in elementary zoology or botany includes the elements of evolution, nothing more than a very brief review need be given here. For fuller information, the student is urged to read some of the references at the end of the chapter. As this is a much misunderstood subject, it may be well to begin by defining it. Darwin defined evolution as "descent with modification," so that resemblances between closely related species depend upon their common inheritance, while their differences depend upon hereditary differences (mutations) accumulated since the time of their last common ancestor. Stated in another way, this means that the species of plants and animals of any period have been derived from similar, previously existing species. No specific lines of descent are implied in these definitions.

THE THEORETICAL BASIS OF EVOLUTION The reasonable theory, developed by Darwin where his predecessors had failed so conspicuously, can be summarized quite briefly. First, all organisms reproduce in excess of the number of offspring that can survive (fig. 126). A single salmon may spawn as many as 128,000,000 eggs. A bullfrog lays around 20,000 eggs annually. *Ascaris lumbricoides* var. *suum*, a common parasite of hogs, has been observed to lay as many as 700,000 eggs in a single twenty-four hour period. It is obvious that 100 per cent survival of all of the young would soon lead to impossibly large numbers of any of these species. But much the same is true for organisms which reproduce slowly. The elephant is probably the slowest reproducer of all animals. Yet Darwin has calculated that the minimal rate of reproduction would, with survival of all young, result in no less than 19,000,000 living descendants of a single pair after 750 years! Obviously, if there were that many descendants from every pair of elephants breeding in the year 1200 A.D., the world could not hold all of the elephants, let alone any other organisms.

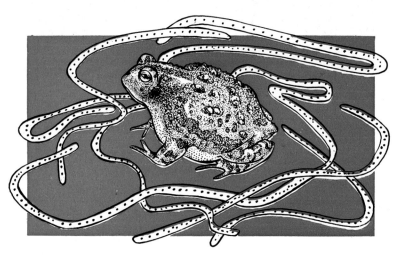

Fig. 126. *The prodigality of nature: a female toad and some of her spawn. The eggs are laid in a jelly string. Actual counts of the eggs in the spawn of individual females have ranged from 4000 to 12000 eggs.*

Nonetheless, adult populations in any area tend to remain approximately constant from year to year, and the differences between annual reproduction and actual populations must represent annual loss through predation, failure to secure necessary food or other requirements of life, disease, or other factors. Modern ecology has shown that natural populations are not so constant as Darwin thought. They may show considerable seasonal or annual fluctuations. But they always remain so far short of their reproductive potential that his argument is unimpaired.

Third, it is too much to expect that the surplus organisms will give up without a struggle. Each will make every possible effort to secure the means of life, to get a mate, and to leave progeny. But as most cannot reach maturity, there must be a severe struggle for the necessities of life.

Fourth, all organisms vary one from an-other, and so the competing plants and animals of any species will represent a wide array of variation (fig. 127). Even the proverbial peas in a pod differ noticeably. If any of these variations confer upon their possessors either an advantage or a disadvantage in securing the means of life and escaping enemies, this should influence their chances of surviving and leaving offspring. Hence this *natural selection* of organisms most fit for competition for the means of life should gradually change the characteristics of a species. The optimum conditions of competition will differ in different parts of the range of a widely distributed species, and

Fig. 127. *The effect of artificial selection upon pigeons. Above, a wild rock pigeon, from which all domestic varieties have been derived. Below, a pouter and a fantail, widely divergent varieties which have been produced by selection by breeders. (Redrawn from Romanes.)*

225

hence the species will tend to break up into distinct units.

DARWIN'S SUMMARY   This argument could scarcely be summarized better than in Darwin's own words. In chapter 3 of the "Origin of Species," he says, ". . . how is it that varieties, which I have called incipient species, become ultimately converted into good and distinct species, which in most cases obviously differ from each other far more than do the varieties in the same species? How do those groups of species, which constitute what are called distinct genera and which differ from each other more than do the species of the same genus, arise? All these results . . . follow from the struggle for life. Owing to this struggle, variations, however slight and from whatever cause proceeding, if they be in any degree profitable to the individuals of a species, in their infinitely complex relations to other organic beings and to their physical conditions of life, will tend to the preservation of such individuals, and will generally be inherited by the offspring. The offspring, also, will thus have a better chance of surviving, for, of the many individuals of any species which are periodically born, but a small number can survive. I have called this principle, by which each slight variation, if useful, is preserved, by the term natural selection. But the expression often used by Mr. Spencer, of the Survival of the Fittest, is more accurate, and is sometimes equally convenient. We have seen that man by selection can certainly produce great results, and can adapt organic beings to his own uses, through the accumulation of slight but useful variations, given him by the hand of Nature. But Natural Selection, we shall hereafter see, is a power incessantly ready for action, and is as immeasurably superior to man's feeble efforts as the works of Nature are to those of Art."

In this summary, Darwin speaks of inheritance. It is obvious that without inheritance of the varying characters of species, selection could accomplish nothing permanently, for the progeny of the most favorable variants of one generation might turn out to be the least fit competitors of the next generation. Darwin had confidence that there must be a regular and stable mechanism of inheritance, but in every edition of the "Origin," he retained the statement that "the laws governing inheritance are for the most part unknown." Filling this deficiency in evolutionary theory has been one of the major achievements of modern genetics.

FIELDS OF EVIDENCE FOR EVOLUTION   The most plausible of theories has little scientific value unless it can be tested. Darwin's success depended upon the great weight of detailed evidence which he marshalled in favor of his theory. This evidence was drawn from many fields of biological research, including domestication of plants and animals, bio-geography, taxonomy, comparative anatomy, embryology, and paleontology. While the relative emphasis on the different fields has changed, these are still the basic sources of evidence for evolution. These fall beyond the scope of the present book, but are adequately covered in the references at the end of the chapter. But to these one more must now be added, and this is genetics, a science unknown to Darwin. When Mendelism was rediscovered at the turn of the century, it was generally regarded as a stumbling block to evolution. The apparent permanence of the gene appeared to provide for recombinations of alleles already present, however it is seemed inconsistent with the origin of anything really new. But in recent years, genetics has achieved a central position in evolutionary theory. It is with this that the balance of the present chapter will be concerned.

57. THE DYNAMICS OF EVOLUTION

THE SOURCES OF VARIABILITY Darwin devoted a considerable portion of the "Origin," as well as several supplementary books, to the demonstration of variability within species. Variability is obviously the first requisite for evolution, because without it competition for the means of subsistence would lead to a reduction in numbers without, however, leading to any qualitative change in the makeup of a population. But equally important for evolution is the requirement that the causes of variability be hereditary, for otherwise the effects of selection from generation to generation could not be cumulative. On this aspect of the problem Darwin was handicapped by lack of knowledge of Mendel's work. In recent years, studies on gene mutation and chromosomal mutation have supplied the necessary data. These are the only known sources of *inheritable* variability, and they appear to be adequate to explain the observed diversification of species.

GENE MUTATION As the main facts of gene mutation were discussed in chapter 13, only some specific, evolutionary aspects need be added here. First, it should be mentioned that for many years, critics of the new science of genetics claimed that the mutants with which geneticists dealt were merely degenerate results of life under laboratory conditions. Hence, they argued, the results of genetic studies could not be applied to evolution, or to other problems of organisms in natural populations. This has been abundantly disproven, for the same mutations that geneticists first studied in the laboratory have been found in nature in such varied organisms as *Drosophila* and *Iris* (fig. 128).

However, there are some more serious objections to the type of mutation ordinarily dealt with by laboratory geneticists. Most of these are more or less obviously abnormalities, and their prospective fate in nature should be elimination by natural selection. This problem has been met in two ways. First, the rates of mutation in nature are sufficiently high (see chapter 13) to give assurance that practically all of the mutations which can occur with appreciable frequency in a particular species must have occurred many times over during its long history. Hence those mutations which have adaptive value under the conditions prevailing in recent times have long since been incorpo-

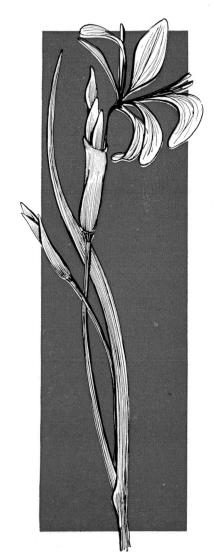

Fig. 128. *The blue flag,* Iris versicolor.
*(Drawn from a specimen in the
Nieuwland Herbarium of the University
of Notre Dame.)*

rated into the normal, wild type genotype of the species under the influence of natural selection. This of course does not preclude the inclusion of different alleles in the genotype of different populations of a species which are living under different conditions, nor does it preclude extensive heterozygosity.★ In summary then, the mutations which we see tend to be abnormal, because the more favorable ones have long since been incorporated into the wild type through the long-continued action of natural selection upon much the same array of recurring mutations.

This first point concerns only rather large, easily identified mutations. These necessarily form the basis of a large part of genetic research for the sake of simplicity, but the spectrum of mutation extends from very gross ones, including lethality and severe defects like vestigial wings, through moderate changes like color substitutions, to very minor ones which can be identified only by the use of special methods. Many geneticists believe that the smallest mutations, which

★ Because this is clearly true, Dobzhansky has recently objected to the use of the term "wild type," on the grounds that it tends to conjure up a picture of an ideal genotype and phenotype for each species, with actual individuals and populations appearing as accidental deviants from this ideal. While this criticism may be correct, still the term has some practical usefulness in describing the outcome of natural selection.

would be missed in the usual genetic experiment, are the ones which are most important for evolution. One reason for this is the unproved belief that a series of minor changes should be more harmoniously incorporated into a complex reaction system (i.e., the total genotype, leading as it does through a complex series of interactions to the adult phenotype) than should one or a few gross changes. Much more important is the fact that the subspecies of a single species and the species of a single genus generally differ from one another by a number of *quantitative* characters, and it has been shown (chapter 10) that such traits are ordinarily based upon swarms of genes, each having a very minor individual effect.

For example, Alden Miller has published a very thorough study of the species and subspecies of juncos (fig. 129). The twenty-one named forms in this genus of sparrows comprise nine species, some of which are broken up into a number of subspecies. These replace one another geographically, but they may interbreed where their ranges meet. The several subspecies of each species differ from one another in such typical quantitative ways as length of wing and tail, length of tarsus, intensity of color and extension of the hood. While no breeding tests were made, birds were taken which were most easily interpreted as natural hybrids. They showed the wide range of variability which is characteristic when many minor genes are segregating. Hence it was considered that multiple factor inheritance, with accumulation of many minor mutants, had played a major role in formation of these subspecies. And because the differences be-

Fig. 129. Junco hiemalis, *the eastern junco.*

228

Fig. 130. Viola tricolor. (*Drawn from a specimen in the Nieuwland Herbarium of the University of Notre Dame.*)

CHROMOSOMAL MUTATION   The various kinds of chromosomal mutations have already been described in chapters 12 and 14. It may now be pointed out that, like gene mutation, this phenomenon is a source of variability upon which natural selection can act. The pattern of synapsis of the chromosomes of hybrids between subspecies or related species often reveals that chromosomal rearrangements are among the differentiating factors. While this method is most readily applicable to *Drosophila* and other dipterans with giant chromosomes, still some positive results have been obtained in many groups. For example, two species of Japanese fishes have been found to differ by two translocations (fig. 131). Many species of insects show chromosomal differences which are most easily interpreted as small deficiencies and duplications. A study of synapsis of the salivary gland chromosomes in hybrids between *Drosophila melanogaster* and *D. simulans* revealed no less than twenty-four rearrangements differentiating the chromosomes of these two species, and others, too small for certain identification, were suspected! Other examples will be discussed below in relation to other topics.

tween the species were similar in kind, it was assumed that these had been formed by the same process acting for a longer time.

Again, when two subspecies of the wild pansy, *Viola tricolor* (fig. 130), were studied, it turned out that no less than nine or ten pairs of genes were involved in the determination of so simple a character as flower color, and other differences were similarly determined. The same process was found to characterize the differentiation of species.

THE STATISTICAL MODIFICATION OF POPULATIONS   Any new mutant must be rather rare when it first arises. Let us assume a breeding population of 500 animals, all

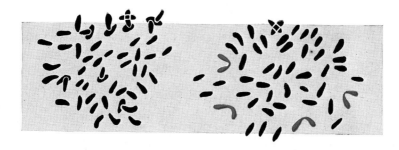

Fig. 131.   *The chromosomes of* Misgurnus anguillicaudatus *(left) and* Barbatula oreas, *closely related species of fishes from Japan. The first has 26 pairs of rod–shaped chromosomes, while the second has 22 rod–shaped pairs and two V–shaped pairs, shown in red. These probably represent unions of previously separate chromosomes. (Redrawn from Makino, Cytologia, vol. 12.)*

homozygous for a gene A, so that A is present 1000 times in the population. Now a single mutation of A to a occurs. The frequency of the mutant is then one in 1000, or 0.001. If a has high selective value, its prospective fate is to increase and become widely distributed through the population. But this can only occur through such processes as reproduction and further mutation, aided by natural selection. As these are finite processes which can be measured, the study of changes in gene frequency in populations has become a fundamental part of the study of evolution.

The starting point for studies of gene frequency is the Hardy-Weinberg Law. This law states that, if alternative forms of a gene are present in a population, and if all genotypes are equally viable, then the original proportions of the genes will be maintained in all subsequent generations. Let the frequency of one allele, A, be q, and that of the other, a, be $1 - q$, so that the sum of their frequencies is 1. Then in the F_2, the frequencies of the genotypes will be $[qA + (1 - q)a]^2 = q^2AA + 2q(1 - q)Aa + (1 - q)^2 aa$, and the frequencies of the genes will still be qA and $1 - qa$. In the typical monohybrid cross, $AA \times aa$, the values of q and $1 - q$ are both 0.5, which simply means that the two alleles are present in equal numbers. In the F_1, the two alleles are still obviously present in equal proportions, as one of each comprises each pair. Substituting numbers in the above equation for the F_2, we get $(0.5A + 0.5a)^2 = 0.25AA + 0.50Aa + 0.25aa$. As this is the familiar 1 : 2 : 1 genotypic ratio of elementary genetics, it is clear that the elementary Mendelian ratios are simply special cases of the Hardy-Weinberg Law. The two kinds of genes are still in a 1 : 1 ratio.

But in natural populations, gene frequencies are not likely to be those of laboratory experiments. The Hardy-Weinberg

Law is still fully applicable. If A is 0.8 and a 0.2, the formula would read $(0.8A + 0.2a)^2 = 0.64AA + 0.32Aa + 0.04aa$. As the sum of the frequencies of the three genotypes is 1, the calculation is verified. If this represented 50 organisms, there would be 100 genes, of which 80 would be A (all 64 genes of the 32 AA organisms, plus 16 genes from the 16 Aa organisms), while 20 would be a (all 4 genes of the 2 aa organisms, plus the other 16 genes from the Aa organisms). Thus the values $q = 0.8$ and $1 - q = 0.2$ are maintained.

This equation may be used another way to determine *gene frequencies* when phenotype frequencies are already known. Thus in a human population in which 84 per cent of the people are Rh-positive and 16 per cent Rh-negative, we know that $(1 - q)^2 = 0.16$, and hence $(1 - q) = 0.4$, and $q = 0.6$. Substituting these values in the equation, $(0.6 Rh + .4 rh)^2 = 0.36 RhRh + 0.48 Rhrh + 0.16 rhrh$. Again, the gene frequencies are maintained $(0.36 + 0.24 = 0.60,$ and $0.24 + 0.16 = 0.40)$.

In these examples, random mating has been assumed. In a preferential mating system, the proportions of genotypes would be altered, but the proportions of genes would remain the same. If, for example, people of the same Rh type tended to marry, the homozygotes would increase at the expense of the heterozygotes. But the values of q and $1 - q$ would remain the same. It may be seen then that the Hardy-Weinberg Law is a conservative factor in evolution, tending to maintain the status quo. No evolution would be possible unless some factors should upset the Hardy-Weinberg equilibrium. The major factors which have been discovered are mutation, natural selection, genetic drift, and migration. The last is beyond the scope of genetics, and so will be mentioned only in passing, but the first three will be discussed below.

MUTATION AND SELECTION It is obvious that, whenever a mutation occurs, there is an increase in the frequency of the mutant gene and a corresponding decrease in the frequency of its allele. If mutation were always in the same direction, as $A \longrightarrow a$, then even the slowest of mutation rates would eventually lead to 100 per cent incidence of a, unless this were prevented by a selective disadvantage. More commonly, mutation may go in either direction, $A \rightleftharpoons a$, but the two rates may be different. In this case, the final result would be an equilibrium, with the two alleles being present in the population in proportions determined by their relative rates of mutation. Whenever data adequate for the determination of these rates are available the equilibrium value is readily calculable.

Natural selection tends to eliminate those genotypes which are least able to compete for the means of life (fig. 132). But this is by no means an all-or-none phenomenon. No one generation sees all of the less fit lost and all of the more fit surviving. Rather, both suffer losses at all stages in the life cycle, but the more fit survive to reproductive age somewhat more often and succeed in leaving young somewhat more often. The result is a gradual shifting of the Hardy-Weinberg equilibrium in favor of superior genotypes.

Thus for every 1000 AA or Aa individuals that survive, only 999 aa individuals may survive. One may say then that the gene a is subject to a negative selection pressure of 0.001, or conversely that A is favored by a positive selection pressure of the same magnitude. The results of a selection pressure of this magnitude have been calculated. Assuming an initial gene frequency of one in a million, it would take 11,739 generations to double the frequency of a dominant mutant, or 321,444 generations to double the frequency of a recessive mutant. When genes are moderately frequent, selection works much more rapidly. But at very low or very high frequencies, change is very slow with mild selection pressures. Because of this, some geneticists feel that some supplementary process must be necessary.

One obvious suggestion is that actual selection pressures may be greater than those used in the calculations. This may be true for major genes, but, as explained above, most students of evolution feel that minor genes influencing quantitative traits are more important for evolution.

Mutation and selection, of course, occur simultaneously, and if both should go in the same direction, the effect might be a rather rapid change. Population size also has an influence on the rate of change produced by

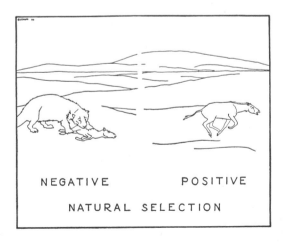

Fig. 132. *Natural selection. (From Simpson, Journal of the Washington Academy of Sciences, vol. 31.)*

NEGATIVE   POSITIVE

NATURAL SELECTION

selection, with moderate sized populations presenting the optimum conditions.

GENETIC DRIFT Some of the most fundamental genetic processes are random processes which derive their regularities from the mathematical laws of chance. Like all random processes, these are subject to sampling errors, and these may cause changes in gene frequencies from generation to generation without regard to the selective values of the alleles involved. Such a change due to sampling errors in the fundamental genetic processes is called *genetic drift*. Thus, in a monohybrid, gene *A* might be retained by the egg while *a* goes to the polar body, or the reverse might occur. In fertilization, whatever the egg might carry, if a sperm with *A* fertilizes the egg, then the sperm with *a* is lost, or vice versa. These are matters of chance. In large populations and with moderate gene frequencies, such chance fluctuations cancel out. But in very small populations, or where a rare gene is concerned, chance fluctuations due to sampling errors may produce important changes. This phenomenon is genetic drift, or the Sewall Wright phenomenon, after the man who has studied it most thoroughly.

Above, we postulated a population of 500 individuals, with a particular mutation occurring once, so that it was present to the extent of one gene in 1000. Even if this gene were favored by a strong selective pressure, it might, by chance be sloughed off into a polar body if it were in a female. Or it might be carried only by a sperm which failed to fertilize an egg. It would then be irretrievably lost, and no amount of selective advantage could restore it, unless a new mutation should occur. Or it might happen that ten sperm carrying the mutant gene would fertilize eggs, thus increasing its frequency very rapidly.

As every new gene must be rare when it first arises, it seems probable that genetic drift frequently impedes or aids the establishment of such genes in a population. But in small populations, the frequency of *any* gene may be subject to accidental fluctuations which swamp out the effects of any but the most severe selective forces. Nor are small populations so rare in nature as might be thought at first. Not only are there the permanently small populations of species approaching extinction, like the whooping crane, which now numbers only about twenty-four birds; and the small populations of species adapted to highly restricted habitats, like small mountain lakes or volcanic craters; but any species may go through seasons or years of scarcity. At these times, genetic drift may play a predominant role in determining the future genotype of the species. Stebbins has called this the "bottleneck" phenomenon.

THE STRUCTURE OF POPULATIONS It appears, then, that evolution must generally occur on the basis of changes in gene frequency in populations. The origin of new alleles must be by mutation. Their fate, however, is determined by natural selection, which in very large populations is too slow even if time be available on a geological scale; yet in very small populations, natural selection may be swamped out by genetic drift, leading to mal-adapted populations. Nevertheless, that evolution has generally led to a rather nice adaptation of organisms to their circumstances of life is one of the most striking facts of natural history. What is the nature of the natural populations, then, which has permitted the observed results? While most natural species comprise an enormous number of individuals at any one time, these do not all constitute a single, potentially interbreeding population. A widely distributed species is almost always broken up into a number of more-or-less isolated subspecies. Furthermore, each subspecies may occupy a rather considerable territory within which the population is not evenly distributed. Rather, it is broken up into a series of moderate sized local populations, and it is these which are the actual breeding populations. Simple proximity probably plays a larger role in the selection of mates than does any other factor. Presumably, these breeding populations are ordinarily too large to be dominated by genetic drift but too small to interfere with the effectiveness of natural selection. But the determination of critical population limits for these purposes is still in the future. Migration between populations, and interbreeding where different subspecies meet, tend to blur the lines between them but do not generally obliterate them.

SELECTION AND NON-ADAPTIVE CHARACTERS One of the common criticisms of the theory of evolution by natural selection of chance mutants is the fact that this should lead to ever-increasing nicety of adaptation of organisms to their conditions of life, yet the adaptive value of many characters of natural species is not evident if it exists. Whether such characters are actually non-adaptive is difficult to decide in specific instances. It must be remembered that the endocrine glands of vertebrates were thought to be functionless until recently. Nonetheless, there is a very good possibility that many characters are actually non-adaptive, and there are several genetic processes which tend to produce such characters. First, they may be pleiotropic effects of genes with other effects which do have selective value. Or they may have become fixed in a population by genetic drift. Or the gene concerned may be closely linked to another which has high selective value. Finally, the gene concerned may have had selective value under previous conditions, as in the case of the vestigial characters (limbs of snakes, vermiform appendix of man, etc.).

58. GENETIC ISOLATING MECHANISMS

Natural selection cannot operate upon single genes, but only upon whole organisms, which include constellations of genes. The various subspecies of a species do not differ from one another in an absolute way by the inclusion or exclusion of specific genes, but rather they differ in the *proportions* of the various genes in the collective genotype. There is normally some crossing between adjacent subspecies wherever they meet, with an interchange of genes resulting. If such an interchange were to be very extensive, it would swamp out the distinctions between the subspecies, and they would become one. Because the dominant school of evolutionary thinking today regards subspecies as the first stage in the formation of new species, the factors which tend to isolate subspecies, and finally species and higher groups, from one another are particularly important. Such isolating mechanisms may be classified into three categories: *restriction of random dispersal*, which prevents potential mates from meeting; *restriction of random mating*, in which potential mates do not interbreed even though they may meet; and *reduction of fertility*, so that crossing results in few offspring or none. As the first two are concerned with geographic, ecological, and behavioral problems, they are beyond the scope of this book. But the reduction of fertility is very much a genetic problem, and it will be taken up below.

INTERSPECIFIC STERILITY AND HYBRID STERILITY Although there is an immense literature on these phenomena, going all the way back to Aristotle, yet there are very few cases which have been successfully analyzed for the genetic factors which result in sterility. At the outset, it should be pointed out that sterility is not an all-or-none phenomenon. If a plant which normally sets 100 seeds sets only 50 in a particular cross, one may properly speak of a 50 per cent reduction in fertility. Actually, such reductions in relative fertility are quite common, especially among plants, and these offer more hope for analysis than do examples of absolute sterility.

Hollingshead and Babcock have analyzed a very interesting case of interspecific sterility in *Crepis*, a common weed. When *C. tectorum* is crossed to another species, for example *C. capillaris* (fig. 133), the outcome depends upon the strain of *tectorum* which is

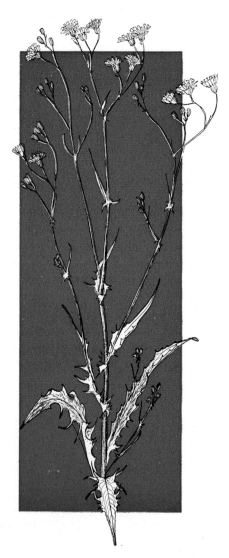

used. The F_1 from some strains is fully viable; that from other strains includes viable plants and plants which die as seedlings in a ratio of 1 : 1; and other strains give a progeny all of which die as seedlings. The evidence indicates that *tectorum* may carry a gene which behaves as a dominant lethal in interspecific crosses. The gene evidently functions harmoniously in the *tectorum* genotype, although no phenotypic effects in the pure species have been found.

A similar case has been analyzed by M. Gordon and others in tropical fishes. In the platyfish, *Xiphophorus maculatus* (*Platypoecilus maculatus* of older literature), there is a dominant, sex-linked gene *Sd*, which causes a black spot on the dorsal fin. This black spot is made up of macromelanophores, very large pigment cells which are capable of producing tumors. In the closely related swordtail, *Xiphophorus helleri*, only the recessive allele is known. These fishes can be hybridized (fig. 134). Hybrids of genotype *Sdsd*, having half of their chromosomes from each parent species, have more heavily pigmented fins than do homozygous *X. maculatus*, and these heavily pigmented fins may become tumorous. Backcrossing to pure *X. helleri* results in hybrids with genotypes predominantly derived from *X. helleri*, and half of these should also carry the gene *Sd*. In these, the pigment cells always produce tumors and cause the death of the fish. It may be seen, then, that the gene *Sd* pro-

Fig. 133. Crepis capillaris, *a common weed which has been the subject of a very fruitful series of genetic–evolutionary studies by Babcock and his collaborators.*

A

Fig. 134. *An interspecific cross in fishes. In part A are a male* X. maculatus *with the spotted-dorsal gene, and a female* X. helleri *with its normal allele. Part B shows the* F_1 *hybrids. The fish with the spotted-dorsal gene shows the trait in an extreme form, actually a melanotic tumor. (Courtesy of Dr. Myron Gordon, from Growth, vol. 10.)*

B

duces only a normal color variant in its proper genetic background; in the hybrid, it produces a more extreme variant of the same character, and it may become malignant; but in a genotype closer to that of *X. helleri*, it becomes lethal.

When sterile hybrids are studied cytologically, the most common finding is that the chromosomes fail to synapse at meiosis. The unsynapsed chromosomes are distributed at random, with the result that most gametes are inviable because they do not contain complete genomes. There is, however, always the possibility of occasional chance segregation of whole genomes in such divisions, and this should lead to a small percentage of viable gametes. This is probably the explanation of the rare instances of successful reproduction by mule mares. Also, complete failure of reduction divisions may lead to viable gametes in plants. These give rise to polyploid progeny.

CHROMOSOMAL REARRANGEMENTS AND HYBRID STERILITY There remains the fundamental question of why the chromosomes of interspecific hybrids fail to synapse. Where unrelated or remotely related species are concerned, simple lack of homology may be an adequate answer. But, if species are closely related, then by definition there should be a considerable degree of homology between their chromosomes. Some insight into this problem may be obtained by examining the chromosomes of those hybrids in which partial synapsis occurs. Such studies generally show that extensive chromosomal rearrangements cause a mechanical inhibition of synapsis. Thus a study of the salivary gland chromosomes of hybrids between *Drosophila melanogaster* and *D. simulans* showed that no less than twenty-four rearrangements, and possibly many more, differentiated the chromosomes of the two species. It is little wonder that synapsis was incomplete.

Yet this cannot be the whole story, as is shown by Dobzhansky's study of hybrids

between different races of *Drosophila pseudoobscura* and *D. persimilis*. Depending upon the particular races of the two species which are selected as parents, synapsis in the hybrid will be complete, partial, or it will fail altogether. If failure of synapsis were the whole cause of hybrid sterility, the first should be fully fertile, the second partially fertile, and the last entirely sterile. But this is not the case: in all three, meiosis is grossly abnormal and the hybrid is completely sterile. Obviously, there is a more fundamental physiological defect in the hybrids.

THE TRANSLOCATION COMPLEXES OF *Oenothera* The evening primrose, *Oenothera* (fig. 135), was one of the original plants studied by De Vries. While its study aided in the redemonstration of Mendel's laws, it soon became apparent that this plant is atypical in four respects. First, most species of the genus show only 50 per cent fertility as compared to *O. hookeri*, a member of the genus which does show typical genetic behavior. Second, when other species are crossed to *hookeri*, "twin hybrids" are produced, that is, there are two classes of offspring, in contrast to the usual uniform F_1. Third, although the twin hybrids demonstrate that the plants must be highly heterozygous, yet they breed true when self-fertilized (the usual mode of reproduction in the genus, except for *hookeri*, which is a cross-fertilized species). Finally, crossing over is rarely needed in interpreting *Oenothera* crosses, but when it does occur, it affects large blocks of characters, and the progeny are so different that they were at first regarded as mutants. They were called "half mutants" in early genetic literature, presumably because they affected half of the progeny.

Preliminary to explaining these unusual features of *Oenothera*, let us review and extend our discussion of translocations, with the aid of figure 136. The chromosomes may be identified by numbering their ends, so that the untranslocated chromosomes of 136A are 1·2 and 3·4, respectively. But when

Fig. 135. *An American* Oenothera. *(From
Cleland and Hammond, Studies in*
Oenothera *Cytogenetics and Phylogeny,
University of Indiana Press.)*

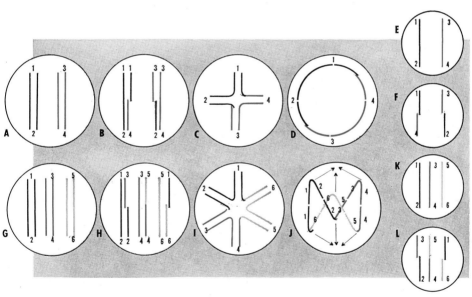

Fig. 136. *Meiotic behavior of translocation complexes. A, two pairs of untranslocated
chromosomes. B, a heterozygous translocation between two pairs of chromosomes.
C, pachytene configuration of the heterozygote. D, metaphase ring, with translocated and
normal chromosomes alternating. E and F, the two types formed by alternate
disjunction. G, three pairs of untranslocated chromosomes. H, a triple
translocation. I, pachytene in the complex translocation heterozygote. Note that the central
segment of each chromosome is not synapsed. J, early anaphase, showing alternate
disjunction of the chromosomes. K and L, the two types of
gametes formed by alternate disjunction.*

a translocation occurs, as in 136B, then there remains one normal chromosome of each pair, but their mates are the translocation products, 1·4 and 3·2. Because homologous point still synapses with homologous point, the translocated chromosomes, sharing homology with two different pairs, bind the tetrads together in a cross figure, as in 136C. In anaphase, alternate members of such a chromosome complex go to one pole, while the others go to the opposite pole. The result is that the two normal chromosomes go to one pole while the two translocated members go to the other pole, as in 136E and F. This is called alternate disjunction.

There is, of course, no reason why only two pairs of chromosomes should be involved in a translocation complex. Figure 136G to L illustrates the behavior of a translocation complex involving three pairs of chromosomes. Again, the specific nature of synapsis results in an alternating position of the normal and translocated chromosomes, and alternate disjunction then results in two types of gametes, one with all of the normal chromosomes, the other with all of the translocated chromosomes. Clearly, the limit to the number of pairs of chromosomes that might be involved in such a translocation complex is the haploid number of the species. O. hookeri has seven pairs of chromosomes, and these all synapse independently. But in some species of Oenothera, the entire set of fourteen chromosomes forms a single ring at synapsis. O. lamarckiana, the species with which De Vries dealt, has a ring of twelve and one pair.

All of the unusual features of the genetics of Oenothera are understandable in terms of the behavior of the translocation complexes, if a few additional details be added. Because of alternate disjunction, only two types of gametes are formed. This should lead to three kinds of zygotes upon self-fertilization, the two homozygous types and the hetero-

zygous type. Only the latter appears in the progeny, because each chromosome complex carries a different recessive lethal gene, so that the homozygotes cannot survive.

The complexes can be identified by crossing to O. hookeri and analyzing the cytological results. The translocated chromosomes are then identified according to the pattern of synapsis with the O. hookeri chromosomes. Each species carries two chromosome complexes, and these can be named. O. lamarckiana has the velans and gaudens complexes. As compared to O. hookeri, velans has the constitution 1·2, 3·4, 5·8, 7·6, 9·10, 11·12, and 13·14. The available data will permit either of two interpretations of the structure of the gaudens complex as follows:

1·2, 3·11, 5·6, 7·12, 9·4, 8·14, 13·10 or

1·2, 3·11, 5·6, 7·13, 9·14, 10·4, 12·8.

The balanced lethals, of course, account for the 50 per cent fertility of Oenothera species. Because the two chromosome complexes of a species are kept so highly separate, their genetic content is quite different, and this is responsible for the twin hybrids upon crossing to O. hookeri. The crossover anomalies result from the structure of the translocation rings, as in figure 136I. Notice that the ends of each chromosome are perfectly paired, but the central segment is kept out of contact with its homologue. Crossing over should occur freely in the paired arms, but these appear to be quite homozygous throughout the genus, so that crossing over is without effects genetically. But the central segments have become strongly differentiated and hence when crossing over rarely does occur, it produces strikingly different types, the half mutants of early genetic literature.

THE FAILURE OF ISOLATING MECHANISMS One of the important aspects of isolating mechanisms short of complete intersterility is that they may occasionally fail. And when they do, the relatively rare hybrids so produced are more likely to backcross to one of the parental types than they are to interbreed among themselves. The result is a slow interchange of genes between the parental species, thus increasing their ranges of variability. This phenomenon was first studied by Edgar Anderson, and he has called it *introgressive hybridization*, a rather imposing name for a fundamentally simple phenomenon. A very nice example is afforded by the sunflowers of California. Two species, *Helianthus annuus* and *H. Bolanderi*, have different ecological requirements, but they do meet in some areas, especially where the activities of man have produced "hybrid habitats," intermediate between the natural habitats of the species. In such areas, the majority of the plants are of one species or the other. But some hybrids are found. These have much reduced fertility, and very few F_2 plants are found. Backcrosses are frequent, and the fertility of the plants increases in each backcross generation, as the genotype more nearly approximates that of a parental species. Finally, both of the parental species in such areas have characteristics in common which are most easily understood on the basis of a slow interchange of genes via the hybrids and backcrosses.

59. POLYPLOIDY IN EVOLUTION

Polyploidy, the phenomenon of multiple sets of chromosomes, was introduced in chapter 14 as one type of chromosomal mutation. It was mentioned that this is common among plants, but rare among animals (presumably because it would upset the balance of the sex-differential chromosomes). Actually, polyploidy appears to be one of the mainsprings of evolution among plants. The first indication of this came about thirty-five years ago, when O. Winge made a comprehensive study of the chromosome numbers of flowering plants. He found that about half of the species studied had twelve or fewer chromosomes. Among those with higher numbers, most were integral multiples of the lower numbers, and prime numbers were conspicuously absent. He concluded that multiplication of whole sets of chromosomes, especially to form allopolyploids, must have been a major factor in the formation of plant species with large chromosome numbers.

POLYPLOID SERIES The chromosome numbers of various species of a genus are often highly suggestive. For example, different species of wheat have either 14, 28, or 42 chromosomes, all even multiples of 7, which is the haploid number of the first group of species. Chrysanthemums are known with chromosome numbers of 18, 36, 54, 72, and 90, all even multiples of 9. Tobacco generally has either 24 or 48 chromosomes, although other numbers are known in the genus. The possibility that such series are formed by doubling of the entire chromosome sets of the basic species is most alluring. But some of the data cannot be handled so simply. The chrysanthemum series ran 18—36—54—72—90. If an 18 chromosome species were doubled, it should give the 36 chromosome tetraploid. But doubling this would give the 72 chromosome octaploid. There seems to be no place here for the 54 chromosome, hexaploid, member of the series. Winge realized this, and he boldly postulated that such a species might have been formed by the doubling of the chromosomes of an originally sterile hybrid. Thus, the 18 chromosome species should produce pollen with 9 chromosomes, and the 36 chromosome species should produce ovules with 18 chromosomes. The hybrid between them would then have 27 chromosomes. Such a hybrid can be obtained, but it is highly sterile because the chromosomes cannot form a series of pairs at meiosis. But if the entire chromosome complement should double, then there would be 54 chromosomes comprising 27 perfectly matched pairs.

SPECIES SYNTHESIS However, the belief that polyploidy has actually played a major role in plant evolution does not rest on logical analysis of numerical series. It actually has been possible to duplicate the hand of nature in synthesizing some natural species, and other artificial species, unknown in nature, have been synthesized in the laboratory by means of allopolyploidy. The drug colchicine has been a very powerful aid in these experiments.

The artificial synthesis of the hemp nettle, *Galeopsis tetrahit*, by forming the allopolyploid from two diploid species of the genus was reviewed in chapter 14. In a similar way, the domestic tobacco, *Nicotiana tabacum* (2n = 48), was synthesized from two species having only 24 chromosomes. But the artificial *tabacum*, although morphologically indistinguishable from the natural species, was unsatisfactory in one respect: although it is fully fertile in crosses to natural *tabacum* when used as the male parent, it is female sterile. The marsh grass *Spartina townsendii* has 126 chromosomes, and it has been proved by resynthesis to be an allopolyploid derived from *S. stricta* (2n = 56) and *S. alterniflora* (2n = 70). In many other instances also, the resynthesis of natural species has been accomplished, thus removing all doubts of the origin of plant species by means of allopolyploidy.

Further, new species have been synthesized which are morphologically as distinct from their progenitors as are natural species, are fertile with their own kind, but are separated from the parent species by a sterility barrier. The case of *Raphanobrassica* was recounted in chapter 14. A hexaploid species of tobacco has been synthesized from a tetraploid and a diploid pair of parental species. And numerous new species of wheat have been synthesized.

60. CONCLUSIONS

A few years ago, Julian Huxley published a book entitled *Evolution, the Modern Synthesis*. This title is particularly appropriate, because the modern study of evolution does require a synthesis of data from all fields of biology, together with geology, paleontology, and a good many other fields. The present chapter has dealt almost exclusively with genetic aspects of evolution, because of the limitations of space. Yet it may be added that evolutionary research was stalemated for years until genetic research reached a level of development at which it could contribute knowledge of the *processes* of evolution.

SUMMARY As conceived today, the primary sources of the variability which forms the raw materials of evolution are gene mutations and chromosomal mutations. Both are inherited and are reshuffled into new constellations of characters on the basis of Mendelian heredity. These various phenotypes must then be tested by natural selection, and the ecological factors to which the organism is continually subjected constitute the major agencies of natural selection. The result is more extensive survival and reproduction for the better adapted, and relative restriction of the expansion of the less well adapted types. Because species are generally divided up into local populations living under quite different conditions, this leads to the formation first of subspecies, then of related but distinct species, and finally of even the highest categories.

There is not, of course, complete unanimity of opinion among students of evolution regarding the relative roles of the various factors in evolution, although there is a remarkable degree of agreement regarding the main aspects of the problem as reported above. It is perhaps best to leave the controversial details to more advanced works on evolution.

Questions and Problems

1. Define:

Allopolyploidy	Introgressive
Bottleneck phenomenon	hybridizat'on
Evolution	Isolating mech-
Genetic drift	anism
Hardy-Weinberg Law	Natural selection
	Species synthesis

2. Explain the theoretical basis of evolution.

3. What are the main fields of evidence for evolution?

4. Discuss the sources of variability which form the raw materials of evolution.

5. What evidence favors very small mutations as the main source of evolutionary variability?

6. Discuss the structure of breeding populations.

7. Under what conditions should a new gene become fixed in a population most rapidly?

8. By what means may various populations of a species become isolated from each other? Why should this have any importance for evolution?

9. Discuss fully the behavior of the gene *Sd* in crosses between the platyfish and the swordtail.

10. Explain how translocation complexes account for the genetic peculiarities of *Oenothera*.

11. It has been said that allopolyploidy is the most completely proven case of evolution. Enlarge upon this statement, taking either a positive or a negative viewpoint.

References

Babcock, Ernest B., 1947. The Genus *Crepis*. Part I. The Taxonomy, Phylogeny, Distribution, and Evolution of *Crepis*. University of California Press. One of the most thorough studies ever published upon a single genus. The genetic viewpoint predominates throughout.

Clausen, Jens, 1951. Stages in the Evolution of Plant Species. Cornell University Press, Ithaca. A very clear and persuasive genetic-evolutionary study of several West Coast genera.

Darwin, Charles, 1859. The Origin of Species. Modern Library Giants Series. Still the foundation of modern evolution, this book will repay careful study.

De Vries, Hugo, 1906. Species and Varieties. Their Origin by Mutation. Open Court Publishing Co., Chicago. This is the major English language work by this distinguished Dutch student of genetics and evolution.

Dobzhansky, Th., 1951. Genetics and the Origin of Species. Third edition. Columbia University Press. This is a classic. The first edition inaugurated the modern genetic study of evolution.

Dodson, Edward O., 1952. A Textbook of Evolution. W. B. Saunders Co., Philadelphia. If you have enjoyed your genetics book, you might like this one too.

Goldschmidt, R. B., 1940. The Material Basis of Evolution. Yale University Press, New Haven. The major dissenter from the dominant school of evolutionary thought states his viewpoint.

Gordon, Myron, 1951. Genetic and Correlated Studies of Normal and Atypical Pigment Cell Growth. Growth, Symposium 10:153-219. This paper summarizes the fascinating work on production of tumors in hybrid fishes.

Mayr, Ernst, 1943. Systematics and the Origin of Species. Columbia University Press, New York. Evolution as seen by a taxonomist.

Miller, Alden H., 1941. Speciation in the Avian Genus *Junco*. University of California Publications in Zoology, 44:173-434. This is a very thorough systematic-evolutionary study of a genus of common birds.

Simpson, G. G., 1953. The Major Features of Evolution. Columbia University Press, New York. The viewpoint of a genetically minded paleontologist.

Stebbins, G. L., 1950. Variation and Evolution in Plants. Columbia University Press, New York. A comprehensive treatment of problems of evolution in plants.

Winge, O., 1917. The chromosomes, their number and general importance. Comptes-Rendus des Travaux Carlsberg Lab., 13:131-275. This is the paper which first established the importance of polyploidy in plant evolution.

CHAPTER 20

Genetics in the Service of Agriculture

Plant and animal breeding were already old sciences when genetics appeared on the scene, yet they may very well be regarded as applied genetics. From the first days of agriculture, farmers have realized that better crops and more productive animals should be obtainable by using only their best stock for breeding. The Greek poet Theognis (520 B.C.) wrote of the care with which farmers selected their breeding stock.

61. PRE-MENDELIAN BREEDING METHODS

Actually, the achievements of pre-Mendelian breeders were considerable. In the year 1900, there probably was not a domestic plant or animal to be found that was not vastly different from its wild ancestors, and the differences undoubtedly were generally improvements from the viewpoint of man. Innumerable varieties had been developed which were suited to diverse localities. But the armamentarium of the breeders was extremely limited, and improvement of agricultural plants and animals has proceeded very much more rapidly since the application of genetics to the practical problems of breeding.

SELECTION The entire biology of the latter half of the nineteenth century was dominated by Darwinism, and so it is natural that *mass selection* should have been the principal tool of the breeder. This means that large progenies were raised, and then the best were selected for further breeding. But the population—not the individual—was the unit of selection. Often this simply meant that the poorest stock was culled. Nonetheless, over a period of many years, a great deal was accomplished by this method.

As a result of many exploratory crosses between local varieties, named breeds and varieties of livestock and plants arose. Once established, the purity of such stock was often highly valued. Efforts to improve them were made principally through mass selection, but some modified types of selection were also used. In corn breeding, for example, superior ears were selected, then all of the seed from a single ear was planted in one row. By comparison of rows, it was possible to get a better check on the performance of specific lines of descent by this *ear-to-row* method than by simple mass selection. It had the advantage that one could keep track of the female parents over a series of generations tested. But it provided no control of the pollen parent.

PEDIGREE SELECTION The value which was placed upon named breeds and varieties (like Holstein-Friesian cattle and White Federation wheat) led to the *pedigree selection* method of breeding, which was designed to maintain the purity of breeds as well as to improve them. In this method, an attempt was made to control all matings, so that the exact pedigree of every animal or plant culture was known. Then the best of each generation was used to breed the next generation.

All of these methods did produce results. But they were often very puzzling to the breeder. In the pedigree method, for example, it was assumed that two horses of identical ancestry ought to be identical, at least in their major characteristics. Yet every breeder saw the results—then inexplicable—of genetic recombination in his pedigreed stocks. They knew that heredity had to be the basis of breeding, yet the elementary principles of heredity were not available for their use. Jay L. Lush, a pioneer of animal breeding, has expressed the dilemma of the breeders of those days with a memory from his early days in college: "I remember being told that the first principle of animal breeding was: like produces like; while the second principle was: like does not always produce like!"[*]

62. MODERN BREEDING

Modern plant and animal breeding utilize virtually all of the principles of genetics, and indeed not a few of those principles were originally discovered by practical breeders. As a result, an adequate treatment of this subject would be a whole book, a textbook of genetics written from the viewpoint of agriculture, like the excellent book of Babcock and Clausen, which is cited at the end of this chapter. All that will be attempted here is to show that genetics is a highly practical science which is intimately related to the welfare of man.

It must not be thought that selection has been replaced by newer methods. It has merely been refined. Under the influence of genetics, breeders no longer select for an ill-defined general superiority, but rather they select for specific genotypes, or at least for specific character complexes.

THE OBJECTIVES OF PLANT AND ANIMAL BREEDING The primary objective of breeders is to provide adequate food for mankind. Obviously, this places great importance upon such quantitative characters as yield of crop plants, annual egg production of chickens, gallons of milk yielded annually per cow, or per cent of butterfat in the milk.

[*] Dunn, Genetics in the 20th Century, 1951. By permission of the Macmillan Company.

Related to yield may be such characters as resistance to disease and insects. But other characteristics may be equally important, for food must be palatable as well as abundant. Hence good table characteristics of flavor, texture, and color must be sought. For grain, this will include flour and baking characteristics. For fresh fruits, it may include ability to withstand shipping to distant markets without deteriorating or becoming badly bruised. For many fruits and vegetables, canning characteristics are important, and in recent years, freezing characteristics have become important. Nutritive values, such as vitamin content and protein content, must also be considered. So many objectives cannot be achieved at once, and so the breeder must strive not for an ideal, all-purpose product, but for a plant or animal well suited for a specific purpose.

Further, an excellent plant or animal for one locality may be a very poor one for another locality. Thus the hybrid corn varieties which are excellent for Iowa may fail in the southwest, under completely different conditions of soil and climate. Similarly, the Hereford and Shorthorn beef cattle, which thrive in the north central and northwestern states, do not stand up well in the heat and drought of the cattle country of south Texas.

But it is not food alone for which the breeder is asked. Lumber was, until recently, taken unmodified from the hand of nature. But in recent years, forest genetics has become an important science, and new varieties of trees have been developed and grown as crops. Many plants are valued as the sources of drugs. These may be of great therapeutic value, like quinine or the antibiotics. Or they may be cultivated primarily for pleasure, like tobacco. Or plant products may be used for both of these purposes, like alcohol. Finally, many plants are used primarily for their beauty. All of these values are made more readily and more abundantly available through the breeder's art. Genetics is an eminently practical science.

MAJOR CONTRIBUTIONS OF GENETICS TO BREEDING Here we are concerned not so much with specific accomplishments as with principles. Perhaps the first major principle of genetics to aid the practical breeder was the basic fact that heredity depends upon stable units, the genes. In the pre-Mendelian days, the blending theory of inheritance was generally accepted. Accordingly, it was expected that a breed should become ever more and more uniform. As this did not happen, it was necessary to assume a very high mutability and a mysterious tendency to revert to ancestral characteristics (atavism). These anomalies were easily understood after 1900, on the basis of stable genes together with a second basic principle, the independent assortment of characters and the consequent segregation of recessives.

Third, elementary genetics made it clear why organisms with identical pedigrees need not have identical hereditary constitutions. Segregation provides for different genotypes within a single progeny. Hence it would be possible, even though most improbable, for two litter mates to share no genes in common. Finally, genetics revealed the possibilities inherent in recombination of factors as a source of variability to supplement mutation.

SOME ACHIEVEMENTS OF THE BREEDERS Even monohybridism has found some successful applications in breeding. For example, the fat of beef cattle may be either white or yellow. This depends upon the presence or absence of a specific enzyme which breaks down yellow pigments of the food into colorless compounds. The dominant gene Y causes the enzyme to be present, while its recessive allele, y, prevents formation of an active enzyme. While neither gene influences the flavor or nutritional value of the beef, yellow fat is regarded as an undesirable market character for esthetic reasons. When a breeder finds it in his herd, he can eliminate it by simple steps. All cows and bulls which have produced yellow fatted calves are known to be heterozygous, hence they can be withdrawn from the breeding stock. And normal relatives of yellow fatted calves can be tested by backcrossing to homozygous yellows. Only those which prove to be of genotype YY should be used for further breeding. Again, there is a very simple relationship between vitamin A content of corn and the number of genes for yellow endosperm. It may be recalled that the endosperm is triploid, and hence the possible genotypes are yyy, Yyy, YYy, and YYY. The first of these genotype subserves only a trace of vitamin A, while each Y adds about 2.5 units per gram of grain.

The breeder may in some instances produce the mutations with which he works. Thus M. Demerec x-rayed *Penicillium notatum* and so produced a mutation which resulted in a four-fold increase in production of penicillin. Demerec's strain of *Penicillium* is now the usual basis of the commercial production of this valuable drug. Induced mutations have been studied fairly extensively in barley, and some have been found to increase yields by a few percent. But generally, the value of experimentally induced mutations for plant and animal breeding has yet to be explored.

COMBINATION BREEDING This subject was introduced in chapter 4 in connection with dihybridism. It was defined as the crossing of different varieties in order to obtain new pure breeding strains with a combination of desired characteristics from both parental stocks. It was pointed out that Mendel himself used this method in order to improve the peas available to his monastery. Among the early Mendelian breeders, Nilsson-Ehle was perhaps the first to urge the importance of this method. He emphasized the importance of making crosses to combine specific characters, not simply to

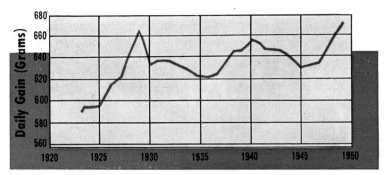

Fig. 139. *Daily gain of pigs in Danish testing stations from 1923 to 1949. Note that the gain fell off when the breeding objectives were changed from economy of gain to quality of carcass about 1928.* (*Modified from Lush, in* Genetics in the 20th Century, *The Macmillan Co.*)

which has been persistently attacked at Svalöf is the improvement of Swedish cereal crops. The results have been great, but of course not all of the increased yield has been due to genetics. Improved methods of cultivation, use of fertilizers, and mechanization of farming have all made important contributions. But it has been possible to assess the contribution of plant breeding by growing the new varieties and the old unimproved varieties side by side under identical conditions. Estimates of the amount of the improvement which is due to plant breeding vary from 12 to 25 per cent of the total improvement, depending upon the particular grain tested. Muntzing estimates the annual value of the increase due to plant breeding as 78,000,000 Kroner for cereal crops alone. Comparable figures are not available for other crops, but Müntzing estimates, very conservatively, that the total annual value of the plant breeding program in Sweden must be at least 100,000,000 Kroner ($20,000,000). Yet the total cost of the Svalöf station from 1886 to 1948 was only 15,000,000 Kroner, only 15 per cent of its minimum annual yield from plant breeding alone!

Finally, some examples may be given of quantitative improvements in livestock. Figure 137 shows a record of the butterfat content of milk from purebred Friesian cows in the Netherlands from 1906 to 1945. Notice that there has been a steady rise over this long period. It is interesting to compare this with figure 138, which shows total production of milk and butterfat as well as percentage of butterfat of Holstein-Friesian cows in the United States. Notice that percentage of butterfat again shows a steady increase, but total production fell off during the war years. Undoubtedly this resulted from poorer care, poorer feed, and other war-caused shortages. It also shows that the butterfat content of the milk is less influenced by environmental factors than is total productivity.

Figures 139 and 140, which are based upon records of pigs in Danish testing stations, are particularly interesting because they show changes which are correlated with changed objectives on the part of the breeders. Until the late 1920's, just gross gain with maximum economy was sought. But then a change in competitive markets made it necessary to emphasize quality of the carcass. With reduced selection for growth rate, it fell off. But meanwhile thickness of the backfat decreased, while the thickness of the belly and the length of the body increased. These are good market qualities. In each case, the changes were in the direction of selection.

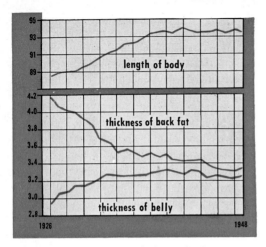

Fig. 140. *Twenty years of selection for changes in market qualities of pigs in Danish testing stations. (Modified from Lush, in Genetics in the 20th Century, The Macmillan Co.)*

CONCLUSION   Thus we see that the application of genetics to the problems of plant and animal breeding has greatly increased the rate of progress in these fields. As this has been a short term development, there is every reason to believe that the greatest achievements of the breeders are still in the future. The demands of man for greater quantities of food grow by the day. As Arne Müntzing has said, "consistent breeding work on this basis is the best way so far known to protect humanity from starvation."*

Questions and Problems

1. Define:

Combination breeding	Inbreeding
Ear-to-row selection	Mass selection
Heterosis	Pedigree selection

* Genetics in the 20th Century. 1951, The Macmillan Co., New York.

2. Agricultural experiment stations are costly. Can you give evidence that this expenditure is a sound investment of public money?

3. Why has plant and animal breeding been more productive since the turn of the century than before?

4. Discuss the breeders' objectives.

5. Discuss the proposition that plant and animal breeding is largely the application of the principles of quantitative inheritance to domestic plants and animals.

6. Can you cite any notable exceptions to the principle stated in question 5?

7. Why don't animals of identical pedigree show identical phenotypes?

8. From a breeder's viewpoint, why is it desirable to propagate fruit trees by vegetative cuttings?

9. Cite examples, other than hybrid corn, in which the exploitation of hybrid vigor has yielded valuable results.

10. How can seedless watermelons be produced?

References

Babcock, E. B. and R. E. Clausen, 1927. Genetics in Relation to Agriculture. Second edition. McGraw-Hill, New York. An old book, but still a very valuable treatment of genetics with emphasis on breeding problems.

Lush, Jay L., 1945. Animal Breeding Plans. Collegiate Press, Ames, Iowa. A textbook of animal breeding by a long-time leader in the field.

———, 1951. Genetics and Animal Breeding. In Genetics in the 20th Century, pp. 493–525. A review of some of the most salient facts.

Müntzing, Arne, 1951. Genetics and Plant Breeding. In Genetics in the 20th Century, pp. 473–492. An excellent brief review.

Stakman, E. C., 1947. Plant diseases are shifty enemies. American Scientist, 35:321–350. Deals with the mutability of plant pathogens and the problems of breeding resistant varieties.

CHAPTER 21

Human Genetics

Since the earliest days of genetics, efforts have been made to apply Mendelian principles to man. It was soon learned that a few normal traits and more pathological traits were inherited on a simple, monofactorial basis. This was made the basis of a premature campaign for eugenic legislation which was characterized by more enthusiasm than factual basis. As a result, human genetics fell into disrepute. Young geneticists did not wish to specialize in a field of dubious standing which offered very little opportunity for experimental work.

Meanwhile, the work of Landsteiner and others on the blood groups, although starting with serology rather than genetics, demonstrated the importance and the practical usefulness of genetics in this important field of medicine. Snyder established a course in medical genetics at Ohio State University, and several other medical schools followed suit. Heredity clinics have been established at a number of universities, outstanding among which are those at the University of Michigan and the University of Minnesota. Gradually, an extensive body of verified information on the genetics of man has been accumulated, and the field may be said to have come into its own with the founding of the American Society of Human Genetics in 1948. Today's student of human genetics is both better informed and more conservative than his predecessors of half a century ago. It will be the purpose of the present chapter to discuss some of the important aspects of human genetics.

63. DIFFICULTIES IN STUDYING HUMAN GENETICS

EXPERIMENTATION VS. PEDIGREES   The progress of human genetics was much slower than that of general genetics partly because there are many serious difficulties which must be overcome in the study of human genetics. The first of these is certainly the fact that the experimental method is not available. When a geneticist working with any other material is confronted with a problem, he sets up a series of experimental crosses to get the data for the solution of his problem. A human geneticist cannot do this. Instead, he must collect pedigrees of families some members of which show the trait under study. Even an extensive pedigree might fail to include a critical cross, necessary to test an hypothesis. But most pedigrees are not very extensive. Some times it is possible to get sound information on only one or two generations, and it is rarely possible to include more than four generations.

Another serious difficulty of the pedigree method is the fact that often—usually—much of the information must be obtained by interviewing members of the families under study. Such information is not always reliable. For example, in a recent study of inheritance of susceptibility to poliomyelitis, families of children admitted to the hospital and diagnosed by the most modern methods were interviewed. Many instances were found in which parents or aunts and uncles had had some crippling disease, but no diagnosis was available. In many instances, the attending physician was no longer living. In another instance, the attending physician was still living, but he had retired and destroyed all of his records, and he had no memory of the case.

Families are sometimes eager to help promote the understanding of any anomaly which has plagued some of their number. But frequently families are most uncooperative, and try to impede the study. This seems to be based upon two premises, both of which are false. First, there is a widespread belief that an hereditary anomaly is necessarily incurable, an inexorable curse. Naturally, anyone who believes this will be loath to acknowledge any such hopeless thing in his family. But such an attitude is unjustifiable. As was shown in chapter 16, genes operate through ordinary physiological channels, and gene-caused anomalies of function are, at least potentially, subject to treatment just as are all other physical disorders. And where successful treatment has not yet been found, every increase in knowledge increases the probability of finding such a treatment.

Second, many people feel that an hereditary anomaly is particularly disgraceful, and so they conceal information from the investigator. They should realize that no person can influence the constitution of the zygote from which he develops, nor of the gametes which he transmits. Recessive deleterious genes are so common that probably everyone carries some in the heterozygous state. And probably every family, if followed out far enough, would show some unfortunate segregants. There is no personal guilt here. On the other hand, non-genetic anomalies are in many instances caused by the stupidity of persons now living. Hence if any disgrace does attach to an anomaly, it should not be to those of genetic origin. And again, ever-increasing knowledge is the first requisite for successful treatment.

SMALL SIZE OF FAMILIES Experimental genetics depends upon the raising of large

progenies, which may approximate the Mendelian ratios rather closely. But even the largest of human families are so small that accidents of sampling are likely to mask any ratio whatever. This can be compensated for to some degree by *pooling* the data from many comparable families. But it is often very difficult to gain reasonable assurance that a large series of marriages are genotypically identical, even if only a single pair of genes is under study. Hence it is necessary to use complex statistical methods to extract a minimum of information from the small samples of data available.

DIFFICULTIES OF DIAGNOSIS Frequently, groups of diseases which are very similar or even identical clinically may be very different genetically. Thus glaucoma, a very serious disease of the eyes, has been reported in both dominant and recessive, sex-linked and autosomal forms. In addition to all of these, it may occur in a non-hereditary form. But all are identical clinically. In other instances, like muscular dystrophy, it may be possible to distinguish the different hereditary forms clinically, if the attending physician is alert to the possibility and is interested. Obviously, a pedigree will be misleading unless persons labeled the same actually carry the same gene. And this is possible only if each case is diagnosed accurately, and preferably diagnosed by the same person. This is not often possible when a pedigree extends over several generations. Further, diagnostic methods change from time to time, and different methods do not always give comparable results.

PENETRANCE In a population homozygous for a mutant gene, sometimes only a limited percentage actually show the trait. Thus if a culture of *Drosophila* is homozygous for the gene for nicked wings (fig. 141), only about 3 per cent of the flies show the character, while the rest are phenotypically normal. One says that the gene has a *pene-*

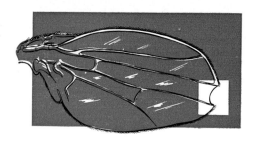

Fig. 141. *Nicked wing, a very low grade vestigial allele, which is characterized by reduced penetrance.*

trance of 3 per cent. It can be easily demonstrated that the normal and nicked progenies are genotypically identical, because the same results are obtained again if the normals are crossed together, or if the nicked flies are crossed together, or if normals and nicked are crossed. In all three crosses, progenies are obtained which have 3 per cent of the flies nicked. The penetrance of a gene may vary all the way from 0+ to 100 per cent. The genes of the older studies all had high penetrance because they were the easiest to understand, and so had to be mastered before progress could be made in more difficult problems.

The explanation of reduced penetrance is that the entire genotype tends toward the development of a normal organism, while the mutant gene simply acts as a differential factor to change the course of development in some small way. The mutant may fail to overcome the normalizing effect of the residual genotype, and so the penetrance is reduced. As it is sometimes expressed, they have the ticket (genotype), but they miss the boat (phenotype).

In man as in other organisms, genes may have reduced penetrance, but the experimental crosses cannot be made to clarify the situation. Obviously, this will complicate the interpretation of pedigrees considerably. A dominant gene with low penetrance may be confusable with a recessive, and other kinds of confusion are easily possible.

Another problem of penetrance in man is that of diagnostic criteria. For example, one recent study of the inheritance of susceptibility to polio used permanent paralysis (fig. 142) as the diagnostic criterion. This led to the conclusion that the gene showed about 30 per cent penetrance. In another study, a positive diagnosis by spinal tap was used as the diagnostic criterion, and this led to the conclusion that the penetrance was nearly 100 per cent. Again, gout is based upon a dominant gene which causes a dis-

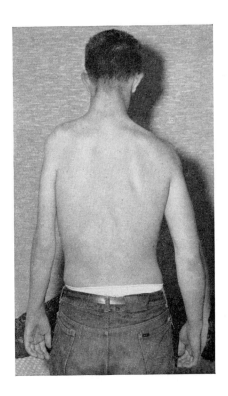

Fig. 142. *Residual effects of poliomyelitis. Note the great asymmetry of the shoulders and the withered left arm. (Courtesy of Dr. John J. Reedy.)*

turbance of nucleic acid metabolism. Uric acid rises to an abnormally high level in the blood and may crystallize out in the joints, causing the painful symptoms of gout. As measured by the latter, the gene shows a rather low penetrance, but it shows around 100 per cent penetrance as measured by the increase in blood level of uric acid.

The whole range of penetrance is known in man. Thus the gene for leukemia shows less than 1 per cent penetrance. The gene for diabetes mellitus has a penetrance of around 10 per cent, while that for multiple exostoses, a bone disease, has a penetrance of 60 per cent. Finally, the blood group genes show 100 per cent penetrance.

EXPRESSIVITY Frequently one and the same genotype may be expressed in different degrees in different individuals, or even on opposite sides of the same individual. To such variable expression of a single gene, the name *expressivity* is given. The gene for crossveinless in *Drosophila*, for example, causes defective development of the cross-veins of the wings. But the defect may range from a barely detectable interruption to complete absence. This at once suggests the possibility that multiple alleles may be involved, but an appropriate series of experimental crosses shows that only one gene, with variable expressivity is involved. In man, brachydactyly is inherited on the basis of a single dominant gene. This is an abnormality in which one or more segments of

the fingers are abnormally short, or even missing (fig. 143). The number of fingers affected is variable. That it is a matter of expressivity rather than of multiple alleles is clear because the two hands of one person may differ in this respect. But in other cases, it may not be so clear, and data involving variable expressivity may be extremely difficult to interpret.

Penetrance and expressivity are often confused, and so it may be well to contrast them. Penetrance is a population characteristic, concerned with the proportion of organisms with a particular genotype which actually shows the trait concerned. Expressivity is an individual characteristic, concerned with the extent of expression of a gene in a single individual.

PHENOCOPIES This subject was discussed at length in chapter 16. It need only be pointed out that man, like all other organisms, is subject to phenocopies. Epilepsy may be based upon hereditary factors, but it can also be produced by head injuries. Cataracts may be based upon a dominant gene, but they may occur as phenocopies after an attack of German measles. Heart defects may be caused genetically or by anxiety states. The statement was made in chapter 16 that probably any gene whatever could be mimicked by a phenocopy if an appropriate experimental agency were chosen. No doubt this is true for man, too. But the phenocopying agents are not always un-

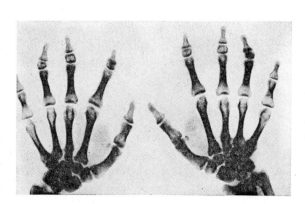

Fig. 143. *Brachydactyly. Note the great reduction of the middle segment of each finger. Compare this with figure 48. (From Komai, in the* Journal of Heredity, vol. 44.)

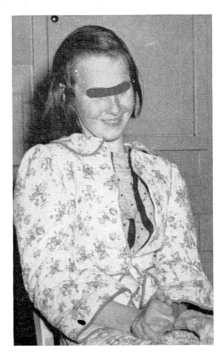

Fig. 144. *This girl is suffering from Huntington's chorea. The early age of incidence in her case leads to a very poor prognosis. (Courtesy of Dr. John J. Reedy and Dr. Hans Mautner.)*

derstood, and this of course leads to misinterpretation of pedigrees.

AGE OF INCIDENCE   Not a few inherited characters make their appearance rather late in life. Huntington's chorea (fig. 144), for example, is a disease which begins with loss of muscular coordination and control and leads to mental deterioration. It is inherited as a simple dominant. But the disease rarely strikes before thirty-five or forty years of age. A carrier for this gene might very well die from other causes at an earlier age, and would then appear in a pedigree as normal. And by that time, he might have had several children. Similar considerations apply to cancer. Many studies prove that specific types of cancer are hereditary in lower mammals. The same has been demonstrated for some of the less common types of cancer in man. But the picture is less clear for the more common types, and the fact that they ordinarily strike late in life may well be one reason. Many a carrier dies of a very different cause long before he has an opportunity to develop the genetic cancer.

64. ADVANTAGES IN STUDYING HUMAN GENETICS

In spite of the numerous disadvantages which one encounters in the study of human inheritance, there are some advantages. The first of these by far is the fact that man is the best known of all organisms. Whatever one may wish to study he may be assured that

there is already a considerable body of related literature. It may not be genetically oriented, but it is available and helpful. If one wishes to study inheritance of susceptibility to a particular disease, for example, he may find no previous literature on the genetic aspect of the problem, but he is sure to find literature on the disease itself.

Further, because man has long taken an especial interest in the study of man, the chances are always good that one can find someone who is interested in other aspects of the same problem, and thus mutual help becomes available.

The study of twins has been a very valuable aid to the progress of human genetics. If a particular trait is genetically determined, then identical twins should be concordant for it much more often than should fraternal twins or ordinary sibs. This makes possible some separation of genetic and environmentally caused variability. Another interesting aspect of twin studies is provided by case histories of identical twins reared apart. In one such study, both members of a pair of twins developed the same mental defect (schizophrenia) at about the same time (within a few weeks). As they had lived apart and in completely different environments for years, there is little room for doubt that the genetic element in the causation of the disease must have been very strong.

65. SOME NORMS OF HUMAN INHERITANCE

The principal methods of study in human genetics are the collection and analysis of pedigrees, and the statistical analysis of the data of the pedigrees. There is no substitute for these, but there are some rules of thumb which are useful. If a rare trait is recessive, the marriage of an affected person (*aa*) to a normal person will most probably be to a homozygous normal (*AA*), and hence none of their children will be affected. But they will all be heterozygous. Albinism (fig. 145) may be taken as an example, as only one person in 20,000 shows the trait. As it depends upon a recessive gene, this corresponds to a gene frequency of about 0.007. Substituting in the Hardy-Weinberg formula, we find that about one person in seventy is a carrier for the gene. Thus an albino marrying a normal person has one

chance in seventy of marrying a carrier of the gene for albinism, and sixty-nine chances in seventy of marrying a homozygous normal person.

Because of the facts discussed in the preceding paragraph, the dominant backcross (*Aa* × *AA*) has considerable practical importance in human genetics. For a person heterozygous for a relatively rare gene is most likely to marry a person homozygous for its normal allele. As a result, none of their children can show the recessive trait, but half will be heterozygous carriers. In this way, recessives may be carried, hidden and unsuspected, until two heterozygous persons chance to marry, and then homozygous recessives may appear. As most people are heterozygous for one or more of the numerous relatively rare recessive genes with which man is burdened, most human marriages are dominant backcrosses for one or more such genes.

The most usual thing by far is that the normal alleles are dominant, and the mutants are recessive. However, there are some outstanding exceptions, like brachydactyly, in which pathological conditions, which are obviously mutations from the normal, are inherited on the basis of dominant genes. Sex-linked recessives (like hemophilia) occupy an intermediate position, in that they show up in the simplex condition in males. It has been observed that of the three types (dominant, sex-linked, and recessive) dominant abnormalities are generally the mildest and recessives are generally the most severe. It is believed that this is because a dominant

Fig. 145. *Albinism in man.*

gene is subject to the full force of natural selection in every generation, while recessives are protected as long as they are heterozygous. Sex-linked recessives again have an intermediate position, because they are protected in heterozygous females but exposed to natural selection in the simplex males.

Human populations are enormously heterozygous. This is a result not only of long-continued mutation but also of the fact that laws and mores of most societies promote outbreeding and censure inbreeding. In a large population with great genetic variability, this should tend to produce marriages which are random in the sense that any two genotypes are equally likely to be brought together in a marriage. This is called *panmixis* or *random mating*. This is probably never completely realized, and in some societies there is actually a high degree of inbreeding (usually in small, isolated populations). One then speaks of *assortive mating* or *nonrandom mating*. In almost any society, some genotypic preferences are shown in selecting marriage partners. People do tend to select partners of similar height and of comparable intelligence, although great disparities may occur in each. In addition to this, the structure of human societies has tended to place restrictions on panmixis. A young man does not have an unlimited field of girls to choose from (or vice versa). Typically, he lives in a community of rather

Fig. 146. *Twins. Victor and Aladar are identical. There is some doubt whether Ida and Irma are identical or fraternal, but their resemblance is certainly very close.*

limited size, and he must choose from among the girls who happen to be there. The problem of who marries whom and why is not as yet the most satisfactorily solved problem in sociology, but simple proximity still plays a very large role. In older societies, in which local communities were both smaller on the average and more isolated from one another than they now are, this factor was undoubtedly often sufficiently strong to make genetic drift a significant thing in human genetics. And in some very small and isolated populations, such as those on small oceanic islands, the degree of inbreeding can be great enough that all of the islanders look very much alike.

But the typical thing in our highly mobile

and mechanized society is a sufficiently close approximation to panmixis to maintain a high degree of heterozygosity. And, with the exception of monozygotic (identical) twins (fig. 146), it is almost certain that no two individuals are ever genotypically identical.

Studies of genetics in man have concentrated upon single gene differences, because these are relatively easy to study. Hundreds of pathological conditions are known which depend upon single gene differences. But very few normal differences between people are so simply determined. The blood groups, the ability or inability to taste phenyl-thio-carbamide (PTC), some characteristics of hair growth, and a few muscular characteristics comprise most of the known list. A few others, like skin color, seem to be conditioned by only a few pairs of independent genes. But most of the differences between persons appear to be quantitative in character, and not much progress has been made in analyzing their inheritance.

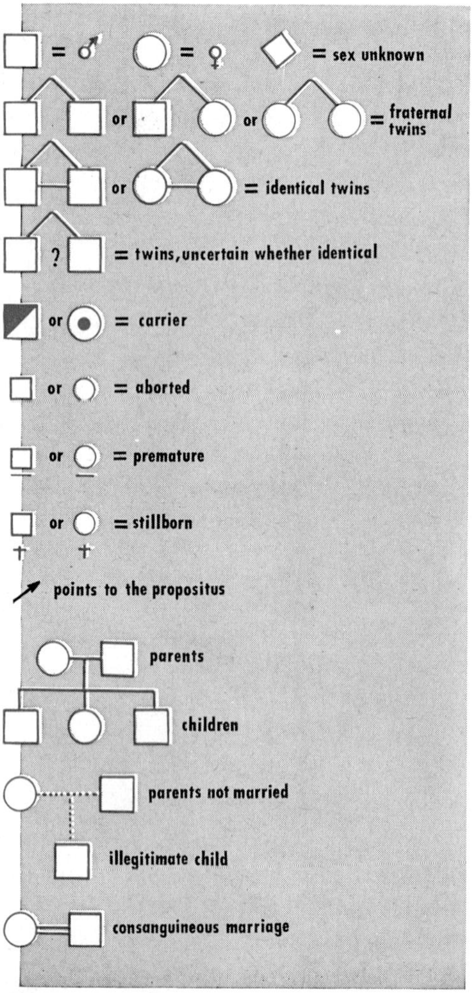

66. PEDIGREE NOTATION

SYMBOLS   In order to avoid chaos, it is necessary to standardize the symbols used in pedigrees as much as possible. A series of such standardized symbols, used and understood by all geneticists, is presented in figure 147. At the outset, a male is indicated by a square and a female by a circle. The conventional ♂ and ♀ of general biology are not used because it has been found that, in association with other pedigree symbols, they are more subject to confusion. Whenever the sex of a person in a pedigree is not known—a stillborn child for example—it is indicated with a diamond.

Fig. 147.   *Standard pedigree symbols. Each symbol is described on the figure.*

A marriage is indicated by a horizontal line connecting the symbols of the partners, and their children are shown by attaching their symbols to a horizontal line beneath the parents. The symbols for twins are connected to the horizontal by lines diverging from a single point. If they are identical twins, then their symbols are also connected by a horizontal line. If it is uncertain whether they are identical or fraternal, then a question mark is written between the symbols.

The ordinary assumption that the parents of a child are married is not always justified, and it is necessary to have some way to symbolize illegitimacy. This is done by connecting the parents and child with dotted lines rather than the usual solid lines. Also, parents may be cousins or other close relatives (consanguineous). Their positions in the pedigree may make this clear, but it is customary to make it more graphic by connecting them with a *double* line.

A person affected by the trait under study is indicated by blacking in his symbol. Heterozygous carriers for recessive genes should not be marked unless they can be identified with certainty, but when this is possible, it can be indicated by blacking half of the symbol, or by putting a black dot in the center of the symbol. An aborted child is indicated by a symbol much smaller than others, while a premature child is indicated by a small symbol which is underlined. A stillborn child is indicated by a small symbol with a cross under it.

A study of a particular family commonly begins with a specific person who comes to the attention of a geneticist for one reason or another. This person is called the *propositus* or *probandus*, and is indicated on the pedigree chart by an arrow pointing to his symbol.

A great deal can be done with these standard pedigree symbols. But sometimes a specific study requires additional, special symbols. This would be true, for example, in a study of linkage. Whenever an author finds it necessary to use symbols in addition to the standard ones, he should publish a key to his symbols along with the pedigree. The study of individual pedigrees is still the most basic method in human genetics, and the pedigrees should be kept as clear and unequivocal as the familial data will permit.

CHARACTERISTICS OF A PEDIGREE FOR A DOMINANT GENE No universally applicable rules for the interpretation of pedigrees can be laid down, however, some commonly applicable characteristics can be pointed out. If a dominant gene is being followed, the most common thing is that the affected parent is heterozygous, and so the mating is actually a backcross. Because any heterozygous person will show the trait, a "skipped"

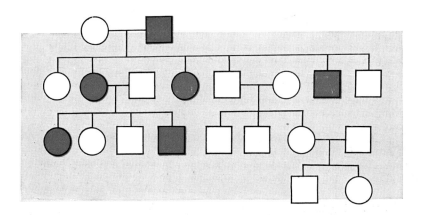

Fig. 148.   *A typical dominant pedigree. Note that there are no skipped generations.*

generation is not possible: an affected person always has an affected parent (unless, of course, a new mutation has occurred). For the same reason, if an affected person is homozygous all of his children would have to show the trait concerned. Obviously, reduced penetrance would disrupt these characteristics. A typical pedigree for a dominant gene is shown in figure 148.

CHARACTERISTICS OF A PEDIGREE FOR A RECESSIVE GENE   In a recessive pedigree, on the other hand, skipped generations are the rule. If an affected person marries a homozygous normal person, all of their children will be normal, although carriers. When a carrier marries a homozygous normal person, their children will all be normal, but half will be carriers. By such dominant backcrosses, a recessive gene may be carried for many generations, and become widely dispersed through a population. But if two such carriers marry, then their children should be in a ratio of three normals to one affected. Naturally, this is more likely to happen if the partners are closely related. Many known recessive genes cause pathological conditions, and it is for this reason that cousin marriages are generally regarded as biologically undesirable. Figure 149 shows a recessive pedigree, including a cousin marriage.

67. INHERITANCE OF PATHOLOGICAL TRAITS

Many references have been made already to the inheritance of pathological conditions, and we may now concentrate our attention upon this situation. The range of severity of inherited pathology covers the entire gamut from such trivial disorders as color blindness to lethal diseases like amaurotic idiocy.

It may be well to consider again what is actually inherited. At the outset, no phenotype is ever inherited as such. What is inherited is a gene, which controls certain norms of development, and so finally leads to a specific phenotype when the conditions of development are within a certain range. Where one speaks of inheritance of an infectious disease, it is clear that the disease could not be produced by the genotype alone: contact with the pathogenic organism is also necessary. But for many of the commoner diseases infection is so nearly universal that the genotype becomes the major factor in determining who gets the disease. One may more properly speak of inheritance of susceptibility in such cases. A good example is poliomyelitis (infantile paralysis). Susceptibility to this disease is inherited on the basis of a single recessive gene. The evi-

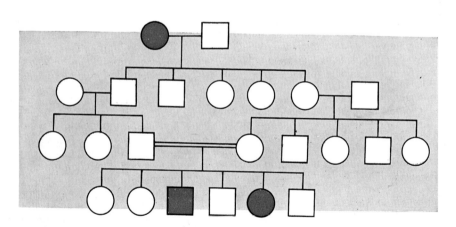

Fig. 149.   *A typical recessive pedigree. Note skips, and the results of a cousin marriage.*

dence indicates that the infection is extremely widespread—perhaps as common as the common cold. But only persons homozygous for the gene for susceptibility to polio actually develop the disease. The total number annually would be regarded as insignificant, were not the results of the disease so often dramatic and disastrous.

On the other hand, there are many constitutional diseases which seem to be more directly related to the genotype than just through a susceptibility. Amaurotic idiocy (fig. 150) is an example. There are two forms of this disease, each inherited on the basis of a single pair of recessive genes. Victims of the infantile form develop a progressive blindness very early, and this is accompanied by deterioration of the cells of the brain. It leads to death by two years of age. No treatment is yet available, but there is some biochemical information about the disease. Its victims are unable to oxidize the lipoid sphyngomyelin. The course of the juvenile form of the disease is very similar, but the onset of symptoms occurs at six to eight years of age. As the victims never reach reproductive age, all cases must result from segregation of the genes of two heterozygous parents. But there does seem to be a one-to-one relationship between the homozygous recessive genotype and the development of the disease. Further examples will be discussed below.

There are many hundreds of inherited pathological traits known in man. A few of these will be cited here, with selection being designed to illustrate diverse types both of disease and of inheritance. Hemolytic jaundice is a disease in which there is an excessive rate of destruction of red blood cells. Part of the hemoglobin so released is converted into bile salts. The resulting high concentration of bile salts in the blood causes their deposition in the skin and in the whites of the eyes, thus causing the yellow color which is the most obvious symptom of jaundice. The disease is based upon a single dominant gene.

Telangiectasis is a disease caused by an insufficient amount of muscular and elastic tissue around the small arterioles. The more extremely deficient arterioles may rupture spontaneously, thus causing hemorrhages which, in some cases, are serious, even fatal. The most common site of bleeding is under the mucous membrane of the nose, and hence the disease is often referred to as spontaneous nosebleed, but the hemorrhages can occur from arterioles under any of the mucous membranes. Smaller hemorrhages

Fig. 150. *Juvenile amaurotic idiocy. This boy developed symptoms at seven years of age. By age 9, when this picture was taken, he was totally blind and extremely low in intelligence. His stance, including the extension of his arms, is quite typical. (Courtesy of Dr. John J. Reedy and Dr. Hans Mautner.)*

commonly cause the appearance of red spots under the skin and mucous membranes. The frequency of hemorrhages commonly increases until about thirty to thirty-five years of age, then it falls off. This trait again is based upon a single dominant gene.

Susceptibility to tuberculosis is inherited on a more complex basis, and the details are not clear. There appear to be at least two pairs of genes involved. Some evidence indicates that resistance is dominant and susceptibility recessive, but others believe that one gene for susceptibility is dominant and another recessive.

Polycystic kidney is a structural defect in which numerous cysts riddle the kidney, thus reducing the total amount of functional kidney tissue to a minimum. While not dangerous in itself, it makes its victims unable to stand any severe stress upon the kidneys, and hence a fatal outcome is common. It is again inherited as a dominant.

Diabetes insipidus is characterized by abnormally high activity of the kidneys. This is unrelated to sugar diabetes, and involves no abnormality of carbohydrate metabolism. As a result of the excessive output by the kidneys, one must also drink unusually large quantities of water. While the disease is considered harmless, it could become dangerous under conditions of water shortage. It is inherited on the basis of a dominant gene with reduced penetrance.

Diabetes mellitus is, of course, the well-known disease characterized by excretion of sugar in the urine. It is caused by failure of the pancreatic islets to secrete insulin, a hormone which is essential to carbohydrate metabolism. The pancreatic failure may, in turn, be caused by an excess of a pituitary secretion, alloxan. Whatever the details, the disease generally appears to be based upon a dominant gene with penetrance reduced to about 10 per cent.

Gastric ulcers is a well-known affliction which is based upon a recessive gene with about 50 per cent penetrance. This disease is particularly interesting because the non-genetic component of penetrance is known. Of the homozygous recessives who are potential ulcer victims, it is those who are extremely nervous and who tend to drive themselves hard who actually develop the ulcers.

Xeroderma pigmentosum (fig. 151) is a type of skin cancer which is highly interesting from a genetic point of view. An affected baby very soon shows an abnormal aversion to light. On exposure to light, the skin reddens, then heavy freckles develop and grow very large. The white skin between the freckles undergoes degenerative changes and frequently becomes tumorous. Death occurs between five and fifteen years of age.

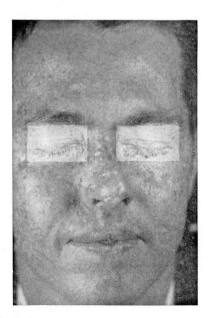

Fig. 151. *Xeroderma pigmentosum. The scars were caused by removal of tumors.* (*Courtesy of Dr. Paul V. Chivington, Jr.*)

From a genetic point of view, there are several interesting aspects of this disease. First, it shows a rather obvious dependence of gene action upon an environmental factor, for lesions develop *only* in those parts of the body exposed to light. Second, the heterozygous carriers of this gene are recognizable by their very heavy freckling, which, unlike ordinary freckling is not associated with red hair. This is often characteristic of the healthy brothers and sisters of the disease victims.

The most interesting aspect of the genetics of xeroderma pigmentosum, however, is its mode of inheritance. It is inherited as a *partially sex-linked* recessive. How can a gene be partially sex-linked? Must it not be either on the X chromosome or on an autosome? The answer to this question requires some additional knowledge of the sex-differential chromosomes of man. In both the X chromosome and the Y chromosome, the centromere divides the chromosome into two segments. One of these is called the *differential* segment, because there appears to be no homology between X and Y in this segment. The differential segment of the X chromosome includes typical sex-linked genes, such as those for color blindness and hemophilia. The differential segment of the Y chromosome includes a number of *holandric* (Greek —entirely male) genes, which can only be transmitted from father to son. Such characters as webbed toes and scaly skin are in-

herited on the basis of holandric genes. On the other side of the centromere is the *homologous* segment, in which the same genes are present in both X and Y chromosomes. Such genes are, of course, sex-linked in the sense that they are in the sex-differential chromosomes. But they cannot show the typical pattern of sex-linked inheritance, which depends upon the male being simplex. Hence genes which may cross over between homologous parts of the X and Y chromosomes are said to be partially sex-linked. Partially sex-linked genes include those for xeroderma pigmentosum, total color blindness (in contrast to red-green color blindness), and retinitis pigmentosa, a degenerative eye disease which leads to blindness. Haldane's map of the X and Y chromosomes of man is presented in figure 152. Distances are calculated from the centromere instead of from an end of the chromosome.

CURABILITY OF GENETIC DEFECTS Such a recital of genetic maladies ought not to be concluded without reemphasizing the fact that genes act through ordinary physiological channels, and therefore genetic diseases should always be subject to treatment and

Fig. 152. A map of the sex-differential chromosomes of man. A, the differential segment of the X chromosome, with typical sex-linked genes. B, the differential segment of the Y chromosome, with holandric genes. C, the homologous segment, with partially sex-linked genes. (Redrawn from Gates.)

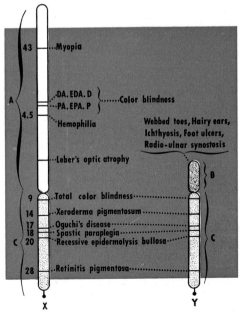

cure on the same basis that other diseases are, provided that the proper treatment is found. For example, jaundice may be treated by removal of the spleen (in which red blood cells are destroyed). Telangiectasis can be treated by cauterizing or tying off the most severely affected arterioles. Tuberculosis has been treated successfully for many years, and recently it has responded well to streptomycin. Diabetes mellitus can be very successfully controlled by the administration of insulin. Even psychic disorders of genetic origin have been treated successfully. Manic-depressive psychosis is generally agreed to have a strong genetic element in its causation, although psychic traumata are also involved. The disease has been very successfully treated with electric shock therapy. Schizophrenia, the commonest and most serious of the prevalent mental diseases, also has a strong genetic factor in its causation, and it can often be treated successfully by means of insulin shock (sublethal doses). Thus the equation which so many people (including many who ought to know better) draw between *hereditary* and *incurable* is unjustified by the facts.

FACTORS WHICH TEND TO INCREASE THE FREQUENCIES OF PATHOLOGICAL GENES If the frequency of pathological genes should rise sufficiently high, it would be disastrous for mankind, and at any level whatever, they present a serious social problem and a challenge. It is therefore important to examine those factors which either raise or lower the frequencies of pathological genes.

New mutation deserves first consideration among the causes of increasing incidence of undesirable genes. As pointed out in chapters 13 and 19, mutation is a random process with respect to the prospective values of the mutants. Because of this the overwhelming majority of all mutations must be undesirable. Hence as mutation proceeds from generation to generation, it must enlarge the burden of undesirable genes at the expense of the more desirable ones.

Some progress has been made in the study of mutation rates in man. Much of what is known on this subject was summarized by Neel and Falls in a paper which is cited at the end of this chapter. There are two principal methods of study. The first is restricted to dominant genes, and depends upon the proportion of mutant children to normal children born of normal parents in a given population during a specified interval. The study of Neel and his collaborators on the mutation rate of the gene for retinoblastoma, an eye cancer, is a good example. Because of the extremely serious nature of this disease, which is fatal in early childhood if the eyeball is not removed before the tumor invades the brain, probably all cases are a matter of record, and most are referred to medical school clinics. Because it is inherited as a dominant, the mutation from normal must have occurred in the parents of the affected child, except in those rare cases where an operated child has reached maturity, married, and had children. Neel and his collaborators interviewed the families of all retinoblastomatous children born in Michigan between 1937 and 1948. The total number of births in the same period was obtained from the records of the Michigan Department of Health. This lead to the conclusion that the mutation occurred at the rate of 23 times per million gametes.

The second method is indirect, and is applicable to either a dominant or a sex-linked recessive mutation. One determines the frequency of the disease and the extent of unfitness it causes (increase over the general death rate). Then one can calculate the mutation rate which would be necessary to offset the loss of the gene through death of its bearers. This is predicated upon the assumption that the gene frequency is remaining constant in the population. When the mutation rate for chondrodystrophy (fig. 153) was calculated by both methods, they gave similar results (about 45 mutations per million gametes), thus tending to verify the methods. The indirect method is considered not applicable to autosomal recessives, because of the difficulty of estimating the effects of heterozygosity upon survival.

A second factor tending to increase the frequencies of undesirable genes is the much discussed one of differential reproductive rates. It is a matter of frequent observation that, if a population be classified by educational levels, or by socio-economic status, or by profession, the average family size will be smallest at the upper levels and largest at the lower levels. Many people have been gravely concerned over whether our intelligence level is being gradually lowered by this reproductive differential. Basic to this is the assumption that these classifications reflect real differences in the intelligence of the people at different levels, and that these are genetically determined. Unquestionably, these assumptions are only partly true—but that part may be a large one. Who will doubt that the average physician is more intelligent than the average unskilled laborer? On the other hand, intelligence is not a simple attribute, but a complex one, and so,

undoubtedly, is its inheritance. Many geneticists feel that the higher intelligence levels can be formed by recombination of the genes of sound but not superior people. Further, it might be mentioned that there has been a tendency in recent years toward larger families at the upper levels of society.

Another aspect of differential reproductive rates concerns the reproductive rates of persons with markedly undesirable genes, such as those for mental deficiency. It has been much publicized that high-grade morons sometimes are extraordinarily fertile. While this is true, the more severe mental deficiencies generally result in complete sterility. Many other undesirable genes seem to depress the fertility of their bearers. This aspect of the problem of differential reproductive rates has probably been overrated in importance.

Fig. 153. *Chondrodystrophy, or achondroplasia. Note the normal size of hands and body, and the abnormally short limbs. This is the most common type of dwarfing in man. (Courtesy of Dr. John J. Reedy and Dr. Hans Mautner.)*

FACTORS TENDING TO DECREASE THE FRE-QUENCIES OF UNDESIRABLE GENES There are also several factors which continually operate to eliminate undesirable genes from human populations. The first of these is natural selection. It is important to emphasize this, because it has often been said that man, through his social institutions, has stopped the beneficial action of natural selection. Man has not yet learned to cancel out the laws of nature: he can direct their action, but he cannot destroy them. It is possible to identify some of the ways that natural selection works in eliminating undesirable genes in man today. A few of these may be recounted. First, undesirable genes often reduce fertility. As an example, a genetically crippled man married a woman with a minor deformity which may or may not have been genetically determined. They were extremely anxious to have children, but were unable to establish a pregnancy. They then reported to an excellent sterility clinic, where they were treated for many years, entirely unsuccessfully. This is not an unusual case history.

Further, victims of severe genetic disorders may have difficulty in securing mates. To take an example, a successful engineer, a brilliant man, was badly crippled by polio. He was very anxious to get married, but he wanted a wife who would represent all of his unsatisfied athletic aspirations. Such girls were not interested in him. Had he been willing to marry a handicapped girl, he would have had no difficulty. But he is still a bachelor. Not infrequently, severely defective people do marry others who are similarly handicapped. But the more serious the defect, the poorer are the chances in general. This is one form of natural selection.

The victims of undesirable genes are also subject to a higher death rate from disease and accidents than is the general population. This is obvious in cases where the phenotype itself is a dangerous disease. But it may be equally effective in other cases, like mental deficiency. A high-grade moron may procreate a large number of children, but how many of them will survive to reproductive age? The author is unable to quote reliable statistics on this question, but doubts very gravely that their survival rate comes near that of better endowed families. We live in a high speed, mechanized society in which fatal accidents may strike at any moment. Natural selection in such a society must favor the ability to think quickly and accurately, and to manipulate high speed machinery (including the automobile) skilfully and accurately. Accidents do not just happen: every careful study indicates that they are caused. This is probably an effective factor in natural selection in modern society.

Another factor which tends to reduce the frequency of undesirable genes is genetic drift. This subject was discussed in chapter 19, and the discussion need not be repeated here. It need only be pointed out that most pathological genes are sufficiently rare (fortunately) that accidents of sampling could have an important bearing on their frequency. Measurements of mutation frequency for hemophilia (about thirty-two mutations per million gametes) indicate that the new mutations within the past few generations should account for more cases of hemophilia than actually exist. The only available explanation is that the difference is accounted for by loss of genes through natural selection and genetic drift. Thus in large populations genetic drift may operate to decrease the frequencies of rare genes. In small, isolated populations, such as commonly occur in backward regions, however, genetic drift may have a great effect on the frequencies of all genes. And, as that effect is independent of selection, it undoubtedly increases the prevalence of many pathological genes. It is for this reason that genetic abnormalities are so common in small, isolated communities.

THE EUGENIC PROBLEM The discussion of human genetics and of man's burden of undesirable genes leads inevitably to the question of whether man can use his knowledge of genetics to improve *himself*, as he has used it to improve his domestic plants and animals. That this might be done was originally proposed by Galton in the pre-Mendelian days. He called the new science which he envisioned *eugenics*, and he defined it as the "study of agencies under social control, that may improve or impair the racial (meaning hereditary) qualities of future generations, either physically or mentally."

Eugenics is generally approached from two very different angles, the negative and the positive. The objective of negative eugenics is the elimination of at least the most severely detrimental genes from human populations. The objective of positive eugenics is to promote the increase of the most desirable genes. Although Galton thought primarily in terms of positive eugenics, with a mentally and physically superior humanity as his goal, the actual eugenic programs of the present century have emphasized the negative aspect, probably because it is superficially simpler.

NEGATIVE EUGENICS The proponents of negative eugenics point out that there are some genetically caused deformities, such as certain types of gross crippling, and mental defects, such as certain types of mental deficiency (fig. 154) and insanity, which are so disastrous in their effects that the victims must always be wards of the state or intolerable burdens upon their families. The birth of such a child is always an unrelieved tragedy for the family, and is likely to be a heavy and unproductive expense for the state. It used to be urged that the state enforce the sterilization of such persons and of known carriers, in the hope that such a program, rigorously carried out, would quickly relieve mankind of its gravest genetic burdens. Many states have enacted such programs into law, but in most states the law has been allowed to become a dead letter.

Negative eugenics has always been highly controversial, and such legislation is not often advocated any longer, because of the weight of technical and moral arguments against it. From a moral viewpoint, it is said that a person who is competent to live and work in society has a right to the integrity of his body, and that that right can be forfeited only in punishment for crime. If he is not competent, then society is obliged to pro-

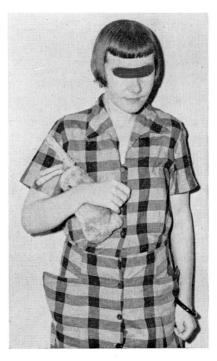

Fig. 154. *Phenylpyruvic oligophrenia, a recessive type of mental deficiency which is characterized by the inability to oxidize phenylpyruvic acid. The toy indicates the infantile mentality of this girl, whose I.Q. is only 32. (Courtesy of Dr. John J. Reedy and Dr. Hans Mautner.)*

vide institutional care. From a technical viewpoint, the returns to be expected from a sterilization program depend upon the mode of inheritance in the case of each gene. The best success would be expected with dominant genes having an early incidence, like retinoblastoma. The results would be poorer if a dominant gene had late incidence, like Huntington's chorea. But the majority of harmful genes are recessive, and hence the number of undetected heterozygous carriers far exceeds the number of identifiable defectives. Most of the defective patients results from the segregation of the genes of heterozygous parents, who may themselves be superior. The author is acquainted with a distinguished professor, who is listed in Who's Who and whose wife earned a Phi Beta Kappa key, whose oldest child is a genetic moron.

It is plain that the detection of heterozygotes is an important problem. Some progress has been made toward its solution. Thus persons heterozygous for the gene for thalassemia major, a dangerous anemia, show alterations of the red blood cells which constitute the harmless thalassemia minor. Progress in the field of identification of heterozygous persons was summarized up to 1948 by Neel in a paper which is cited at the end of this chapter. But this problem is further complicated by the fact that human populations are so highly heterozygous that probably most people are heterozygous for some seriously harmful genes. Muller has estimated that the average person is heterozygous for at least eight such genes. Because of this, a thorough program of elimination of carriers of defective heredity would be patently impossible. Yet the ability to identify heterozygotes would be invaluable to genetic counsellors: it would make it possible to advise carriers of the same defective gene against marriage.

In view of the grave problems discussed above, it seems just as well to let the compulsory eugenics laws remain unenforced. On the other hand, because each birth of a serious defective is a profound tragedy, known carriers for the more serious defects should certainly be advised, preferably before marriage. Many will feel that it is worth while to take a risk where the probability of a normal child is as good as three to one. On the other hand, some will not if the defect is sufficiently serious. Again, people get married for many reasons, some of which are by no means adequate. If offered a good, socially acceptable excuse for backing out, many would do so, and thus prevent an unfortunate and unsuccessful marriage. This is a real service, for marriage will test the mettle of the best, and it is only for mature people who really want it.

POSITIVE EUGENICS The general objective of positive eugenics is to increase the frequencies of the most favorable genes in human populations. But, while it is easy to define the gross abnormalities which are the targets of negative eugenics, it is very difficult to define the objectives of positive eugenics so exactly. In a general way, the objectives are sound physical health and superior intelligence. Specific genes have generally not been identified, and it seems probable that these are influenced by whole constellations of quantitative genes. But the objectives cannot be simple anyway, for diversity is as important to the welfare of man as is superiority. We must have technicians as well as scientists and physicians, clerks as well as lawyers, laborers as well as executives. In a population of potential Phi Beta Kappa's, many of these essential jobs would have to be done by very highly frustrated and unhappy people. Nevertheless, few will wish to claim that society has yet had the services of either as much or as good brain power as is desirable.

A central problem for the positive eugenicists is the fact that people at the upper levels of our society, by whatever method those levels may be defined, generally do not have families as large as do those at lower levels. The assumption is made that the various levels of society reflect the general levels of genetic endowment. This cannot be entirely true, as educational opportunity and other external factors have a great deal of influence on one's station in life. But in a free, competitive society, it is very difficult to maintain an undeserved position, and people from even the humblest ranks do rise to high positions. So perhaps there is good correlation between socio-economic status and intelligence in our society. As mentioned above, the perpetuation of the best genotypes may depend upon reproduction by the best endowed persons, or it may depend upon recombination of the genes of good but not superior genotypes. If the latter is the case, there is not much for the positive eugenicist to do, but if the former is the case, it is important to learn why the best endowed people do not have larger families, and to take steps to remove those causes.

The cause of the low reproductive rate among the more highly educated is a complex sociological problem and is beyond the scope of the present work. Some of the problems revolve around delayed time of marriage required by advanced education, reduced libido resulting from the sedentary life, poor economic position in the early years of marriage coupled with the high cost of maternity and housing, and the high cost of education for their children.

Suggested programs for positive eugenics generally aim at removing these reasons for the reluctance of highly educated people to have large families. Some of these suggestions may be recounted. The first is perhaps that marriage subsidies should be granted to superior young couples to make it feasible for them to marry and have children during their college and graduate years (the best years for child-bearing). Another perennial suggestion is the establishment of a *family* wage system, with substantial salary increases upon marriage and upon the birth of each child. Because the cost of maternity often appears as a disaster to a young couple not yet well established financially, low cost maternity clinics are important in programs for positive eugenics. These are already available at all medical schools, but most people do not live close enough to use them, and the number of applicants exceeds available facilities so much that really needy applicants must be rejected. Very closely related is the high cost of housing, which has been heavily publicized (and attacked) in recent years.

Another important aspect of the problem is the cost of higher education. Many people who really want a large family do not have one because they feel that they must provide maximal educational opportunity for their children, and they realize that they cannot do this for a large family. It has therefore been suggested that college scholarships should be established which are to be awarded to outstanding students who are members of large families.

A final aspect of positive eugenics is the fact that many people do not have children because they cannot establish a pregnancy. Sterility is a widespread problem which is not appreciated by the general public. A discussion of the causes and treatment of sterility does not belong here. However, it should be emphasized that sterility is caused by specific anatomical or physiological defects, and these can often be treated successfully. Sterility clinics are now fairly common, and gynecologists are generally trained in the treatment of sterility. It is also important to emphasize the fact that sterility is a mutual problem of husband and wife.

The defect which prevents conception is found in the husband almost as often as in his wife. And many a man who has cursed his wife's barrenness has remained childless because false pride has kept him from submitting to examination.

In general, positive eugenics is not encumbered by the moral problems which beset negative eugenics. But it is beset by practical problems which are as great: an adequate program would be costly, and could perhaps be done only through the government. If the measures were applied equally to the entire public, they would not have the desired eugenic effect. And if some method were devised for applying them selectively, let us say to the upper third of each college class, or to some similar group of proven superiority, then there would be the greatest difficulty in securing public consent. So it appears that the successful utilization "of agencies under social control, that may improve . . . . the racial qualities of future generations" is still far in the future. Meanwhile, we may take some satisfaction in the fact that the average size of families of college graduates has increased somewhat in the past few years.

68. SOCIAL VALUES OF GENETICS

Probably the majority of geneticists are paid as teachers. Their job is to investigate fundamental problems in genetics and to transmit the knowledge gained, not only for the training of more geneticists, but for the benefit of biologists generally, for the training of physicians, and for its value to the general public, for which, in modern society, some understanding of science has become a requirement of general culture. Probably the second largest group of geneticists is made up of the plant and animal breeders, whose contribution to society was discussed at length in chapter 20.

But there are some more specifically social functions of genetics, sometimes performed by laboratory geneticists, sometimes by genetically trained physicians, and now ever more commonly performed by men specifically trained as human geneticists, and staffing *heredity clinics*. It will be the purpose of the present section to discuss some of these functions.

MARRIAGE PROGNOSIS One of the commonest services asked of a geneticist is prediction of the probability that, if a young couple should marry, their children will show some particular familial defect. For example, a couple both of whom had just graduated from college with high honors were engaged to be married. The girl had a brother who was a moron, probably genetically caused. Her fiance knew of no comparable affliction in his own family, nor did his parents, who are living. It was necessary to tell the girl that there is a 50 per cent probability that she is a carrier, but as her fiance was probably homozygous normal, their children would probably be normal also. But she may transmit the gene for mental deficiency, and it may show up in later generations. Of course, there was also a small probability that her fiance was heterozygous, and they then would have a probability of about one eighth of having a deficient child (only one eighth because the probability of her being a carrier is one half). Actually, this couple decided to take the risk, and all of their children are normal.

In another instance, both parties have had poliomyelitis, and they want to know what is the probability that their children will have the disease. As susceptibility is inherited on the basis of a recessive gene, it is necessary to tell them that they are both homozygous and can only have homozygous children. Hence all of their children will almost certainly have the disease unless adequate preventive measures intervene. In this instance, the couple were married and had four children, of which the first three all had polio, while the fourth was still an infant when the parents were last interviewed. Today, with gamma globulin and the Salk serum, the polio genotype may not be so serious a disadvantage.

Sometimes advice is sought after marriage, because an abnormal child has already been born. A couple had an anencephalic child (lacking the brain) which died on the day of birth. The father recalled that his parents had had two similar children which also died on the day of birth. The parents wanted to know the probability that an additional child would also be anencephalic. The condition has not been studied extensively, but studies have been published which indicate an hereditary basis for it. The occurrence three times in this one family supports that probability. There are two possible modes of inheritance which are consistent with this pedigree (fig. 155). It might be based upon a recessive gene, which would require that both parents be heterozygous (they are unrelated, and there is no record of the defect in the mother's family). Or it might be based upon a dominant with reduced penetrance. If the first is correct, then the probability of any future pregnancy leading to an anencephalic child would be 25 per cent. If the second possibility is correct, then the probability of a future child inheriting the gene for anencephaly is 50 per cent. But a child with the gene may appear normal, like the father. Actually, this couple has had two more children, both normal.

CLINICAL DIAGNOSIS Genetic information may also be a considerable aid in diagnosis of disease. There is the case of a man who was hospitalized with gastric hemorrhages. Gastric ulcer was suspected, but the man's father said that he had always had profuse nosebleeds. Therefore the possibility was suggested that this man might also have telangiectasis, with the principal distended vessel in the stomach. An exploratory operation was performed, and the expected dilated vessel found and removed. And thus an "ulcer" patient was released from the hospital after minor treatment. It may be said that any disease which can be diagnosed after genetic information is given can be diagnosed without it too. This is no doubt true, for diagnosis depends first upon the symptoms of the patient. But in many instances, a correct diagnosis is actually made only after genetic information is obtained, and in many others genetic information would no doubt shorten the road to a correct diagnosis.

PREVENTION OF DISEASE Genetic information may be of considerable value in the prevention of disease, because it provides a basis for detecting potential victims before they develop symptoms. Manic-depressive psychosis, for example, is a very serious

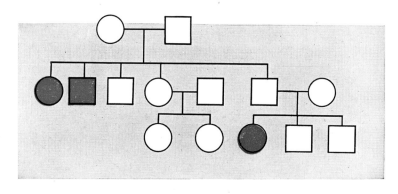

Fig. 155. *A pedigree for anencephaly.*

mental disease which has a strong hereditary factor in its causation. But psychic traumata are also necessary for its clinical manifestation. If the physician knows that there is a history of manic-depression in a family, he can be especially watchful of the mental hygiene of the children, and he can be prepared to refer them to a qualified specialist if necessary. In this way, their mental health can be assured, when otherwise they would be much more likely to develop the disease.

Snyder has reported a very nice example of potential disease prevention by genetic means in the case of hemolytic icterus. This is a type of jaundice in which the rate of destruction of red blood cells by the spleen is abnormally high. The disease may run a very rapid course to fatality. But, fortunately, preclinical signs of the disease can be detected in the blood of a potential victim, and the disease can be prevented by removal of the spleen. The disease is based upon a dominant gene. In the case reported by L. H. Snyder, a patient was operated upon in time to save his life, and his children were tested for blood signs. A son was found to show the typical blood picture of preclinical hemolytic icterus, and was urged to submit to the preventive operation. He refused, and some time later was brought into the hospital *too late* to be saved. It would be manifestly impossible to examine everyone for preclinical hemolytic icterus, but it would be practical, as a routine matter, to examine the near relatives of known hemolytic icterus patients. Much the same applies to numerous hereditary ills.

PATERNITY TESTS   The subject of determination of paternity in contested cases, or of parentage when more than one set of parents claim the same child, was discussed at length in chapter 8. Here it need only be mentioned that this is one of the important functions of genetics in society.

ADVICE ON EUGENICS PROGRAMS   Finally, it may be mentioned that the advice of competent geneticists should always be sought before setting up any eugenic program, whether negative or positive. This seems so obvious that it ought to be unnecessary to mention it, yet legislatures have been inadequately advised in the past.

69. RÉSUMÉ AND PROSPECT

In the preceding pages, the development of genetics has been traced from its elementary beginnings to its present highly complex state, from the monohybrid cross to quantitative inheritance and linkage, to the theory of the gene and cytoplasmic inheritance. Especially in the later chapters, some insight has been afforded into the trends of current research in genetics. Where geneticists first sought only a clarification of the ratios of inheritance in accordance with the Mendelian laws, today the goals include an understanding of the exact physiological mechanisms through which genes obtain their effects, and, indeed, an understanding of the chemistry and organization of the gene itself. Where the first geneticists found the apparent permanence of the gene to be a stumbling block in the way of the understanding of evolution, the geneticists of today have made their science the cornerstone of evolution through studies on mutation and on population genetics.

The growth of applied genetics has been spectacular, particularly in plant and animal breeding. These sciences were, of course, thousands of years old when genetics was first introduced. Their achievements in pregenetic days were great. Probably there was not a single domestic plant or animal in use which did not differ greatly from its wild ancestors. With the advent of genetics, however, a rational theory was for the first time available to the breeders. They were swift to recognize its value, and it probably is not an overstatement to say that the breeders have made more progress in the last fifty years than in all of the preceding millenia.

Not the least of the achievements of genetics has been the growth of human genetics. The simple demonstration that the Mendelian laws apply to man as well as to lower organisms is itself highly significant. But geneticists have gone far beyond that, and have shown the exact bases of inheritance of many specific disorders, thus providing the physician with a powerful—though as yet inadequately used—diagnostic and preventive tool. And through eugenic measures we may at least hope to lighten man's burden of sorrow and add some measure to his competence to cope with the problems which beset him.

All of this has been accomplished within a very short span of time—within the lifetime of some men now living. Every discovery has, while solving one problem, focused attention upon several more problems for research, while providing new concepts and tools for use in their investigation. Thus the scope of genetics and its potential for achievement have grown ever broader. If we may draw an analogy between the development of genetics and that of older sciences such as chemistry and physics, then it may be confidently said that the great achievements of the past fifty years are but a prelude to a much greater future.

Questions and Problems

1. Define:

Age of incidence	Panmixis
Assortive mating	Partial sex-linkage
Consanguineous	Pedigree
Eugenics	Penetrance
Experiment	Pooled data
Expressivity	Propositus
Holandric	

2. The following are pedigrees for polio. Show how each is compatible with the mode of inheritance discussed in the text:

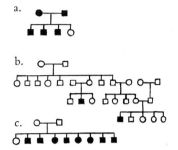

3. The following is a pedigree for manic-depressive psychosis. How would you interpret it genetically:

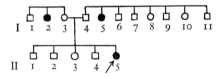

4. Discuss the limitations of the pedigree method as compared to the experimental method.

5. Discuss the curability of genetically caused diseases, and cite examples of such diseases which are subject to successful treatment at present.

6. What is meant by reduced penetrance? Might your interpretation of the pedigree for manic-depression in problem 3 be changed if you were told that I-2 and 3 are probably of identical genotype, with I-3 appearing normal because of reduced penetrance?

7. What are some of the advantages of the study of inheritance in man?

8. Why should the dominant backcross be important for human genetics?

9. Why should the same disease be more severe when inherited as a recessive than when inherited as a dominant?

10. What is meant by panmixis? To what extent is it ordinarily achieved in human populations?

11. Can you think of any American populations in which panmixis is notably restricted or lacking, in other words, in which there is a high degree of inbreeding? What factors are responsible for this?

12. Discuss the problem of the inheritance of disease as such versus the inheritance of susceptibility.

13. Suppose that a person with a polycystic

kidney were to suffer a kidney infection. How do you think his chances of recovery would compare with those of a structurally normal person with the same infection? What importance might this have for preventive medicine?

14. How can a gene be said to be *partially* sex-linked? Give an example in man.

15. What are the main factors which tend to increase the frequencies of undesirable genes?

16. What evidence is there for the effectiveness of natural selection in man today?

17. To what extent should genetic drift favor the elimination of undesirable genes?

18. What are the objectives of negative eugenics?

19. What are the main arguments for and against negative eugenics?

20. What is the importance of the development of means of identifying persons heterozygous for recessive genes?

21. Formulate objectives for a potential program of positive eugenics.

22. How good would you consider the chances of winning public approval for an effective program of positive eugenics?

References

Colin, E. C., 1946. Elements of Genetics. Second edition. Blakiston Co., New York. A very simple elementary genetics book which emphasizes heredity in man.

Gates, R. R., 1946. Human Genetics. The Macmillan Co., New York. This two volume work is an encyclopedic treatment of the subject.

Neel, J. V., 1949. The detection of genetic carriers of hereditary disease. American Journal of Human Genetics, 1:19–36. The most comprehensive treatment of the subject yet available.

Neel, J. V. and H. F. Falls, 1951. The rate of mutation of the gene responsible for retinoblastoma in man. Science, 114:419–422. Includes a brief review of the problem of mutation rates in man.

Neel, J. V. and W. J. Schull, 1955. Human Heredity. University of Chicago Press.

Reed, S. C., 1955. Counseling in Medical Genetics. W. B. Saunders Co., Philadelphia.

Snyder, L. H., 1941. Medical Genetics. Duke University Press, Durham.

——, 1946. Principles of Heredity. Fourth edition. D. C. Heath, Boston. These very readable books present the viewpoint of one of the founders of human genetics in America.

Sorsby, Arnold, 1953. Clinical Genetics. C. V. Mosby Co., St. Louis. A very thorough treatment of the genetic aspects of clinical problems.

Stern, Curt, 1949. Principles of Human Genetics. W. H. Freeman Co., San Francisco. An excellent textbook of genetics, based upon human examples as far as possible.

Treasury of Human Inheritance. Galton Laboratory, London. This is a series of papers representing research in human genetics at the Galton Laboratory over a period of many years. It is a very valuable source of information on the subjects covered.

CHAPTER 22

Historical Retrospect

There are very few sciences for which a definite date of origin can be given. Genetics is one of those few, for, although men had wrested with the problems of heredity since remote antiquity, no one had gained any insight until less than a century ago. Then one cold February evening in 1865, Gregor Mendel, a monk who had experimented with garden peas for eight years, read a paper explaining his experiments before a small scientific society. And in that short paper (reproduced here on pages 285–311) were the elements of genetics, as developed in the early chapters of this book. But before discussing Mendel, it may be well to review the efforts of some of his predecessors to understand the principles of heredity.

70. SOME PREMENDELIAN STUDENTS OF HEREDITY

It is a matter of common observation that organisms are, in some measure, molded by the environment. The best seed produces only a mediocre crop in poor soil. The skin of man is tanned when exposed to the sun. The theory that these *acquired characters* gradually blend into the hereditary make-up of organisms is a very old one, although it is associated principally with the name of Lamarck. This French zoologist developed a theory of evolution based upon the inheritance of acquired characters. However, experiments set up to test such inheritance (as amputating the tails of mice for many successive generations) always gave negative results, and so the theory was discarded by almost all biologists. It is unfortunate that Lamarck is remembered primarily for this outmoded theory, for he was a gifted zoologist, with great accomplishments in comparative anatomy and taxonomy. He came very close to the cell theory thirty years before Schleiden and Schwann.

In 1863 and 1864, a French botanist, Naudin, published papers which included data which were probably adequate for the derivation of the Mendelian laws, yet he missed. Especially significant is the work of Dzierzon with bees, for it was probably known to Mendel. Both men were Silesian priests, and both were enthusiastic bee breeders. It was Dzierzon who first discovered the fact that male bees hatch from unfertilized eggs, while females hatch from fertilized eggs. He noted that the sons of hybrid mothers were of the two grandparental types in equal numbers. This may have alerted Mendel to the importance of ratios among the offspring.

Another unsuccessful attempt to understand heredity was that of Darwin. According to his theory of *pangenesis*, every organ in the body produces minute particles, the pangenes, which pass through the blood to the gametes. In the embryo, each pangene is responsible for the development of an organ like the one from which it came. This concept is quite harmonious with the inheritance of acquired characters, which Darwin accepted. Yet Darwin could not have regarded pangenesis as anything more than a working hypothesis, for in every edition of the "Origin of Species" he retained the statement that "the laws governing inheritance are for the most part unknown."

One more "pre-Mendelian" student of heredity whose work was published after Mendel's, but in ignorance of the latter, was August Weismann. He became professor of zoology at Freiburg in 1867, and for forty years exercised a profound influence on biological thinking in relation to heredity and evolution. He reasoned that the chromosomes must be the bearers of heredity, because only the chromosomes behaved in an orderly, predictable fashion at cell division. Because each embryo begins with the fusion of two gametes, he predicted that reduction divisions would be found in the formation of gametes. Otherwise, the hereditary material would be doubled at every generation. Embryonic differentiation he believed to result from the progressive loss of hereditary material during the embryonic mitoses. This required the idea that germ cells were set aside in the earliest embryonic stages as reservoirs of completely undifferentiated—and therefore genetically complete—cells. These latter ideas have been completely disproved, as was shown in chapter 16. As the germ cells are the only bridge between generations, and as he believed them to be at all stages distinct from all somatic cells, he spoke of "the continuity of the germplasm" or the "immortality of the germplasm" from the Adam of a species to its last member. This he contrasted with the differentiated and mortal body or soma.

71. GREGOR JOHANN MENDEL: BIOGRAPHICAL SKETCH

These, then, are some of the brilliant predecessors of the modest monk, who, on February 22, 1865 read to the Brünn Society for the Study of Natural Science a paper on "Experiments in Plant Hybridization." In this paper, he set forth the fundamental laws of heredity, yet no questions were asked,

and no discussion followed his paper. It was published in the following year in the Proceedings of the society, where it remained almost unnoticed until 1900. Yet the rediscovery of this paper produced an effect comparable to that of the "Origin of Species." Who *was* this man who, unrecognized in his own time, has had so great an effect upon our time?

Johann Mendel was born in 1822 in the village of Heinzendorf in Silesia. His parents were peasants, and his father, although a small landholder, was still bound by the old feudal law of corvee to work three days a week for the Countess Waldburg. Mendel attended the village school, in which natural science was taught, an unusual thing at the time. Further, Father Schreiber, the village priest, spent much time instructing the peasants in the grafting of fruit trees, and in other techniques of scientific farming. The elder Mendel was one of his most eager students, and hence it appears that Johann was, from earliest childhood, influenced in the direction of botanical and agricultural pursuits.

The school master recognized Johann's genius, and urged his parents to send him away for further schooling. This was done at the cost of much sacrifice for the family and genuine privation for Johann. In 1838, his father was struck by a rolling log while working on the estate of the countess. His chest was crushed, and he was never again able to work his farm. Further help from home was out of the question, but Johann was able to continue his schooling because his younger sister, Theresia, very generously gave him her dowry, and because he was able to earn a frugal living by private teaching.

MENDEL AS A MONK AND TEACHER After graduating from the gymnasium, Mendel attended the Philosophical Institute at Olmütz, where he distinguished himself. But these, too, were very difficult years, and his health was frail. In his autobiography,* he wrote that he "felt that it would not be possible for him to endure such exertions still further, and he saw himself forced therefore after the completion of his philosophical studies to enter a profession in which he would be freed of the bitter necessities of life. His circumstances determined his choice of profession. He applied and was received in the Augustinian monastery of St. Thomas in Altbrünn." And so in September 1843, he entered the monastery of St. Thomas, where he took the name *Gregor*, with which he always signed himself.

Because of the above statement in his autobiography, some have doubted the sincerity of Mendel's religious profession. Yet he appears to have been an exemplary member of the monastic community. Later, as abbot, he showed more than ordinary concern for the spiritual life of the community, and his associates have all attested the practical character of his faith. It is known that the possibility of his entering the priesthood had long been under discussion in the Mendel family, and, in selling his farm, his father had even made provisions in the sales contract for some help toward the education of Johann "if the latter as he now designs should enter the priesthood."† Thus it appears, while his circumstances determined his final choice, that he was already much interested in the priesthood. Had the family been more prosperous, he might have become a parish priest rather than a monk.

After his ordination, Mendel was soon assigned to duty as a temporary teacher of mathematics and Greek in a nearby high school. Although his service was highly re-

garded, he could not be given a permanent appointment, because he lacked the necessary teaching credentials. He was therefore urged to take the examination for teachers of natural science. This he did in the spring of 1850, but he failed. That he failed is hardly surprising, for the examination was ordinarily taken on the basis of university training, and Mendel was entirely self-taught in science. However, one of the examiners persuaded the abbot to send Mendel to the University of Vienna for further training. He attended the university for two years (1851–1853), and in 1854 he was appointed substitute teacher of natural science in the Brünn Modern School (an advanced technical high school). In May 1856, he again took the examination for the teaching credential, and again he failed. There is no reliable information available on why he failed this time, but it seems unlikely that this gifted candidate was not adequately prepared. Some have thought that anticlericalism prejudiced some of the examiners, while others believe that he showed unusual independence of thought, and that his avid defense of theories contrary to those of the examiners aroused their antipathy. At any rate, he failed, and he never again applied for his credentials, hence during the entire fourteen years of his service at the Brünn Modern School his title was merely substitute teacher, although he was on regular, full-time duty. He began his experiments with peas soon after his second failure, and a school inspector has expressed the opinion that the experiments were undertaken as a result of a dispute with the examiner for botany. If this is correct, then we are much indebted to the examining board for failing its most gifted candidate.

Mendel's teaching years were his happiest. Through the recollections of his students there appears a man of reserve and humility, but still a warm and human man, with great enthusiasm for his boys and for the sciences

* Mendel's autobiography was written in the third person, as a part of his application for admission to the examination for high school teachers in 1850.

† Iltis, The Life of Mendel. Translated by Eden and Cedar Paul. W. W. Norton Co., New York.

which he taught them (fig. 156). He was skilled in making difficult material clear. The boys were frequent visitors to the monastery, where he showed them his microscope and his telescope, his bees and his tamed animals, but especially his garden plants. Yet he never hinted that he was himself carrying out original investigations.

MENDEL AS ABBOT   In March 1868, the abbot died, and on March 30, Mendel's brother monks unanimously elected him to that high office, thus conferring upon him that honor which the rest of the world had withheld. He wrote to the botanist Nägeli that "on March 30 my unimportant self was elected life-long head, by the chapter of the monastery to which I belong. From the very modest position of teacher of experimental physics I thus find myself moved into a sphere in which much appears strange to me, and it will take some time and effort before I feel at home in it. This shall not prevent me from continuing the hybridization experiments of which I have become so fond; I even hope to be able to devote more time and attention to them, once I have become familiar with my new position."* This was to be an unrealized hope, however, for Mendel found that the sympathetic direction of his staff, the fostering of the religious life of the monastic community, and the care and restoration of the monastery took ever more and more of his time. But most of all, his time and energy were consumed by a bitter dispute with the state over taxation. In 1874, a law for taxation of the monasteries was passed. Mendel regarded the law as unconstitutional, and

* Supplement to Genetics, vol. 35, "Birth of Genetics."

Fig. 156.   *Statue of Mendel at Brünn, by Charlemont. (From Iltis, Life of Mendel, W. W. Norton Co.)*

fought it until his death ten years later. To one raised in the American tradition, the whole controversy is difficult to understand. It seems self-evident that a prompt court hearing should have settled the constitutional question, as Mendel wished. But the Imperial Austrian government took the viewpoint that it was beneath the dignity of the government to discuss the validity of its laws with individual citizens. After Mendel's death, his successor obtained a settlement by acknowledging the law and then applying for exemptions to such an extent that little or none of the tax was payable.

EICHLING'S INTERVIEW WITH MENDEL
One of the best glimpses of Mendel's personality comes from this period. In 1942 Mr. C. W. Eichling, a flower and seed dealer of New Orleans, published in the Journal of Heredity his recollections of a visit with Mendel in 1878, when Mr. Eichling had been a young man of 22 years. Mr. Eichling wrote as follows: "In the summer of 1878 I was traveling representative for Louis Roempler, one of the large novelty plant-and-seed firms of Nancy, France. . . .

"Not one of the leaders in the horticultural industry interviewed that summer mentioned the name of Mendel. Not until I reached Erfurt and called on Ernest Benary, the Nestor of European seed growers and breeders, did I hear Mendel's name mentioned . . . . Benary mentioned Mendel . . . . and his experiments with garden peas, *Pisum sativum*. I told Benary that Brünn was on my itinerary . . . . and he suggested that I try to meet the Abbot if possible.

"On my arrival at Brünn I called on the only customer I had in the quaint old city of about 70,000 inhabitants. After our business was concluded, I asked about the Abbot Mendel. My customer stared at me in some astonishment and registered mild amusement at my inquiry. I was told that, while *der Herr Abt* was one of the best beloved clerics

in Brünn, not a soul believed his experiments were anything more than a pastime, and his theories anything more than the maunderings of a charming putterer. . . .

"My first impression was a genuine and pleasant surprise. My customer's account had built in my mind a picture of an old, wrinkled, spooky, monk. Coming toward me was a fine looking, spectacled priest, smiling and extending a welcoming hand. His countenance expressed both determination and kindliness. I judged him to be about fifty years old . . . . having been told that German was the Abbot's favorite language we were soon in a lively conversation.

"I told Mendel that Ernest Benary had requested me to call on him and I discovered then that Mendel knew of nearly all the important men in the plant and seed line. . . .

"We then perused my catalogue together, and Mendel displayed great interest in the rare plants I had to offer and asked many questions about their propagation. . . .

"It was now mid-day and the monastery bell called to dinner to which the Abbot invited me. A substantial meal, served in the Abbot's study, consisted of soup, home-grown vegetables, home made bread, exquisite ham and beer. After a little chat, the Abbot invited me to walk with him through his extensive gardens. The grounds were kept as clean as a pin. I was shown beds of well grown vegetables and fruit trees of many varieties, each tree with a label. Mendel pointed with pride to a pair of espaliers against a wall, well loaded with fruit. . . .

"I repeat here that at the time I met Mendel I knew practically nothing of his discoveries and experiments and he forbore to enlighten me on the subject. He did show me several beds of green peas in full bearing, which he said he had reshaped in height as well as in type of fruit to serve his establishment to better advantage. I asked him how he did it and he replied: 'It is just a little trick, but there is a long story connected with it which would take too long to tell'. . . .

"I told Mendel that I had promised to make a report to Benary regarding these experiments, but Mendel changed the subject and asked me to inspect his hothouse. . . .

"Mendel asked me about my school days. . . . He was of the opinion that I should have gone through Heidelberg University. He became enthusiastic when he spoke of his own student years in Vienna and we even recalled some of our favorite student songs such as 'Gaudeamus igitur'—'Vom Hoh'n Olymp'—'Edite, bibite collegiales,' etc. . . .

"My time to leave had arrived, and I thanked the Abbot for his great kindness to me, a young stranger. I knew from his hearty handshake and his blessing that I had made a friend. He accompanied me to the gate and made me promise to call on him again. This was not to be, because other plans prevented my returning.

"It is strange that when I asked Mendel about his work with the peas, he deliberately changed the subject. It could not have been that he had any desire to withhold the facts from me, for he had published the two immortal papers on his discoveries a dozen years before. It would seem that a direct invitation to talk about what must have been a very important episode in his life would have been eagerly seized upon. Could it be that this reticence was due to the complete oblivion his publications had achieved? Actually to have found the key to the riddle of heredity, and to have his discovery completely ignored both by his friends and by the scientific public must have been a tragic blow. . . . But the patronizing letter from Nägeli, advising him to spend his time more profitably, would have been enough to quench the enthusiasm of a very hardy soul indeed. Be that as it may, by failing to draw the master out with a sympathetic question I missed a priceless chance, in that garden sixty-four summers ago, to hear from the lips of the founder of Genetics how he made the discovery which today is recognized as marking an epoch in the study of life."

ILLNESS AND DEATH After several years of poor health, Mendel became acutely ill on January 4, 1884, and he died two days later of heart failure and Bright's disease. After a funeral mass on January 9, the founder of genetics was buried in the monastery cemetery. His funeral was attended by the dignitaries of church and state, and by a great throng which included students who honored the memory of an inspiring teacher, poor people who mourned, as Iltis has said, "a true disciple of Christ, who knew how to give alms and not to humiliate the receiver,"[*] but there were none present who suspected that they were burying a great scientist.

[*] Iltis, in Genetics in the 20th Century, 1951, The Macmillan Co., New York.

Fig. 157. *Hugo de Vries.*
(*From Genetics, vol. 4.*)

Fig. 158. *Carl Correns.*
(*From Genetics, vol. 13.*)

72. THE REDISCOVERY OF MENDEL AND MENDELISM

One of Mendel's successors has quoted him as saying, with regard to his experiments in heredity, "My time will surely come." It did come in the spring of 1900, and the story of his rediscovery and his long overdue recognition, achieved through the independent efforts of three men, is one of high drama, seldom equalled in the history of science. These three men were Hugo de Vries, Carl Correns, and Erich von Tschermak.

De Vries (fig. 157) was a distinguished Dutch botanist, whose studies in evolution had led him to make Mendelian crosses in

ten genera of plants, upon which he published first in the Proceedings of the French Academy of Sciences, then more fully in the March 1900 issue of the Reports of the German Botanical Society. In the second paper, he acknowledged the priority of Mendel. Meanwhile, Carl Correns (fig. 158), a young German botanist, was writing up the results of similar experiments on corn and peas, and he published his paper in the April issue of the Reports of the German Botanical Society. He included the statement that, "I thought that I had found something new. But then I convinced myself that the Abbot Gregor Mendel in Brünn, had, during the sixties, not only obtained the same results through extensive experiments with peas, which lasted for many years, as did de Vries and I, but had also given exactly the same explanation, as far as that was possible in the sixties."*

Erich von Tschermak (fig. 159) was a Viennese plant breeder, who in January 1900 had submitted a post-doctoral thesis in which he had also described the results of two years

* 1950, The Birth of Genetics. Supplement to Genetics, vol. 35.

Fig. 159. *Erich von Tschermak.*
(*From Genetics, vol. 27.*)

of study upon inheritance in peas. Publication of the entire thesis was planned, but when the papers of de Vries and Correns appeared, he felt that a summary of his thesis should be published promptly, and so he prepared a brief note for the June issue of the Reports of the German Botanical Society. In commenting upon these events, von Tschermak wrote ". . . . The three rediscoverers were fully aware of the fact that the independent discovery of the laws of heredity in 1900 was far from being the accomplishment that it had been in Mendel's time since it was made considerably easier by the work which had appeared in the interval. . . . Consequently the three rediscoverers were less interested in being celebrated as rediscoverers of rules they themselves designated 'Mendel's laws', than in the successful utilization of these laws for the development of their various fields: de Vries for the mutation theory, Correns for fundamental research in inheritance, and I for practical plant breeding."*

Of this famous triumvirate, only von Tschermak is still living at this writing. He has fulfilled the high promise of his youth, for he has been one of the most productive of the Mendelian plant breeders.

73. WHY WAS MENDEL'S RECOGNITION SO LONG DELAYED?

The question of why Mendel's recognition was so long delayed has vexed the historians of science. It is known that the Proceedings of the Brünn Society were in the libraries of most of the universities of Europe and America. Yet busy scientists may not have opened a journal in which they did not expect to find anything of importance.

MENDEL'S CORRESPONDENCE WITH NÄGELI Mendel sent a reprint of his paper to at least one botanist who ought to have recognized its value: Carl Nägeli, a specialist in plant hybridization, who was often regarded as the most distinguished botanist of his time. But Nägeli replied in condescending tone, saying with respect to the pea experiments, that they "are not completed but that they should really just begin," a severe stricture considering that Mendel's paper was based on over 10,000 plants. Nägeli expressed willingness to repeat the experiments if Mendel would send him seed. Mendel sent him no less than 140 packages of seeds with complete directions, but no experiments were ever carried to completion. Mendel and Nägeli remained in correspondence until 1873, mostly in regard to experiments with the hawkweed, *Hieracium*, in which Nägeli was much interested. In spite of this, Nägeli did not consider Mendel worthy of mention in a book on heredity which he published in 1884.

MENDEL AND DARWIN Bateson has suggested that Mendel would have achieved the recognition which he deserved during his life time had Darwin read his paper. Darwin was familiar with the literature on hybridization, and he realized that the weakest aspect of his theory of the origin of species lay in the lack of reliable information on heredity. Bateson believed that Darwin would have recognized and publicized the value of Mendel's work. That Darwin did not have Mendel's paper is certain, for his library has been thoroughly searched. Bateson may well be right, but the thesis is unprovable, and it may well be wrong, for surely the same thing would have been said of Nägeli were not the history of his relationship to Mendel known.

Another factor may have been the mathematical treatment of his data. Although this was an important feature in Mendel's success, quantitative biology was then unheard of, and it must have seemed strange and incomprehensible to biologists accustomed to thinking only in qualitative terms.

Whatever the real cause may have been,

* Journal of Heredity, 1951.

few if any discoveries of comparable magnitude have been so completely ignored in the time of the discoverer. Mendel's paper was cited, however, in W. O. Focke's comprehensive bibliography of plant hybridization, which was published in 1881. It was through this reference that the three rediscoverers found that Mendel had priority over them by thirty-five years. But Mendel had said that "my time will surely come": it did come in the spring of 1900, and it will last as long as mankind honors its benefactors.

GENETICS, A YOUNG SCIENCE   In concluding this historical survey, it may be profitable to emphasize the fact that these events are recent ones. At the time of this writing, there is still living at least one man who has talked with Mendel (Mr. C. W. Eichling, who was quoted above). And one of the three rediscoverers, von Tschermak, is still living. Of those men who joined the ranks of the new science at the turn of the century, a goodly company are still with us, so that there are today many living links with the first days of genetics.

74. SOME NOTES ON THE LATER HISTORY OF GENETICS

Much of the subsequent history of genetics has already been recounted in the preceding chapters. However, a brief summary may be in order here. The first major task of the early geneticists was to demonstrate the universality of the Mendelian laws, by exploring the simplest types of inheritance in a wide variety of plants and animals. Correns was a leader in this work in Germany, with his studies on corn and other plants. Bateson and Punnett did the pioneer work in England, working especially with chickens and sweet peas. Cuénot in France and William Castle in the United States took the lead in mammalian genetics. Simultaneously, some of the more complex problems were being attacked. Correns quickly turned to problems of cytoplasmic inheritance. Bateson and Punnett led the way in the investigation of collaboration of factors, and Johannsen developed the pure line concept, which proved to be the key to the old nature-nurture problem. As early as 1906, Nilsson-Ehle published a paper which established genetics as the rational basis of plant breeding, and the role of genetics in both plant and animal breeding has grown steadily since that time.

In 1910, Thomas Hunt Morgan introduced the use of the fruit fly, *Drosophila melanogaster*, into genetic research. The pages which precede attest how potent a catalyst for the development of genetics this proved to be. But even more important than so fortunate a choice of experimental organisms was the group of collaborators which Morgan attracted, first at Columbia University and later at California Institute of Technology. These included such men as H. J. Muller, who, like Morgan himself, later became a Nobel laureate; A. H. Sturtevant; and Calvin Bridges. The combination led not only to the most thorough understanding of a single organism that has yet been achieved, but more specifically it led in the following fifteen years to the full vindication of the chromosome theory of inheritance, the understanding of sex linkage, linkage and chromosome mapping, and finally to the theory of the gene, as published by Morgan in 1926. During this same period, Goldschmidt, in Germany, and Bridges, in Morgan's laboratory, carried on experiments which are the foundation of today's understanding of the determination of sex.

It was also during this period that the first steps were taken toward the development of hybrid corn. About 1905, G. H. Shull began his investigations of inbred lines of corn, and his insight into the relationship between the deterioration of inbred lines and hybrid vigor led to the production of superior hybrids. But these were not commercially practical because of the poor seed set of the inbred parents. D. F. Jones overcame this difficulty in 1917 by the introduction of the double-cross method. From that point on, hybrid corn became simply a matter of the exploration of the most desirable double-crosses, and this has been a major occupation of maize breeders since that time.

Muller discovered the induction of mutations by x-rays in 1929, and this has been a powerful stimulus not only to studies on mutation, but also to studies on the nature of the gene. This was followed in 1933 by the discovery of the salivary gland chromosomes by the German cytologists, Heitz and Bauer, and by their use in cytogenetics by the American, T. S. Painter. Bridges, however, more than anyone else, was responsible for the exploitation of the salivary gland chromosomes. The study of the salivary gland chromosomes showed that the position effects, which had been discovered in 1925 by Sturtevant and Morgan, were much more frequent and important than had been supposed. Paralleling this were the extensive and brilliant studies of A. F. Blakeslee and his many collaborators at Smith College on the chromosomal mutants of *Datura*, the Jimson weed. Goldschmidt then made the various facts associated with position effects the basis for a concerted attack upon the idea of genes as discrete particles. Another very important factor in the development of the theory of the gene was the rise of biochemical genetics. Some experiments in this field had been carried out even during the first two decades of the present century, especially by the English geneticists, but it received its greatest impetus much more recently. Beadle and Ephrussi, during the early thirties, investigated the biochemical genetics of eye pigments in *Drosophila* and some other insects. While they produced some valuable results, the most important

outcome of this work was the search for an organism more readily adapted to the study of genetic problems from a biochemical point of view, and the resulting investigations of the mold *Neurospora* by Beadle and many collaborators.

The biochemical genetics of *Neurospora* is also one of the most important recent developments in physiological genetics, which is, however, a much older field of investigation. Goldschmidt began his work in this field early in the present century, while Sewall Wright, of the University of Chicago, has been active in this field since 1916.

Some mention should be made of the saddest chapter in the history of genetics. During the twenties, Russia achieved a position of distinction in genetics, under the leadership of such men as N. K. Koltzoff, a world leader in animal genetics and cytology, and N. I. Vavilov, a plant breeder and plant geographer of the greatest magnitude. But a young plant breeder, named T. D. Lysenko, teamed up in the early thirties with a Marxist philosopher, named J. J. Prezent. The result has been disastrous for the development of genetics. In 1936, Lysenko challenged Vavilov, not on the grounds that he had repeated the basic Mendelian experiments and found them erroneous, but rather on the grounds that this was foreign science, that it was an evil thing born in a monastery at the hands of a priest and nurtured by Morgan within the shadow of Wall Street, and that it was idealistic and so incompatible with dialectical materialism. As Goldschmidt has pointed out, such nonsense may be raised by charlatans or fanatics in any country, but in a free country the sense of humor of their colleagues has free reign and prevents any disastrous effects of such aberrations. In Russia, however, this was not possible, for Lysenko convinced the political authorities that the geneticists were actually enemies of the state, and so the power of the state backed him up and prevented the free discussion which is the necessary condition for intellectual progress. By the beginning of World War II, Koltzoff, who was a very old man, had been forced to close his laboratory, and Vavilov had been sent to a forced labor camp in Siberia. There he died, probably in 1942.

In the place of the fine science of genetics which these martyrs for science had developed in Russia, Lysenko established a form of Lamarckism which he called Michurinism, after an earlier Russian plant breeder. All Russian geneticists then had to give at least lip service to Michurinism. Nonetheless, some bold men still continued to publish papers in the fine tradition of their predecessors. Then in 1948, Lysenko announced that the Central Committee of the Communist Party had examined his position and had approved it: henceforth, no deviation from Michurin-Lysenko biology would be permitted. Since the death of Stalin, there have been some indications that there may be a return to a sounder policy with regard to genetics in Russia. Scientists throughout the world will watch these developments with hopeful interest.

One of the most active aspects of genetics today is the application of genetics to problems of evolution. At the turn of the century, the new science of genetics seemed to be a stumbling block in the way of evolution. The apparent permanence of the gene seemed to preclude any evolution which might go beyond a mere reshuffling of a few alleles. But increasing knowledge of mutation removed that difficulty, and, when Dobzhansky published the first edition of "Genetics and the Origin of Species," the majority of biologists were quickly convinced that the dynamics of evolution lay in the field of population genetics. No one has been more active than Dobzhansky himself in the exploitation of this field, but mention should also be made of R. A. Fisher and Sewall Wright, who have taken the lead in the mathematical analysis of population genetics, and of Goldschmidt, who has played an important role by protesting too easy an acceptance of incompletely analyzed ideas, and by proposing alternatives to the more fashionable hypotheses.

Certainly the genetic research of the near future will continue to emphasize the physiology of the gene and the application of genetics to problems of evolution. Human genetics will continue to be studied intensively, and its applications will become ever more important. For the more distant developments, some of the students of today will be responsible.

References

Dodson, Edward O., 1955. Mendel and the rediscovery of his work. Scientific Monthly, 81:187–195. A more complete report on some of the material of this chapter.

Dunn, L. C. (editor), 1951. Genetics in the 20th Century. The Macmillan Co., New York. This is a collection of papers presented by distinguished geneticists at the Golden Jubilee of Genetics sponsored by the Genetics Society of America in 1950.

Eichling, C. W., 1942. I talked with Mendel. Journal of Heredity, 33:243–246.

Iltis, H., 1932. Life of Mendel. W. W. Norton and Co., New York.

Mendel, Gregor, 1866. Versuche über Pflanzen-Hybriden. Reprinted as a facsimile reproduction of the original in the Journal of Heredity, 42:3–47. In translation, Experiments in Plant Hybridization. 1948. Harvard University Press, Cambridge.

Punnett, R. C., 1950. Early days of genetics. Heredity, 4:1–10. This paper comprises the fascinating reminiscences, upon the occasion of the fiftieth anniversary of the rediscovery of Mendelism, of one of the most active of the early geneticists.

Stern, C. (editor), 1950. The Birth of Genetics. Supplement to Genetics, 35 (no. 5, pt. 2):1–47. This includes Mendel's letters to Nägeli and the original papers of de Vries, Correns, and von Tschermak, all in English translation.

von Tschermak-Seysenegg, Erich, 1951. The rediscovery of Gregor Mendel's work. Journal of Heredity, 42:163–171.

APPENDIX A

Experiments in Plant-Hybridisation*

By Gregor Mendel

INTRODUCTORY REMARKS

Experience of artificial fertilisation, such as is effected with ornamental plants in order to obtain new variations in colour, has led to the experiments which will here be discussed. The striking regularity with which the same hybrid forms always reappeared whenever fertilisation took place between the same species induced further experiments to be undertaken, the object of which was to follow up the developments of the hybrids in their progeny.

To this object numerous careful observers, such as Kölreuter, Gärtner, Herbert, Lecoq, Wichura and others, have devoted a part of their lives with inexhaustible perseverance. Gärtner especially, in his work "Die Bastarderzeugung im Pflanzenreiche" (The Production of Hybrids in the Vegetable Kingdom), has recorded very valuable observations; and quite recently Wichura published the results of some profound investigations into the hybrids of the Willow. That, so far, no generally applicable law governing the formation and development of hybrids has been successfully formulated can hardly be wondered at by anyone who is acquainted with the extent of the task, and can appreciate the difficulties with which experiments of this class have to contend. A final decision can only be arrived at when we shall have before us the results of detailed experiments made on plants belonging to the most diverse orders.

Those who survey the work done in this department will arrive at the conviction that among all the numerous experiments made, not one has been carried out to such an extent and in such a way as to make it possible to determine the number of different forms under which the offspring of hybrids appear, or to arrange these forms with certainty according to their separate generations, or definitely to ascertain their statistical relations.[1]

[1] [It is to the clear conception of these three primary necessities that the whole success of Mendel's work is due. So far as I know this conception was absolutely new in his day.]

It requires indeed some courage to undertake a labour of such far-reaching extent; this appears, however, to be the only right way by which we can finally reach the solution of a question the importance of which cannot be overestimated in connection with the history of the evolution of organic forms.

* Reprinted by permission of the Royal Horticultural Society of London. The original paper was published in the *Verh. naturf. Ver. in Brünn, Abhandlungen,* iv. 1865, which appeared in 1866.

This was taken from the translation of the original article which was published by the Harvard University Press, Cambridge, Mass. in 1950. This translation included footnotes added and minor changes suggested by Professor W. Bateson, enclosed within [   ].

The paper now presented records the results of such a detailed experiment. This experiment was practically confined to a small plant group, and is now, after eight years' pursuit, concluded in all essentials. Whether the plan upon which the separate experiments were conducted and carried out was the best suited to attain the desired end is left to the friendly decision of the reader.

SELECTION OF THE EXPERIMENTAL PLANTS

The value and utility of any experiment are determined by the fitness of the material to the purpose for which it is used, and thus in the case before us it cannot be immaterial what plants are subjected to experiment and in what manner such experiments are conducted.

The selection of the plant group which shall serve for experiments of this kind must be made with all possible care if it be desired to avoid from the outset every risk of questionable results.

The experimental plants must necessarily—

1. Possess constant differentiating characters.

2. The hybrids of such plants must, during the flowering period, be protected from the influence of all foreign pollen, or be easily capable of such protection.

The hybrids and their offspring should suffer no marked disturbance in their fertility in the successive generations.

Accidental impregnation by foreign pollen, if it occurred during the experiments and were not recognized, would lead to entirely erroneous conclusions. Reduced fertility or entire sterility of certain forms, such as occurs in the offspring of many hybrids, would render the experiments very difficult or entirely frustrate them. In order to discover the relations in which the hybrid forms stand towards each other and also towards their progenitors it appears to be necessary that all members of the series developed in each successive generation should be, *without exception*, subjected to observation.

At the very outset special attention was devoted to the *Leguminosae* on account of their peculiar floral structure. Experiments which were made with several members of this family led to the result that the genus *Pisum* was found to possess the necessary qualifications.

Some thoroughly distinct forms of this genus possess characters which are constant, and easily and certainly recognizable, and when their hybrids are mutually crossed they yield perfectly fertile progeny. Furthermore, a disturbance through foreign pollen cannot easily occur, since the fertilising organs are closely packed inside the keel and the anther bursts within the bud, so that the stigma becomes covered with pollen even before the flower opens. This circumstance is of especial importance. As additional advantages worth mentioning. there may be cited the easy culture of these plants in the open ground and in pots, and also their relatively short period of growth. Artificial fertilisation is certainly a somewhat elaborate process, but nearly always succeeds. For this purpose the bud is opened before it is perfectly developed, the keel is removed, and each stamen carefully extracted by means of forceps, after which the stigma can at once be dusted over with the foreign pollen.

In all, thirty-four more or less distinct varieties of Peas were obtained from several seedsmen and subjected to a two years' trial. In the case of one variety there were noticed, among a larger number of plants all alike, a few forms which were markedly different. These, however, did not vary in the following year, and agreed entirely with another variety obtained from the same seedsman; the seeds were therefore doubtless merely accidentally mixed. All the other varieties yielded perfectly constant and similar off-spring; at any rate, no essential difference was observed during two trial years. For fertilisation twenty-two of these were selected and cultivated during the whole period of the experiments. They remained constant without any exception.

Their systematic classification is difficult and uncertain. If we adopt the strictest definition of a species, according to which only those individuals belong to a species which under precisely the same circumstances display precisely similar characters, no two of these varieties could be referred to one species. According to the opinion of experts, however, the majority belong to the species *Pisum sativum*; while the rest are regarded and classed, some as sub-species of *P. sativum*, and some as independent species, such as *P. quadratum*, *P. saccharatum*, and *P. umbellatum*. The positions, however, which may be assigned to them in a classificatory system are quite immaterial for the purposes of the experiments in question. It has so far been found to be just as impossible to draw a sharp line between the hybrids of species and varieties as between species and varieties themselves.

DIVISION AND ARRANGEMENT OF THE EXPERIMENTS

If two plants which differ constantly in one or several characters be crossed, numerous experiments have demonstrated that the common characters are transmitted unchanged to the hybrids and their progeny; but each pair of differentiating characters, on the other hand, unite in the hybrid to form a new character, which in the progeny of the hybrid is usually variable. The object of the experiment was to observe these variations in the case of each pair of differentiating characters, and to deduce the law according to which they appear in the successive generations. The experiment resolves itself therefore into just as many separate experiments as there are constantly differentiating characters presented in the experimental plants.

The various forms of Peas selected for crossing showed differences in the length and colour of the stem; in the size and form of the leaves; in the position, colour, and size of the flowers; in the length of the flower stalk; in the colour, form, and size of the pods; in the form and size of the seeds; and in the colour of the seed-coats and of the albumen [cotyledons]. Some of the characters noted do not permit of a sharp and certain separation, since the difference is of a "more or less" nature, which is often difficult to define. Such characters could not be utilised for the separate experiments; these could only be applied to characters which stand out clearly and definitely in the plants. Lastly, the result must show whether they, in their entirety, observe a regular behaviour in their hybrid unions, and whether from these facts any conclusion can be come to regarding those characters which possess a subordinate significance in the type.

The characters which were selected for experiment relate:

1. To the *difference in the form of the ripe seeds*. These are either round or roundish, the depressions, if any, occur on the surface, being always only shallow; or they are irregularly angular and deeply wrinkled (*P. quadratum*).

2. To the *difference in the colour of the seed albumen* (endosperm).[1] The albumen of the ripe seeds is either pale yellow, bright yellow and orange coloured, or it possesses a more or less intense green tint. This difference of colour is easily seen in the seeds as [= if] their coats are transparent.

3. To the *difference in the colour of the seed-coat*. This is either white, with which character white flowers are constantly correlated; or it is grey, grey-brown, leather-brown, with or without violet spotting, in which case the colour of the standards is

violet, that of the wings purple, and the stem in the axils of the leaves is of a reddish tint. The grey seed-coats become dark brown in boiling water.

4. To the *difference in the form of the ripe pods*. These are either simply inflated, not contracted in places; or they are deeply constricted between the seeds and more or less wrinkled (*P. saccharatum*).

5. To the *difference in the colour of the unripe pods*. They are either light to dark green, or vividly yellow, in which colouring the stalks, leaf-veins, and calyx participate.[2]

[1] [Mendel uses the terms "albumen" and "endosperm" somewhat loosely to denote the cotyledons, containing food-material, within the seed.]

[2] One species possesses a beautifully brownish-red coloured pod, which when ripening turns to violet and blue. Trials with this character were only begun last year. [Of these further experiments it seems no account was published. Correns has since worked with such a variety.]

6. To the *difference in the position of the flowers*. They are either axial, that is, distributed along the main stem; or they are terminal, that is, bunched at the top of the stem and arranged almost in a false umbel; in this case the upper part of the stem is more or less widened in section (*P. umbellatum*).[3]

[3] [This is often called the Mummy Pea. It shows slight fasciation. The form I know has white standard and salmon-red wings.]

7. To the *difference in the length of the stem*. The length of the stem[4] is very various in

[4] [In my account of these experiments (*R.H.S. Journal*, vol. xxv. p. 54) I misunderstood this paragraph and took "axis" to mean the *floral* axis, instead of the main axis of the plant. The unit of measurement, being indicated in the original by a dash ('), I carelessly took to have been an *inch*, but the translation here given is evidently correct.]

some forms; it is, however, a constant character for each, in so far that healthy plants,

grown in the same soil, are only subject to unimportant variations in this character.

In experiments with this character, in order to be able to discriminate with certainty, the long axis of 6 to 7 ft. was always crossed with the short one of 3/4 ft. to 1 1/2 ft.

Each two of the differentiating characters enumerated above were united by cross-fertilisation. There were made for the

1st trial 60 fertilisations on 15 plants.					
2nd "	58	"	"	10	"
3rd "	35	"	"	10	"
4th "	40	"	"	10	"
5th "	23	"	"	5	"
6th "	34	"	"	10	"
7th "	37	"	"	10	"

From a larger number of plants of the same variety only the most vigorous were chosen for fertilisation. Weakly plants always afford uncertain results, because even in the first generation of hybrids, and still more so in the subsequent ones, many of the offspring either entirely fail to flower or only form a few and inferior seeds.

Furthermore, in all the experiments reciprocal crossings were effected in such a way that each of the two varieties which in one set of fertilisation served as seed-bearer in the other set was used as the pollen plant.

The plants were grown in garden beds, a few also in pots, and were maintained in their naturally upright position by means of sticks, branches of trees, and strings stretched between. For each experiment a number of pot plants were placed during the blooming period in a greenhouse, to serve as control plants for the main experiment in the open as regards possible disturbance by insects. Among the insects[1] which visit Peas the

[1] [It is somewhat surprising that no mention is made of Thrips, which swarm in Pea flowers. I had come to the conclusion that this is a real source of error and I see Laxton held the same opinion.]

beetle *Bruchus pisi* might be detrimental to the experiments should it appear in numbers. The female of this species is known to lay the eggs in the flower, and in so doing opens the keel; upon the tarsi of one specimen, which was caught in a flower, some pollen grains could clearly be seen under a lens. Mention must also be made of a circumstance which possibly might lead to the introduction of foreign pollen. It occurs, for instance, in some rare cases that certain parts of an otherwise quite normally developed flower wither, resulting in a partial exposure of the fertilising organs. A defective development of the keel has also been observed, owing to which the stigma and anthers remained partially uncovered.[1] It also some-

[1] [This also happens in Sweet Peas.]

times happens that the pollen does not reach full perfection. In this event there occurs a gradual lengthening of the pistil during the blooming period, until the stigmatic tip protrudes at the point of the keel. This remarkable appearance has also been observed in hybrids of *Phaseolus* and *Lathyrus*.

The risk of false impregnation by foreign pollen is, however, a very slight one with *Pisum*, and is quite incapable of disturbing the general result. Among more than 10,000 plants which were carefully examined there were only a very few cases where an indubitable false impregnation had occurred. Since in the greenhouse such a case was never remarked, it may well be supposed that *Bruchus pisi*, and possibly also the described abnormalities in the floral structure, were to blame.

[F_1] THE FORMS OF THE HYBRIDS[2]

[2] [Mendel throughout speaks of his cross-bred Peas as "hybrids," a term which many restrict to the offspring of two distinct *species*. He, as he explains, held this to be only a question of degree.]

Experiments which in previous years were made with ornamental plants have already afforded evidence that the hybrids, as a rule, are not exactly intermediate between the parental species. With some of the more striking characters, those, for instance, which relate to the form and size of the leaves, the pubescence of the several parts, &c., the intermediate, indeed, is nearly always to be seen; in other cases, however, one of the two parental characters is so preponderant that it is difficult, or quite impossible, to detect the other in the hybrid.

This is precisely the case with the Pea hybrids. In the case of each of the seven crosses the hybrid-character resembles[3] that

[3] [Note that Mendel, with true penetration, avoids speaking of the hybrid-character as "transmitted" by either parent, thus escaping the error pervading the older views of heredity.]

of one of the parental forms so closely that the other either escapes observation completely or cannot be detected with certainty. This circumstance is of great importance in the determination and classification of the forms under which the offspring of the hybrids appear. Henceforth in this paper those characters which are transmitted entire, or almost unchanged in the hybridisation, and therefore in themselves constitute the characters of the hybrid, are termed the *dominant*, and those which become latent in the process *recessive*. The expression "recessive" has been chosen because the characters thereby designated withdraw or entirely disappear in the hybrids, but nevertheless reappear unchanged in their progeny, as will be demonstrated later on.

It was furthermore shown by the whole of the experiments that it is perfectly immaterial whether the dominant character belongs to the seed-bearer or to the pollen-parent; the form of the hybrid remains identical in both cases. This interesting fact was also emphasised by Gärtner, with the remark that even the most practised expert is not in a position to determine in a hybrid which of the two parental species was the seed or the pollen plant.[1]

[1] [Gärtner, p. 223.]

Of the differentiating characters which were used in the experiments the following are dominant:

1. The round or roundish form of the seed with or without shallow depressions.

2. The yellow colouring of the seed albumen [cotyledons].

3. The grey, grey-brown, or leather-brown colour of the seedcoat, in association with violet-red blossoms and reddish spots in the leaf axils.

4. The simply inflated form of the pod.

5. The green colouring of the unripe pod in association with the same colour in the stems, the leaf-veins and the calyx.

6. The distribution of the flowers along the stem.

7. The greater length of stem.

With regard to this last character it must be stated that the longer of the two parental stems is usually exceeded by the hybrid, a fact which is possibly only attributable to the greater luxuriance which appears in all parts of plants when stems of very different length are crossed. Thus, for instance, in repeated experiments, stems of 1 ft. and 6 ft. in length yielded without exception hybrids which varied in length between 6 ft. and 7 1/2 ft.

The hybrid seeds in the experiments with seed-coat are often more spotted, and the spots sometimes coalesce into small bluish-violet patches. The spotting also frequently appears even when it is absent as a parental character.[1]

[1] [This refers to the coats of the seeds borne by F_1 plants.]

The hybrid forms of the seed-shape and of the albumen [colour] are developed im-mediately after the artificial fertilisation by the mere influence of the foreign pollen. They can, therefore, be observed even in the first year of experiment, whilst all the other characters naturally only appear in the following year in such plants as have been raised from the crossed seed.

[F_2] THE GENERATION [BRED] FROM THE HYBRIDS

In this generation there reappear, together with the dominant characters, also the recessive ones with their peculiarities fully developed, and this occurs in the definitely expressed average proportion of three to one, so that among each four plants of this generation three display the dominant character and one the recessive. This relates without exception to all the characters which were investigated in the experiments. The angular wrinkled form of the seed, the green colour of the albumen, the white colour of the seed-coats and the flowers, the constrictions of the pods, the yellow colour of the unripe pod, of the stalk, of the calyx, and of the leaf venation, the umbel-like form of the inflorescence, and the dwarfed stem, all reappear in the numerical proportion given, without any essential alteration. *Transitional forms were not observed in any experiment.*

Since the hybrids resulting from reciprocal crosses are formed alike and present no appreciable difference in their subsequent development, consequently the results [of the reciprocal crosses] can be reckoned together in each experiment. The relative numbers which were obtained for each pair of differentiating characters are as follows:

Expt. 1. Form of seed.—From 253 hybrids 7,324 seeds were obtained in the second trial year. Among them were 5,474 round or roundish ones and 1,850 angular wrinkled ones. Therefrom the ratio 2.96 to 1 is deduced.

Expt. 2. Colour of albumen.—258 plants

yielded 8,023 seeds, 6,022 yellow, and 2,001 green; their ratio, therefore, is as 3.01 to 1.

In these two experiments each pod yielded usually both kinds of seeds. In well-developed pods which contained on the average six to nine seeds, it often happened that all the seeds were round (Expt. 1) or all yellow (Expt. 2); on the other hand there were never observed more than five wrinkled or five green ones in one pod. It appears to make no difference whether the pods are developed early or later in the hybrid or whether they spring from the main axis or from a lateral one. In some few plants only a few seeds developed in the first formed pods, and these possessed exclusively one of the two characters, but in the subsequently developed pods the normal proportions were maintained nevertheless.

As in separate pods, so did the distribution of the characters vary in separate plants. By way of illustration the first ten individuals from both series of experiments may serve.

	EXPERIMENT I		EXPERIMENT 2	
	Form of Seed		Color of Albumen	
Plants	Round	Angular	Yellow	Green
1	45	12	25	11
2	27	8	32	7
3	24	7	14	5
4	19	10	70	27
5	32	11	24	13
6	26	6	20	6
7	88	24	32	13
8	22	10	44	9
9	28	6	50	14
10	25	7	44	18

As extremes in the distribution of the two seed characters in one plant, there were observed in Expt. 1 an instance of 43 round and only 2 angular, and another of 14 round and 15 angular seeds. In Expt. 2 there was a case of 32 yellow and only 1 green seed, but also one of 20 yellow and 19 green.

These two experiments are important for the determination of the average ratios, because with a smaller number of experimental plants they show that very considerable fluctuations may occur. In counting the seeds, also, especially in Expt. 2, some care is requisite, since in some of the seeds of many plants the green colour of the albumen is less developed, and at first may be easily overlooked. The cause of this partial disappearance of the green colouring has no connection with the hybrid-character of the plants, as it likewise occurs in the parental variety. This peculiarity [bleaching] is also confined to the individual and is not inherited by the offspring. In luxuriant plants this appearance was frequently noted. Seeds which are damaged by insects during their development often vary in colour and form, but, with a little practice in sorting, errors are easily avoided. It is almost superfluous to mention that the pods must remain on the plants until they are thoroughly ripened and have become dried, since it is only then that the shape and colour of the seed are fully developed.

Expt. 3. Colour of the seed-coats.— Among 929 plants 705 bore violet-red flowers and grey-brown seed-coats; 224 had white flowers and white seed-coats, giving the proportion 3.15 to 1.

Expt. 4. Form of pods.—Of 1,181 plants 882 had them simply inflated, and in 299 they were constricted. Resulting ratio, 2.95 to 1.

Expt. 5. Colour of the unripe pods.—The number of trial plants was 580, of which 428 had green pods and 152 yellow ones. Consequently these stand in the ratio 2.82 to 1.

Expt. 6. Position of flowers.—Among 858 cases 651 had inflorescences axial and 207 terminal. Ratio, 3.14 to 1.

Expt. 7. Length of stem.—Out of 1,064 plants, in 787 cases the stem was long, and in 277 short. Hence a mutual ratio of 2.84 to 1. In this experiment the dwarfed plants were carefully lifted and transferred to a special bed. This precaution was necessary, as otherwise they would have perished through being overgrown by their tall relatives. Even in their quite young state they can be easily picked out by their compact growth and thick dark-green foliage.[1]

[1] [This is true also of the dwarf or "Cupid" Sweet Peas.]

If now the results of the whole of the experiments be brought together, there is found, as between the number of forms with the dominant and recessive characters, an average ratio of 2.98 to 1, or 3 to 1.

The dominant character can have here a *double signification*—viz. that of a parental character, or a hybrid-character.[2] In which

[2] [This paragraph presents the view of the hybrid-character as something incidental to the hybrid, and not "transmitted" to it—a true and fundamental conception here expressed probably for the first time.]

of the two significations it appears in each separate case can only be determined by the following generation. As a parental character it must pass over unchanged to the whole of the offspring; as a hybrid-character, on the other hand, it must maintain the same behaviour as in the first generation [F_2].

[F_3] THE SECOND GENERATION [BRED] FROM THE HYBRIDS

Those forms which in the first generation [F_2] exhibit the recessive character do not further vary in the second generation [F_3] as regards this character; they remain constant in their offspring.

It is otherwise with those which possess the dominant character in the first generation [bred from the hybrids]. Of these *two*-thirds yield offspring which display the dominant and recessive characters in the proportion of 3 to 1, and thereby show exactly the same ratio as the hybrid forms, while only *one*-third remains with the dominant character constant.

The separate experiments yielded the following results:

Expt. 1. Among 565 plants which were raised from round seeds of the first generation, 193 yielded round seeds only, and remained therefore constant in this character; 372, however, gave both round and wrinkled seeds, in the proportion of 3 to 1. The number of the hybrids, therefore, as compared with the constants is 1.93 to 1.

Expt. 2. Of 519 plants which were raised from seeds whose albumen was of yellow colour in the first generation, 166 yielded exclusively yellow, while 353 yielded yellow and green seeds in the proportion of 3 to 1. There resulted, therefore, a division into hybrid and constant forms in the proportion of 2.13 to 1.

For each separate trial in the following experiments 100 plants were selected which displayed the dominant character in the first generation, and in order to ascertain the significance of this, ten seeds of each were cultivated.

Expt. 3. The offspring of 36 plants yielded exclusively grey-brown seed-coats, while of the offspring of 64 plants some had grey-brown and some had white.

Expt. 4. The offspring of 29 plants had only simply inflated pods; of the offspring of 71, on the other hand, some had inflated and some constricted.

Expt. 5. The offspring of 40 plants had only green pods; of the offspring of 60 plants some had green, some yellow ones.

Expt. 6. The offspring of 33 plants had only axial flowers; of the offspring of 67, on the other hand, some had axial and some terminal flowers.

Expt. 7. The offspring of 28 plants inherited the long axis, and those of 72 plants some the long and some the short axis.

In each of these experiments a certain number of the plants came constant with the dominant character. For the determination of the proportion in which the separation of the forms with the constantly persistent character results, the two first experiments are of especial importance, since in these a larger number of plants can be compared. The ratios 1.93 to 1 and 2.13 to 1 gave together almost exactly the average ratio of 2 to 1. The sixth experiment gave a quite concordant result; in the others the ratio varies more or less, as was only to be expected in view of the smaller number of 100 trial plants. Experiment 5, which shows the greatest departure, was repeated, and then, in lieu of the ratio of 60 and 40, that of 65 and 35 resulted. *The average ratio of 2 to 1 appears, therefore, as fixed with certainty.* It is therefore demonstrated that, of those forms which possess the dominant character in the first generation, two-thirds have the hybrid-character, while one-third remains constant with the dominant character.

The ratio of 3 to 1, in accordance with which the distribution of the dominant and recessive characters results in the first generation, resolves itself therefore in all experiments into the ratio of 2 : 1 : 1 if the dominant character be differentiated according to its significance as a hybrid-character or as a parental one. Since the members of the first generation [F_2] spring directly from the seed of the hybrids [F_1], *it is now clear that the hybrids form seeds having one or other of the two differentiating characters, and of these one-half develop again the hybrid form, while the other half yield plants which remain constant and receive the dominant or the recessive characters [respectively] in equal numbers.*

THE SUBSEQUENT GENERATIONS [BRED] FROM THE HYBRIDS

The proportions in which the descendants of the hybrids develop and split up in the first and second generations presumably hold good for all subsequent progeny. Experiments 1 and 2 have already been carried through six generations, 3 and 7 through five, and 4, 5, and 6 through four, these experiments being continued from the third generation with a small number of plants,

and no departure from the rule has been perceptible. The offspring of the hybrids separated in each generation in the ratio of 2 : 1 : 1 into hybrids and constant forms.

If A be taken as denoting one of the two constant characters, for instance the dominant, a, the recessive, and Aa the hybrid form in which both are conjoined, the expression

$$A + 2Aa + a$$

shows the terms in the series for the progeny of the hybrids of two differentiating characters.

The observation made by Gärtner, Kölreuter, and others, that hybrids are inclined to revert to the parental forms, is also confirmed by the experiments described. It is seen that the number of the hybrids which arise from one fertilisation, as compared with the number of forms which become constant, and their progeny from generation to generation, is continually diminishing, but that nevertheless they could not entirely disappear. If an average equality of fertility in all plants in all generations be assumed, and if, furthermore, each hybrid forms seed of which one-half yields hybrids again, while the other half is constant to both characters in equal proportions, the ratio of numbers for the offspring in each generation is seen by the following summary, in which A and a denote again the two parental characters, and Aa the hybrid forms. For brevity's sake it may be assumed that each plant in each generation furnishes only 4 seeds.

Generation	A	Aa	a	RATIOS $A : Aa : a$
1	1	2	1	1 : 2 : 1
2	6	4	6	3 : 2 : 3
3	28	8	28	7 : 2 : 7
4	120	16	120	15 : 2 : 15
5	496	32	496	31 : 2 : 31
n				$2^n-1 : 2 : 2^n-1$

In the tenth generation, for instance, $2^n - 1 = 1023$. There result, therefore, in each 2,084 plants which arise in this generation

1,023 with the constant dominant character, 1,023 with the recessive character, and only two hybrids.

THE OFFSPRING OF HYBRIDS IN WHICH SEVERAL DIFFERENTIATING CHARACTERS ARE ASSOCIATED

In the experiments above described plants were used which differed only in one essential character.[1] The next task consisted in

[1] [This statement of Mendel's in the light of present knowledge is open to some misconception. Though his work makes it evident that such varieties may exist, it is very unlikely that Mendel could have had seven pairs of varieties such that the members of each pair differed from each other in *only* one considerable character (*wesentliches Merkmal*). The point is probably of little theoretical or practical consequence, but a rather heavy stress is thrown on "*wesentlich.*"]

ascertaining whether the law of development discovered in these applied to each pair of differentiating characters when several diverse characters are united in the hybrid by crossing. As regards the form of the hybrids in these cases, the experiments showed throughout that this invariably more nearly approaches to that one of the two parental plants which possesses the greater number of dominant characters. If, for instance, the seed plant has a short stem, terminal white flowers, and simply inflated pods; the pollen plant, on the other hand, a long stem, violet-red flowers distributed along the stem, and constricted pods; the hybrid resembles the seed parent only in the form of the pod; in the other characters it agrees with the pollen parent. Should one of the two parental types possess only dominant characters, then the hybrid is scarcely or not at all distinguishable from it.

Two experiments were made with a considerable number of plants. In the first ex-

periment the parental plants differed in the form of the seed and in the colour of the albumen; in the second in the form of the seed, in the colour of the albumen, and in the colour of the seed-coats. Experiments with seed characters give the result in the simplest and most certain way.

In order to facilitate study of the data in these experiments, the different characters of the seed plant will be indicated by A, B, C, those of the pollen plant by a, b, c, and the hybrid forms of the characters by Aa, Bb, and Cc.

Expt. 1.—

AB, seed parents;	ab, pollen parents;
A, form round;	a, form wrinkled;
B, albumen yellow.	b, albumen green.

The fertilised seeds appeared round and yellow like those of the seed parents. The plants raised therefrom yielded seeds of four sorts, which frequently presented themselves in one pod. In all, 556 seeds were yielded by 15 plants, and of these there were:

315 round and yellow,
101 wrinkled and yellow,
108 round and green,
32 wrinkled and green.

All were sown the following year. Eleven of the round yellow seeds did not yield plants, and three plants did not form seeds. Among the rest:

38 had round yellow seeds	AB
65 round yellow and green seeds	ABb
60 round yellow and wrinkled yellow seeds	AaB
138 round yellow and green, wrinkled yellow and green seeds	$AaBb$

From the wrinkled yellow seeds 96 resulting plants bore seed, of which:

28 had only wrinkled yellow seeds	aB
68 wrinkled yellow and green seeds	aBb

From 108 round green seeds 102 resulting plants fruited, of which:

> 35 had only round green seeds Ab
> 67 round and wrinkled green seeds Aab.

The wrinkled green seeds yielded 30 plants which bore seeds all of like character; they remained constant ab.

The offspring of the hybrids appeared therefore under nine different forms, some of them in very unequal numbers. When these are collected and co-ordinated we find:

38 plants with the sign AB				
35	"	"	"	" Ab
28	"	"	"	" aB
30	"	"	"	" ab
65	"	"	"	" ABb
68	"	"	"	" aBb
60	"	"	"	" AaB
67	"	"	"	" Aab
138	"	"	"	" $AaBb$.

The whole of the forms may be classed into three essentially different groups. The first includes those with the signs AB, Ab, aB, and ab: they possess only constant characters and do not vary again in the next generation. Each of these forms is represented on the average thirty-three times. The second group includes the signs ABb, aBb, AaB, Aab: these are constant in one character and hybrid in another, and vary in the next generation only as regards the hybrid-character. Each of these appears on an average sixty-five times. The form $AaBb$ occurs 138 times: it is hybrid in both characters, and behaves exactly as do the hybrids from which it is derived.

If the numbers in which the forms belonging to these classes appear be compared, the ratios of 1, 2, 4 are unmistakably evident. The numbers 32, 65, 138 present very fair approximations to the ratio numbers of 33, 66, 132.

The developmental series consists, therefore, of nine classes, of which four appear

therein always once and are constant in both characters; the forms AB, ab, resemble the parental forms, the two other present combinations between the conjoined characters A, a, B, b, which combinations are likewise possibly constant. Four classes appear always twice, and are constant in one character and hybrid in the other. One class appears four times, and is hybrid in both characters. Consequently the offspring of the hybrids, if two kinds of differentiating characters are combined therein, are represented by the expression

$$AB + Ab + aB + ab + 2ABb + 2aBb + 2AaB + 2Aab + 4AaBb.$$

This expression is indisputably a combination series in which the two expressions for the characters A and a, B and b are combined. We arrive at the full number of the classes of the series by the combination of the expressions:

$$A + 2Aa + a$$
$$B + 2Bb + b.$$

Expt. 2.

ABC, seed parents;	abc, pollen parents;
A, form round;	a, form wrinkled;
B, albumen yellow;	b, albumen green;
C, seed-coat grey-brown.	c, seed-coat white.

This experiment was made in precisely the same way as the previous one. Among all the experiments it demanded the most time and trouble. From 24 hybrids 687 seeds were obtained in all: these were all either spotted, grey-brown or grey-green, round or wrinkled.[1] From these in the following

1 [Note that Mendel does not state the cotyledon-colour of the first crosses in this case; for as the coats were thick, it could not have been seen without opening or peeling the seeds.]

year 639 plants fruited, and, as further investigation showed, there were among them:

8 plants *ABC*		22 plants *ABCc*		45 plants *ABbCc*		
14 "	*ABc*	17 "	*AbCc*	36 "	*aBbCc*	
9 "	*AbC*	25 "	*aBCc*	38 "	*AaBCc*	
11 "	*Abc*	20 "	*abCc*	40 "	*AabCc*	
8 "	*aBC*	15 "	*ABbC*	49 "	*AaBbC*	
10 "	*aBc*	18 "	*ABbc*	48 "	*AaBbc*	
10 "	*abC*	19 "	*aBbC*			
7 "	*abc*	24 "	*aBbc*			
		14 "	*AaBC*	78 "	*AaBbCc*	
		18 "	*AaBc*			
		20 "	*AabC*			
		16 "	*Aabc*			

The whole expression contains 27 terms. Of these 8 are constant in all characters, and each appears on the average 10 times; 12 are constant in two characters, and hybrid in the third; each appears on the average 19 times; 6 are constant in one character and hybrid in the other two; each appears on the average 43 times. One form appears 78 times and is hybrid in all of the characters. The ratios 10, 19, 43, 78 agree so closely with the ratios 10, 20, 40, 80, or 1, 2, 4, 8, that this last undoubtedly represents the true value.

The development of the hybrids when the original parents differ in three characters results therefore according to the following expression:

$$ABC + ABc + AbC + Abc + aBC +$$
$$aBc + abC + abc + 2\ ABCc + 2\ AbCc$$
$$+ 2\ aBCc + 2\ abCc + 2\ ABbC + 2\ ABbc$$
$$+ 2\ aBbC + 2\ aBbc + 2\ AaBC + 2\ AaBc$$
$$+ 2\ AabC + 2\ Aabc + 4\ ABbCc + 4$$
$$aBbCc + 4\ AaBCc + 4\ AabCc + 4\ AaBbC$$
$$+ 4\ AaBbc + 8\ AaBbCc.$$

Here also is involved a combination series in which the expressions for the characters *A* and *a*, *B* and *b*, *C* and *c*, are united. The expressions

$$A + 2Aa + a$$
$$B + 2Bb + b$$
$$C + 2Cc + c$$

give all the classes of the series. The constant

combinations which occur therein agree with all combinations which are possible between the characters *A*, *B*, *C*, *a*, *b*, *c*; two thereof, *ABC* and *abc*, resemble the two original parental stocks.

In addition, further experiments were made with a smaller number of experimental plants in which the remaining characters by twos and threes were united as hybrids: all yielded approximately the same results. There is therefore no doubt that for the whole of the characters involved in the experiments the principle applies that *the offspring of the hybrids in which several essentially different characters are combined exhibit the terms of a series of combinations, in which the developmental series for each pair of differentiating characters are united.* It is demonstrated at the same time that *the relation of each pair of different characters in hybrid union is independent of the other differences in the two original parental stocks.*

If *n* represents the number of the differentiating characters in the two original stocks, 3^n gives the number of terms of the combination series, 4^n the number of individuals which belong to the series, and 2^n the number of unions which remain constant. The series therefore contains, if the original stocks differ in four characters, $3^4 = 81$ classes, $4^4 = 256$ individuals, and $2^4 = 16$ constant forms; or, which is the same, among each 256 offspring of the hybrids there are 81 different combinations, 16 of which are constant.

All constant combinations which in Peas are possible by the combination of the said seven differentiating characters were actually obtained by repeated crossing. Their number is given by $2^7 = 128$. Thereby is simultaneously given the practical proof *that the constant characters which appear in the several varieties of a group of plants may be obtained in all the associations which are possible according to the [mathematical] laws of combination, by means of repeated artificial fertilisation.*

As regards the flowering time of the hybrids, the experiments are not yet concluded. It can, however, already be stated that the time stands almost exactly between those of the seed and pollen parents, and that the constitution of the hybrids with respect to this character probably follows the rule ascertained in the case of the other characters. The forms which are selected for experiments of this class must have a difference of at least twenty days from the middle flowering period of one to that of the other; furthermore, the seeds when sown must all be placed at the same depth in the earth, so that they may germinate simultaneously. Also, during the whole flowering period, the more important variations in temperature must be taken into account, and the partial hastening or delaying of the flowering which may result therefrom. It is clear that this experiment presents many difficulties to be overcome and necessitates great attention.

If we endeavour to collate in a brief form the results arrived at, we find that those differentiating characters, which admit of easy and certain recognition in the experimental plants, all behave exactly alike in their hybrid associations. The offspring of the hybrids of each pair of differentiating characters are, one-half, hybrid again, while the other half are constant in equal proportions having the characters of the seed and pollen parents respectively. If several differentiating characters are combined by cross-fertilisation in a hybrid, the resulting offspring form the terms of a combination series in which the combination series for each pair of differentiating characters are united.

The uniformity of behaviour shown by the whole of the characters submitted to experiment permits, and fully justifies, the acceptance of the principle that a similar relation exists in the other characters which appear less sharply defined in plants, and therefore could not be included in the separate experiments. An experiment with peduncles of different lengths gave on the whole a fairly satisfactory result, although the differentiation and serial arrangement of the forms could not be effected with that certainty which is indispensable for correct experiment.

THE REPRODUCTIVE CELLS OF THE HYBRIDS

The results of the previously described experiments led to further experiments, the results of which appear fitted to afford some conclusions as regards the composition of the egg and pollen cells of hybrids. An important clue is afforded in *Pisum* by the circumstance that among the progeny of the hybrids constant forms appear, and that this occurs, too, in respect of all combinations of the associated characters. So far as experience goes, we find it in every case confirmed that constant progeny can only be formed when the egg cells and the fertilising pollen are of like character, so that both are provided with the material for creating quite similar individuals, as is the case with the normal fertilisation of pure species. We must therefore regard it as certain that exactly similar factors must be at work also in the production of the constant forms in the hybrid plants. Since the various constant forms are produced in *one* plant, or even in *one* flower of a plant, the conclusion appears logical that in the ovaries of the hybrids there are formed as many sorts of egg cells, and in the anthers as many sorts of pollen cells, as there are possible constant combination forms, and that these egg and pollen cells agree in their internal composition with those of the separate forms.

In point of fact it is possible to demonstrate theoretically that this hypothesis would fully suffice to account for the development of the hybrids in the separate generations, if we might at the same time assume that the various kinds of egg and pollen cells were formed in the hybrids on the average in equal numbers.[1]

[1] [This and the preceding paragraph contain the essence of the Mendelian principles of heredity.]

In order to bring these assumptions to an experimental proof, the following experiments were designed. Two forms which were constantly different in the form of the seed and the colour of the albumen were united by fertilisation.

If the differentiating characters are again indicated as *A, B, a, b*, we have:

AB, seed parent;   *ab*, pollen parent;
  A, form round;   *a*, form wrinkled;
  B, albumen yellow.   *b*, albumen green.

The artificially fertilised seeds were sown together with several seeds of both original stocks, and the most vigorous examples were chosen for the reciprocal crossing. There were fertilised:

1. The hybrids with the pollen of *AB*.
2. The hybrids with the pollen of *ab*.
3. *AB* with the pollen of the hybrids.
4. *ab* with the pollen of the hybrids.

For each of these four experiments the whole of the flowers on three plants were fertilised. If the above theory be correct, there must be developed on the hybrids egg and pollen cells of the forms *AB, Ab, aB, ab*, and there would be combined:

1. The egg cells *AB, Ab, aB, ab* with the pollen cells *AB*.
2. The egg cells *AB, Ab, aB, ab* with the pollen cells *ab*.
3. The egg cells *AB* with the pollen cells *AB, Ab, aB, ab*.
4. The egg cells *ab* with the pollen cells *AB, Ab, aB, ab*.

From each of these experiments there could then result only the following forms:

1. *AB, ABb, AaB, AaBb*.
2. *AaBb, Aab, aBb, ab*.
3. *AB, ABb, AaB, AaBb*.
4. *AaBb, Aab, aBb, ab*.

If, furthermore, the several forms of the egg and pollen cells of the hybrids were produced on an average in equal numbers, then in each experiment the said four combinations should stand in the same ratio to each other. A perfect agreement in the numerical relations was, however, not to be expected, since in each fertilisation, even in normal cases, some egg cells remain undeveloped or subsequently die, and many even of the well-formed seeds fail to germinate when sown. The above assumption is also limited in so far that, while it demands the formation of an equal number of the various sorts of egg and pollen cells, it does not require that this should apply to each separate hybrid with mathematical exactness.

The first and second experiments had primarily the object of proving the composition of the hybrid egg cells, while the third and fourth experiments were to decide that of the pollen cells.[1] As is shown by the above

[1] [To prove, namely, that both were similarly differentiated, and not one or other only.]

demonstration the first and third experiments and the second and fourth experiments should produce precisely the same combinations, and even in the second year the result should be partially visible in the form and colour of the artificially fertilised seed. In the first and third experiments the dominant characters of form and colour, *A* and *B*, appear in each union, and are also partly constant and partly in hybrid union with the recessive characters *a* and *b*, for which reason they must impress their peculiarity upon the whole of the seeds. All seeds should therefore appear round and yellow, if the theory be justified. In the second and fourth experiments, on the other hand, one union is hybrid in form and in colour, and consequently the seeds are round and yellow; another is hybrid in form, but constant in the recessive character of colour, whence the seeds are round and green; the third is constant in the recessive character of form but hybrid in colour, consequently the seeds are wrinkled and yellow; the fourth is constant in both recessive characters, so that the seeds are wrinkled and green. In both these experiments there were consequently four sorts of seed to be expected—viz. round and yellow, round and green, wrinkled and yellow, wrinkled and green.

The crop fulfilled these expectations perfectly. There were obtained in the

1st Experiment, 98 exclusively round yellow seeds;

3rd Experiment, 94 exclusively round yellow seeds.

In the 2d Experiment, 31 round and yellow, 26 round and green, 27 wrinkled and yellow, 26 wrinkled and green seeds.

In the 4th Experiment, 24 round and yellow, 25 round and green, 22 wrinkled and yellow, 26 wrinkled and green seeds.

There could scarcely be now any doubt of the success of the experiment; the next generation must afford the final proof. From the seed sown there resulted for the first experiment 90 plants, and for the third 87 plants which fruited: these yielded for the

1ST EXP.	3RD EXP.	
20	25	round yellow seeds . . . . AB
23	19	round yellow and green seeds. . . . . ABb
25	22	round and wrinkled yellow seeds. . AaB
22	21	round and wrinkled green and yellow seeds . . . . AaBb

In the second and fourth experiments the round and yellow seeds yielded plants with round and wrinkled yellow and green seeds, AaBb.

From the round green seeds, plants re-

sulted with round and wrinkled green seeds, Aab.

The wrinkled yellow seeds gave plants with wrinkled yellow and green seeds, aBb.

From the wrinkled green seeds plants were raised which yielded again only wrinkled and green seeds, ab.

Although in these two experiments likewise some seeds did not germinate, the figures arrived at already in the previous year were not affected thereby, since each kind of seed gave plants which, as regards their seed, were like each other and different from the others. There resulted therefore from the

2D EXP.	4TH EXP.	
31	24	plants of the form AaBb
26	25	" " " " Aab
27	22	" " " " aBb
26	27	" " " " ab

In all the experiments, therefore, there appeared all the forms which the proposed theory demands, and they came in nearly equal numbers.

In a further experiment the characters of flower-colour and length of stem were experimented upon, and selection was so made that in the third year of the experiment each character ought to appear in half of all the plants if the above theory were correct. A, B, a, b serve again as indicating the various characters.

A, violet-red flowers.   a, white flowers.
B, axis long.   b, axis short.

The form Ab was fertilised with ab, which produced the hybrid Aab. Furthermore, aB was also fertilised with ab, whence the hybrid aBb. In the second year, for further fertilisation, the hybrid Aab was used as seed parent, and hybrid aBb as pollen parent.

Seed parent, Aab.
Possible egg cells, Ab,ab.
Pollen parent, aBb.
Pollen cells, aB,ab.

From the fertilisation between the possible egg and pollen cells four combinations should result, viz.,

$$AaBb + aBb + Aab + ab.$$

From this it is perceived that, according to the above theory, in the third year of the experiment out of all the plants

Half should have violet-red flowers (Aa)
Classes 1, 3
Half should have white flowers (a)
Classes 2, 4
Half should have a long axis (Bb)
Classes 1, 2
Half should have a short axis (b)
Classes 3, 4

From 45 fertilisations of the second year 187 seeds resulted, of which only 166 reached the flowering stage in the third year. Among these the separate classes appeared in the numbers following:

CLASS	COLOR OF FLOWER	STEM	
1	violet-red	long	47 times
2	white	long	40 "
3	violet-red	short	38 "
4	white	short	41 "

There subsequently appeared

The violet-red flower-colour (Aa) in 85 plants.
The white flower-colour (a) in 81 plants.
The long stem (Bb) in 87 plants.
The short stem (b) in 79 plants.

The theory adduced is therefore satisfactorily confirmed in this experiment also.

For the characters of form of pod, colour of pod, and position of flowers, experiments were also made on a small scale, and results obtained in perfect agreement. All combinations which were possible through the union of the differentiating characters duly appeared, and in nearly equal numbers.

Experimentally, therefore, the theory is confirmed that *the pea hybrids form egg and pollen cells which, in their constitution, represent in equal numbers all constant forms which result from the combination of the characters united in fertilisation.*

The difference of the forms among the progeny of the hybrids, as well as the respective ratios of the numbers in which they are observed, find a sufficient explanation in the principle above deduced. The simplest case is afforded by the developmental series of each pair of differentiating characters. This series is represented by the expression $A + 2Aa + a$, in which A and a signify the forms with constant differentiating characters, and Aa the hybrid form of both. It includes in three different classes four individuals. In the formation of these, pollen and egg cells of the form A and a take part on the average equally in the fertilisation; hence each form [occurs] twice, since four individuals are formed. There participate consequently in the fertilisation

The pollen cells $A + A + a + a$
The egg cells $A + A + a + a$.

It remains, therefore, purely a matter of chance which of the two sorts of pollen will become united with each separate egg cell. According, however, to the law of probability, it will always happen, on the average of many cases, that each pollen form, A and a, will unite equally often with each egg cell form, A and a, consequently one of the two pollen cells A in the fertilisation will meet with the egg cell A and the other with an egg cell a, and so likewise one pollen cell a will unite with an egg cell A, and the other with egg cell a.

Pollen cells	A	A a	a
	$\downarrow$	$\times$	$\downarrow$
Egg cells	A	A a	a

The result of the fertilisation may be made

clear by putting the signs for the conjoined egg and pollen cells in the form of fractions, those for the pollen cells above and those for the egg cells below the line. We then have

$$\frac{A}{A} + \frac{A}{a} + \frac{a}{A} + \frac{a}{a}.$$

In the first and fourth term the egg and pollen cells are of like kind, consequently the product of their union must be constant, viz. A and a; in the second and third, on the other hand, there again results a union of the two differentiating characters of the stocks, consequently the forms resulting from these fertilisations are identical with those of the hybrid from which they sprang. *There occurs accordingly a repeated hybridisation.* This explains the striking fact that the hybrids are able to produce, besides the two parental forms, offspring which are like themselves; $\frac{A}{a}$ and $\frac{a}{A}$ both give the same union Aa, since,

as already remarked above, it makes no difference in the result of fertilisation to which of the two characters the pollen or egg cells belong. We may write then

$$\frac{A}{A} + \frac{A}{a} + \frac{a}{A} + \frac{a}{a} = A + 2Aa + a.$$

This represents the average result of the self-fertilisation of the hybrids when two differentiating characters are united in them. In individual flowers and in individual plants, however, the ratios in which the forms of the series are produced may suffer not inconsiderable fluctuations.[1] Apart from

[1] [Whether segregation by such units is more than purely fortuitous may perhaps be determined by seriation.]

the fact that the numbers in which both sorts of egg cells occur in the seed vessels can only be regarded as equal on the average, it remains purely a matter of chance which of the two sorts of pollen may fertilise each separate egg cell. For this reason the separate values must necessarily be subject to fluctuations, and there are even extreme cases possible, as were described earlier in connection with the experiments on the form of the seed and the colour of the albumen. The true ratios of the numbers can only be ascertained by an average deduced from the sum of as many single values as possible; the greater the number, the more are merely chance effects eliminated.

The developmental series for hybrids in which two kinds of differentiating characters are united contains, among sixteen individuals, nine different forms, viz.,

$$AB + Ab + aB + ab + 2ABb +$$
$$2aBb + 2AaB + 2Aab + 4AaBb.$$

Between the differentiating characters of the original stocks, Aa and Bb, four constant combinations are possible, and consequently the hybrids produce the corresponding four forms of egg and pollen cells AB, Ab, aB, ab, and each of these will on the average figure four times in the fertilisation, since sixteen individuals are included in the series. Therefore the participators in the fertilisation are (as shown below):

Pollen cells $AB + AB + AB + AB + Ab + Ab + Ab + Ab$
$\qquad\qquad + aB + aB + aB + aB + ab + ab + ab + ab.$

Egg cells $\quad AB + AB + AB + AB + Ab + Ab + Ab + Ab$
$\qquad\qquad + aB + aB + aB + aB + ab + ab + ab + ab.$

In the process of fertilisation each pollen form unites on an average equally often with each egg cell form, so that each of the four pollen cells *AB* unites once with one of the forms of egg cell *AB, Ab, aB, ab*. In precisely the same way the rest of the pollen cells of the forms *Ab, aB, ab* unite with all the other egg cells. We obtain therefore the results indicated at the bottom of this page.

In precisely similar fashion is the developmental series of hybrids exhibited when three kinds of differentiating characters are conjoined in them. The hybrids form eight various kinds of egg and pollen cells—*ABC, ABc, AbC, Abc, aBC, aBc, abC, abc*—and each pollen form unites itself again on the average once with each form of egg cell.

The law of combination of different characters, which governs the development of the hybrids, finds therefore its foundation and explanation in the principle enunciated, that the hybrids produce egg cells and pollen cells which in equal numbers represent all constant forms which result from the combinations of the characters brought together in fertilisation.

EXPERIMENTS WITH HYBRIDS OF OTHER SPECIES OF PLANTS

It must be the object of further experiments to ascertain whether the law of development discovered for *Pisum* applies also to the hybrids of other plants. To this end several experiments were recently commenced. Two minor experiments with species of *Phaseolus* have been completed, and may be here mentioned.

An experiment with *Phaseolus vulgaris* and *Phaseolus nanus* gave results in perfect agreement. *Ph. nanus* had, together with the dwarf axis, simply inflated, green pods. *Ph. vulgaris* had, on the other hand, an axis 10 feet to 12 feet high, and yellow-coloured pods, constricted when ripe. The ratios of the numbers in which the different forms appeared in the separate generations were the same as with *Pisum*. Also the development of the constant combinations resulted according to the law of simple combination of characters, exactly as in the case of *Pisum*. There were obtained

CONSTANT COMBINATIONS	AXIS	COLOUR OF THE UNRIPE PODS	FORM OF THE RIPE PODS
1	long	green	inflated
2	"	"	constricted
3	"	yellow	inflated
4	"	"	constricted
5	short	green	inflated
6	"	"	constricted
7	"	yellow	inflated
8	"	"	constricted

The green colour of the pod, the inflated forms, and the long axis were, as in *Pisum*, dominant characters.

Another experiment with two very differ-

$$\frac{AB}{AB}+\frac{AB}{Ab}+\frac{AB}{aB}+\frac{AB}{ab}+\frac{Ab}{AB}+\frac{Ab}{Ab}+\frac{Ab}{aB}+\frac{Ab}{ab}$$

$$+\frac{aB}{AB}+\frac{aB}{Ab}+\frac{aB}{aB}+\frac{aB}{ab}+\frac{ab}{AB}+\frac{ab}{Ab}+\frac{ab}{aB}+\frac{ab}{ab},$$

or

$$AB + ABb + AaB + AaBb + ABb + Ab + AaBb + Aab + AaB$$

$$+ AaBb + aB + aBb + AaBb + Aab + aBb + ab = AB$$

$$+ Ab + aB + ab + 2ABb + 2aBb + 2AaB + 2Aab + 4AaBb.[1]$$

[1] [In the original the sign of equality (=) is here represented by +, evidently a misprint.]

ent species of *Phaseolus* had only a partial result. *Phaseolus nanus*, L., served as seed parent, a perfectly constant species, with white flowers in short racemes and small white seeds in straight, inflated, smooth pods; as pollen parent was used *Ph. multiflorus*, W., with tall winding stem, purple-red flowers in very long racemes, rough, sickle-shaped crooked pods, and large seeds which bore black flecks and splashes on a peach-blood-red ground.

The hybrids had the greatest similarity to the pollen parent, but the flowers appeared less intensely coloured. Their fertility was very limited; from seventeen plants, which together developed many hundreds of flowers, only forty-nine seeds in all were obtained. These were of medium size, and were flecked and splashed similarly to those of *Ph. multiflorus*, while the ground colour was not materially different. The next year forty-four plants were raised from these seeds, of which only thirty-one reached the flowering stage. The characters of *Ph. nanus*, which had been altogether latent in the hybrids, reappeared in various combinations; their ratio, however, with relation to the dominant plants was necessarily very fluctuating owing to the small number of trial plants. With certain characters, as in those of the axis and the form of pod it was, however, as in the case of *Pisum*, almost exactly 1 : 3.

Insignificant as the results of this experiment may be as regards the determination of the relative numbers in which the various forms appeared, it presents, on the other hand, the phenomenon of a remarkable change of colour in the flowers and seed of the hybrids. In *Pisum* it is known that the characters of the flower- and seed-colour present themselves unchanged in the first and further generations, and that the offspring of the hybrids display exclusively the one or the other of the characters of the original stocks. It is otherwise in the experiment we are considering. The white flowers

and the seed-colour of *Ph. nanus* appeared, it is true, at once in the first generation [*from the hybrids*] in one fairly fertile example, but the remaining thirty plants developed flower-colours which were of various grades of purple-red to pale violet. The colouring of the seed-coat was no less varied than that of the flowers. No plant could rank as fully fertile; many produced no fruit at all; others only yielded fruits from the flowers last produced, which did not ripen. From fifteen plants only were well-developed seeds obtained. The greatest disposition to infertility was seen in the forms with preponderantly red flowers, since out of sixteen of these only four yielded ripe seed. Three of these had a similar seed pattern to *Ph. multiflorus*, but with a more or less pale ground colour; the fourth plant yielded only one seed of plain brown tint. The forms with preponderantly violet-coloured flowers had dark brown, black-brown, and quite black seeds.

The experiment was continued through two more generations under similar unfavorable circumstances, since even among the offspring of fairly fertile plants there came again some which were less fertile or even quite sterile. Other flower- and seed-colours than those cited did not subsequently present themselves. The forms which in the first generation [bred from the hybrids] contained one or more of the recessive characters remained, as regards these, constant without exception. Also of those plants which possessed violet flowers and brown or black seed, some did not vary again in these respects in the next generation; the majority, however, yielded, together with offspring exactly like themselves, some which displayed white flowers and white seed-coats. The red flowering plants remained so slightly fertile that nothing can be said with certainty as regards their further development.

Despite the many disturbing factors with which the observations had to contend, it is nevertheless seen by this experiment that the development of the hybrids, with regard to those characters which concern the form of the plants, follows the same laws as in *Pisum*. With regard to the colour characters, it certainly appears difficult to perceive a substantial agreement. Apart from the fact that from the union of a white and a purple-red colouring a whole series of colours results [in F_2], from purple to pale violet and white, the circumstance is a striking one that among thirty-one flowering plants only one received the recessive character of the white colour, while in *Pisum* this occurs on the average in every fourth plant.

Even these enigmatical results, however, might probably be explained by the law governing *Pisum* if we might assume that the colour of the flowers and seeds of *Ph. multiflorus* is a combination of two or more entirely independent colours, which individually act like any other constant character in the plant. If the flower-colour A were a combination of the individual characters $A_1 + A_2 + \ldots$ which produce the total impression of a purple coloration, then by fertilisation with the differentiating character, white colour, a, there would be produced the hybrid unions $A_1a + A_2a + \ldots$ and so would it be with the corresponding colouring of the seed-coats.[1] According to

[1] [As it fails to take account of factors introduced by the albino this representation is imperfect. It is however interesting to know that Mendel realized the fact of the existence of compound characters, and that the rarity of the white recessives was a consequence of this resolution.]

the above assumption, each of these hybrid colour unions would be independent, and would consequently develop quite independently from the others. It is then easily seen that from the combination of the separate developmental series a complete colour-series must result. If, for instance, $A = A_1 + A_2$, then the hybrids A_1a and A_2a form the developmental series—

$$A_1 + 2A_1a + a, \qquad A_2 + 2A_2a + a.$$

The members of this series can enter into nine different combinations, and each of these denotes another colour—

1 A_1A_2	2 A_1aA_2	1 A_2a
2 A_1A_2a	4 A_1aA_2a	2 A_2aa
1 A_1a	2 A_1aa	1 aa.

The figures prescribed for the separate combinations also indicate how many plants with the corresponding colouring belong to the series. Since the total is sixteen, the whole of the colours are on the average distributed over each sixteen plants, but, as the series itself indicates, in unequal proportions.

Should the colour development really happen in this way, we could offer an explanation of the case above described, viz. that the white flowers and seed-coat colour only appeared once among thirty-one plants of the first generation. This colouring appears only once in the series, and could therefore also only be developed once in the average in each sixteen, and with three colour characters only once even in sixty-four plants.

It must, nevertheless, not be forgotten that the explanation here attempted is based on a mere hypothesis, only supported by the very imperfect result of the experiment just described. It would, however, be well worth while to follow up the development of colour in hybrids by similar experiments, since it is probable that in this way we might learn the significance of the extraordinary variety in the colouring of our ornamental flowers.

So far, little at present is known with certainty beyond the fact that the colour of the flowers in most ornamental plants is an extremely variable character. The opinion has often been expressed that the stability of the species is greatly disturbed or entirely upset by cultivation, and consequently there is an inclination to regard the development of cultivated forms as a matter of chance devoid of rules; the colouring of ornamental plants is indeed usually cited as an example of great instability. It is, however, not clear why the simple transference into garden soil should result in such a thorough and persistent revolution in the plant organism. No one will seriously maintain that in the open country the development of plants is ruled by other laws than in the garden bed. Here, as there, changes of type must take place if the conditions of life be altered, and the species possesses the capacity of fitting itself to its new environment. It is willingly granted that by cultivation the origination of new varieties is favoured, and that by man's labour many varieties are acquired which, under natural conditions, would be lost; but nothing justifies the assumption that the tendency to the formation of varieties is so extraordinarily increased that the species speedily lose all stability, and their offspring diverge into an endless series of extremely variable forms. Were the change in the conditions the sole cause of variability we might expect that those cultivated plants which are grown for centuries under almost identical conditions would again attain constancy. That, as is well known, is not the case, since it is precisely under such circumstances that not only the most varied but also the most variable forms are found. It is only the *Leguminosae*, like *Pisum, Phaseolus*,[1] *Lens*, whose or-

[1] [*Phaseolus* nevertheless is insect-fertilised.]

gans of fertilisation are protected by the keel, which constitute a noteworthy exception. Even here there have arisen numerous varieties during a cultural period of more than 1000 years under most various conditions; these maintain, however, under unchanging environments a stability as great as that of species growing wild.

It is more than probable that as regards the variability of cultivated plants there exists a factor which so far has received little attention. Various experiments force us to the conclusion that our cultivated plants, with few exceptions, are *members of various hybrid series*, whose further development in con-

formity with law is varied and interrupted by frequent crossings *inter se*. The circumstance must not be overlooked that cultivated plants are mostly grown in great numbers and close together, affording the most favourable conditions for reciprocal fertilisation between the varieties present and the species itself. The probability of this is supported by the fact that among the great array of variable forms solitary examples are always found, which in one character or another remain constant, if only foreign influence be carefully excluded. These forms behave precisely as do those which are known to be members of the compound hybrid series. Also with the most susceptible of all characters, that of colour, it cannot escape the careful observer that in the separate forms the inclination to vary is displayed in very different degrees. Among plants which arise from *one* spontaneous fertilisation there are often some whose offspring vary widely in the constitution and arrangement of the colours, while that of others shows little deviation, and among a greater number solitary examples occur which transmit the colour of the flowers unchanged to their offspring. The cultivated species of *Dianthus* afford an instructive example of this. A white-flowered example of *Dianthus caryophyllus*, which itself was derived from a white-flowered variety, was shut up during its blooming period in a greenhouse; the numerous seeds obtained therefrom yielded plants entirely white-flowered like itself. A similar result was obtained from a subspecies, with red flowers somewhat flushed with violet, and one with flowers white, striped with red. Many others, on the other hand, which were similarly protected, yielded progeny which were more or less variously coloured and marked.

Whoever studies the coloration which results, in ornamental plants, from similar fertilisation, can hardly escape the conviction that here also the development follows a definite law, which possibly finds its expression *in the combination of several independent colour characters.*

CONCLUDING REMARKS

It can hardly fail to be of interest to compare the observations made regarding *Pisum* with the results arrived at by the two authorities in this branch of knowledge, Kölreuter and Gärtner, in their investigations. According to the opinion of both, the hybrids in outward appearance present either a form intermediate between the original species, or they closely resemble either the one or the other type, and sometimes can hardly be discriminated from it. From their seeds usually arise, if the fertilisation was effected by their own pollen, various forms which differ from the normal type. As a rule, the majority of individuals obtained by one fertilisation maintain the hybrid form, while some few others come more like the seed parent, and one or other individual approaches the pollen parent. This, however, is not the case with all hybrids without exception. Sometimes the offspring have more nearly approached, some the one and some the other of the two original stocks, or they all incline more to one or the other side; while in other cases *they remain perfectly like the hybrid* and continue constant in their offspring. The hybrids of varieties behave like hybrids of species, but they possess greater variability of form and a more pronounced tendency to revert to the original types.

With regard to the form of the hybrids and their development, as a rule an agreement with the observations made in *Pisum* is unmistakable. It is otherwise with the exceptional cases cited. Gärtner confesses even that the exact determination whether a form bears a greater resemblance to one or to the other of the two original species often involved great difficulty, so much depending upon the subjective point of view of the ob-

server. Another circumstance could, however, contribute to render the results fluctuating and uncertain, despite the most careful observation and differentiation. For the experiments, plants were mostly used which rank as good species and are differentiated by a large number of characters. In addition to the sharply defined characters, where it is a question of greater or less similarity, those characters must also be taken into account which are often difficult to define in words, but yet suffice, as every plant specialist knows, to give the forms a peculiar appearance. If it be accepted that the development of hybrids follows the law which is valid for *Pisum*, the series in each separate experiment must contain very many forms, since the number of the terms, as is known, increases, with the number of the differentiating characters, as the powers of three. With a relatively small number of experimental plants the result therefore could only be approximately right, and in single cases might fluctuate considerably. If, for instance, the two original stocks differ in seven characters, and 100 or 200 plants were raised from the seeds of their hybrids to determine the grade of relationship of the offspring, we can easily see how uncertain the decision must become, since for seven differentiating characters the combination series contain 16,384 individuals under 2187 various forms; now one and then another relationship could assert its predominance, just according as chance presented this or that form to the observer in a majority of cases.

If, furthermore, there appear among the differentiating characters at the same time *dominant* characters, which are transmitted entire or nearly unchanged to the hybrids, then in the terms of the developmental series that one of the two original parents which possesses the majority of dominant characters must always be predominant. In the experiment described relative to *Pisum*, in which three kinds of differentiating characters were concerned, all the dominant characters belonged to the seed parent. Although the terms of the series in their internal composition approach both original parents equally, yet in this experiment the type of the seed parent obtained so great a preponderance that out of each sixty-four plants of the first generation fifty-four exactly resembled it, or only differed in one character. It is seen how rash it must be under such circumstances to draw from the external resemblances of hybrids conclusions as to their internal nature.

Gärtner mentions that in those cases where the development was regular, among the offspring of the hybrids, the two original species were not reproduced, but only a few individuals which approached them. With very extended developmental series it could not in fact be otherwise. For seven differentiating characters, for instance, among more than 16,000 individuals—offspring of the hybrids—each of the two original species would occur only once. It is therefore hardly possible that these should appear at all among a small number of experimental plants; with some probability, however, we might reckon upon the appearance in the series of a few forms which approach them.

We meet with an *essential difference* in those hybrids which remain constant in their progeny and propagate themselves as truly as the pure species. According to Gärtner, to this class belong the *remarkably fertile hybrids, Aquilegia atropurpurea canadensis, Lavatera pseudolbia thuringiaca, Geum urbano-rivale,* and some *Dianthus* hybrids; and, according to Wichura, the hybrids of the Willow family. For the history of the evolution of plants this circumstance is of special importance, since constant hybrids acquire the status of new species. The correctness of the facts is guaranteed by eminent observers, and cannot be doubted. Gärtner

had an opportunity of following up *Dianthus Armeria deltoides* to the tenth generation, since it regularly propagated itself in the garden.

With *Pisum* it was shown by experiment that the hybrids form egg and pollen cells of *different* kinds, and that herein lies the reason of the variability of their offspring. In other hybrids, likewise, whose offspring behave similarly we may assume a like cause; for those, on the other hand, which remain constant, the assumption appears justifiable that their reproductive cells are all alike and agree with the foundation-cell [fertilised ovum] of the hybrid. In the opinion of renowned physiologists, for the purpose of propagation one pollen cell and one egg cell unite in Phanerogams[1] into a single cell, which is

[1] In *Pisum* it is placed beyond doubt that for the formation of the new embryo a perfect union of the elements of both reproductive cells must take place. How could we otherwise explain that among the offspring of the hybrids both original types reappear in equal numbers and with all their peculiarities? If the influence of the egg cell upon the pollen cell were only external, if it fulfilled the *rôle* of a nurse only, then the result of each artificial fertilisation could be no other than that the developed hybrid should exactly resemble the pollen parent, or at any rate do so very closely. This the experiments so far have in no wise confirmed. An evident proof of the complete union of the contents of both cells is afforded by the experience gained on all sides that it is immaterial, as regards the form of the hybrid, which of the original species is the seed parent or which the pollen parent.

capable by assimilation and formation of new cells to become an independent organism. This development follows a constant law, which is founded on the material composition and arrangement of the elements which meet in the cell in a vivifying union. If the reproductive cells be of the same kind and agree with the foundation cell [fertilized ovum] of the mother plant, then the development of the new individual will follow the same law which rules the mother plant. If it chance that an egg cell unites with a *dissimilar* pollen cell, we must then assume that between those elements of both cells, which determine opposite characters, some sort of compromise is effected. The resulting compound cell becomes the foundation of the hybrid organism, the development of which necessarily follows a different scheme from that obtaining in each of the two original species. If the compromise be taken to be a complete one, in the sense, namely, that the hybrid embryo is formed from two similar cells, in which the differences are *entirely and permanently accommodated* together, the further result follows that the hybrids, like any other stable plant species, reproduce themselves truly in their offspring. The reproductive cells which are formed in their seed vessels and anthers are of one kind, and agree with the fundamental compound cell [fertilised ovum].

With regard to those hybrids whose progeny is *variable* we may perhaps assume that between the differentiating elements of the egg and pollen cells there also occurs a compromise, in so far that the formation of a cell as foundation of the hybrid becomes possible; but, nevertheless, the arrangement between the conflicting elements is only temporary and does not endure throughout the life of the hybrid plant. Since, in the habit of the plant, no changes are perceptible during the whole period of vegetation, we must further assume that it is only possible for the differentiating elements to liberate themselves from the enforced union when the fertilising cells are developed. In the formation of these cells all existing elements participate, in an entirely free and equal arrangement, by which it is only the differentiating ones which mutually separate themselves. In this way the production would be rendered possible of as many sorts of egg and pollen cells as there are combinations possible of the formative elements.

The attribution attempted here of the essential difference in the development of hybrids to *a permanent or temporary union* of the differing cell elements can, of course, only claim the value of an hypothesis for which the lack of definite data offers a wide scope. Some justification of the opinion expressed lies in the evidence afforded by *Pisum* that the behaviour of each pair of differentiating characters in hybrid union is independent of the other differences between the two original plants, and, further, that the hybrid produces just so many kinds of egg and pollen cells as there are possible constant combination forms. The differentiating characters of two plants can finally, however, only depend upon differences in the composition and grouping of the elements which exist in the foundation-cells [fertilised ova] of the same in vital interaction.[1]

[1] *"Welche in den Grundzellen derselben in lebendiger Wechselwirkung stehen."*

Even the validity of the law formulated for *Pisum* requires still to be confirmed, and a repetition of the more important experiments is consequently much to be desired, that, for instance, relating to the composition of the hybrid fertilising cells. A differential [element] may easily escape the single observer,[2] which although at the outset may

[2] *"Dem einzelnen Beobachter kann leicht ein Differenziale entgehen."*

appear to be unimportant, may yet accumulate to such an extent that it must not be ignored in the total result. Whether the variable hybrids of other plant species observe an entire agreement must also be first decided experimentally. In the meantime we may assume that in material points an essential difference can scarcely occur, since the unity in the developmental plan of organic life is beyond question.

In conclusion, the experiments carried out by Kölreuter, Gärtner, and others with respect to *the transformation of one species into another by artificial fertilisation* merit special mention. Particular importance has been attached to these experiments and Gärtner reckons them among "the most difficult of all in hybridisation."

If a species *A* is to be transformed into a species *B*, both must be united by fertilisation and the resulting hybrids then be fertilised with the pollen of *B*; then, out of the various offspring resulting, that form would be selected which stood in nearest relation to *B* and once more be fertilised with *B* pollen, and so continuously until finally a form is arrived at which is like *B* and constant in its progeny. By this process the species *A* would change into the species *B*. Gärtner alone has effected thirty such experiments with plants of genera *Aquilegia, Dianthus, Geum, Lavatera, Lychnis, Malva, Nicotiana,* and *Oenothera.* The period of transformation was not alike for all species. While with some a triple fertilisation sufficed, with others this had to be repeated five or six times, and even in the same species fluctuations were observed in various experiments. Gärtner ascribes this difference to the circumstance that "the specific [*typische*] power by which a species, during reproduction, effects the change and transformation of the maternal type varies considerably in different plants, and that, consequently, the periods within which the one species is changed into the other must also vary, as also the number of generations, so that the transformation in some species is perfected in more, and in others in fewer generations." Further, the same observer remarks "that in these transformation experiments a good deal depends upon which type and which individual be chosen for further transformation."

If it may be assumed that in these experiments the constitution of the forms resulted in a similar way to that of *Pisum,* the entire process of transformation would find a fairly simple explanation. The hybrid forms as

many kinds of egg cells as there are constant combinations possible of the characters conjoined therein, and one of these is always of the same kind as that of the fertilising pollen cells. Consequently there always exists the possibility with all such experiments that even from the second fertilisation there may result a constant form identical with that of the pollen parent. Whether this really be obtained depends in each separate case upon the number of the experimental plants, as well as upon the number of differentiating characters which are united by the fertilisation. Let us, for instance, assume that the plants selected for experiment differed in three characters, and the species *ABC* is to be transformed into the other species *abc* by repeated fertilisation with the pollen of the latter; the hybrids resulting from the first cross form eight different kinds of egg cells, viz.,

$$ABC, ABc, AbC, aBC, Abc, aBc, abC, abc.$$

These in the second year of experiment are united again with the pollen cells *abc,* and we obtain the series

$$AaBbCc + AaBbc + AabCc +$$
$$aBbCc + Aabc + aBbc + abCc + abc.$$

Since the form *abc* occurs once in the series of eight terms, it is consequently little likely that it would be missing among the experimental plants, even were these raised in a smaller number, and the transformation would be perfected already by a second fertilisation. If by chance it did not appear, then the fertilisation must be repeated with one of those forms nearest akin, *Aabc, aBbc, abCc.* It is perceived that such an experiment must extend the farther *the smaller the number of experimental plants and the larger the number of differentiating characters* in the two original species; and that, furthermore, in the same species there can easily occur a delay of one or even of two generations such as Gärtner observed. The transformation of widely divergent species could generally only be completed in five or six years of experiment, since the number of different egg cells which are formed in the hybrid increases, as the powers of two, with the number of differentiating characters.

Gärtner found by repeated experiments that the respective period of transformation varies in many species, so that frequently a species A can be transformed into a species B a generation sooner than can species B into species A. He deduces therefrom that Kölreuter's opinion can hardly be maintained that "the two natures in hybrids are perfectly in equilibrium." It appears, however, that Kölreuter does not merit this criticism, but that Gärtner rather has overlooked a material point, to which he himself elsewhere draws attention, viz. that "it depends which individual is chosen for further transformation." Experiments which in this connection were carried out with two species of *Pisum* demonstrated that as regards the choice of the fittest individuals for the purpose of further fertilisation it may make a great difference which of two species is transformed into the other. The two experimental plants differed in five characters, while at the same time those of species A were all dominant and those of species B all recessive. For mutual transformation A was fertilised with pollen of B, and B with pollen of A, and this was repeated with both hybrids the following year. With the first experiment $\frac{B}{A}$ there were eighty-seven plants available in the third year of experiment for selection of the individuals for further crossing, and these were of the possible thirty-two forms; with the second experiment $\frac{A}{B}$ seventy-three plants resulted, which *agreed throughout perfectly in habit with the pollen parent*; in their internal composition, however, they must have been just as varied as the forms in the other experiment. A definite selection was consequently only possible with the first experiment; with the second the selection had to be made at random, merely. Of the latter only a portion of the flowers were crossed with the A pollen, the others were left to fertilise themselves. Among each five plants which were selected in both experiments for fertilisation there agreed, as the following year's culture showed, with the pollen parent:

1ST EXPERIMENT	2ND EXPERIMENT		
2 plants	—	in all characters
3 "	—	" 4 "
—	2 plants	" 3 "
—	2 "	" 2 "
—	1 plant	" 1 character

In the first experiment, therefore, the transformation was completed; in the second, which was not continued further, two or more fertilisations would probably have been required.

Although the case may not frequently occur in which the dominant characters belong exclusively to one or the other of the original parent plants, it will always make a difference which of the two possesses the majority of dominants. If the pollen parent has the majority, then the selection of forms for further crossing will afford a less degree of certainty than in the reverse case, which must imply a delay in the period of transformation, provided that the experiment is only considered as completed when a form is arrived at which not only exactly resembles the pollen plant in form, but also remains as constant in its progeny.

Gärtner, by the results of these transformation experiments, was led to oppose the opinion of those naturalists who dispute the stability of plant species and believe in a continuous evolution of vegetation. He perceives[1] in the complete transformation of

[1] ["Es sieht" in the original is clearly a misprint for "Er sieht."]

one species into another an indubitable proof that species are fixed within limits beyond which they cannot change. Although this opinion cannot be unconditionally accepted, we find on the other hand in Gärtner's experiments a noteworthy confirmation of that supposition regarding variability of cultivated plants which has already been expressed.

Among the experimental species there were cultivated plants, such as *Aquilegia atropurpurea* and *canadensis*, *Dianthus caryophyllus*, *chinensis*, and *japonicus*, *Nicotiana rustica* and *paniculata*, and hybrids between these species lost none of their stability after four or five generations.

APPENDIX B

Laboratory Suggestions

Any organism which can be studied in the laboratory can be used for genetic experiments, but the bulk of genetic knowledge has been obtained from a small number of organisms, including man, mouse, corn, tobacco, the evening primrose (*Oenothera*), *Paramecium*, *Neurospora* and other molds, and especially *Drosophila*. The following exercises are based upon *Drosophila*, corn, and man, with a few other organisms being used to a minor extent. The selection is based primarily upon practical considerations of availability and simplicity of use.

In scheduling experiments, it is advisable to introduce living materials as soon as possible, with preserved materials being used to fill other periods as needed. It is also useful to take part of the laboratory time for use as an oral quiz period on genetic problems. A tentative schedule is presented below, based upon the assumption that there are sixteen laboratory periods, one week apart:

WEEK	EXPERIMENT
1	*Drosophila* morphology; plant sorghum seeds.
2	*Drosophila* I—monohybrid cross.
3	Complete sorghum experiment; continue *Drosophila* I.

WEEK	EXPERIMENT
4	Mate F_1 of *Drosophila* I; corn I—monohybridism.
5	PTC pedigree in man; *Drosophila* II—sex-linkage.
6	Complete *Drosophila* I; corn II— dihybridism.
7	*Drosophila* II—mate F_1 flies.
8	Mitosis and Meiosis.
9	Complete *Drosophila* II; *Drosophila* III—dihybridism.
10	Blood typing.
11	*Drosophila* III—mate F_1 flies; corn III—linkage; *Drosophila* IV—linkage.
12	Biometry.
13	*Drosophila* III—complete; *Drosophila* V.
14	Corn IV—complex ratios.
15	Complete *Drosophila* IV.
16	Complete *Drosophila* V.

Such a schedule cannot be hard and fast, because the flies do not necessarily conform to a rigid academic schedule. Hence it is necessary to modify any schedule as the semester proceeds. If time permits, it is highly desirable to move the exercise on mitosis and meiosis up toward the beginning of the semester. A teacher whose primary interests lie in the field of genetics will want to change this schedule radically to emphasize those materials in which he is most interested and which are most readily available in his own laboratory. The present suggestions are intended primarily for that majority of teachers who must rely upon materials available from commercial supply houses. For simplicity, detailed directions are grouped below according to the organism studied.

75. DROSOPHILA EXPERIMENTS

CULTURE OF *Drosophila* The flies are ordinarily grown in half-pint milk bottles stoppered with cotton plugs which are wrapped in gauze. In the bottom of the bottle there should be a layer of agar medium about an inch thick. The flies do not feed upon this, but upon yeast which grows upon this medium. It is necessary to add a mold inhibitor to the medium, as otherwise mold may destroy the cultures. For this purpose, Moldex (sodium para-hydroxybenzoic acid) is most commonly used, but in laboratories which are heavily infested with molds, Dowicide A is more satisfactory. Many good formulas for culture media have been published. The following medium (modified from McDonough, Science, 118: 288) is currently in use in the author's laboratory:

15 grams agar-agar, shreds or powder
Water, 500 cc.
3/4 gram Dowicide A in 10 cc. 95% ethyl alcohol
125 cc. molasses.
110 grams corn meal in 250 cc. of water.

Heat the 500 cc. of water, and dissolve agar-agar in hot water. Add the remaining ingredients in the order stated. Mix well. Pour into culture bottles and allow to cool. Slip a narrow strip of stiff paper into each bottle to provide a good surface for pupation. Stopper the bottles and store in a refrigerator after they have cooled. A few hours before they are to be used, the culture bottles should be innoculated with brewer's yeast and allowed to warm up to room temperature.

While cultures can be grown at room temperature, most reliable results are obtained by growing them in an incubator at 25° C. If a few pairs of flies are put into a fresh culture bottle, there should be a dense population within a few weeks. Transfers to fresh culture bottles should be made every four to six weeks in order to maintain healthy stock cultures. It may be desirable to keep the students' cultures in smaller containers, such as 60 cc. shell vials.

EXERCISE ON MORPHOLOGY OF *Drosophila* AND ON HANDLING THE ORGANISM Living flies should be issued to the students. It is necessary to anesthetize the flies in order to handle them. An anesthetizing bottle can be made by fitting a half-pint bottle with a cork. Drive a long nail into the under side of the cork, and then wrap a bit of cotton and gauze around the head of the nail. To anesthetize the flies, pour a few drops of ether on the pad on the nail, then replace the cork in the bottle, which will soon fill with ether vapor. Now hold the culture bottle with its bottom toward the light. As the flies are positively phototropic, most will gather at the bottom of the bottle. Those remaining on the stopper can be shaken off by loosening the stopper and then shaking it in the mouth of the bottle. Remove stoppers from the culture bottle and the etherizing bottle, then quickly invert the culture bottle over the etherizing bottle, holding their mouths together so that flies cannot escape. Keep the ether bottle upright, so that the ether (which is heavier than air) will not spill into the culture bottle. The ether bottle may, however, be slanted somewhat toward the light to attract the flies. A sharp blow on the side of the culture bottle will help drive flies down into the ether bottle. Separate the bottles and quickly replace stoppers. Leave the flies in the etherizing bottle only a few seconds after the flies stop moving, then dump them onto a white card for examination and study.

Do not attempt to examine more than 30 or 40 flies at a time, or they will revive and fly away before you have finished. If the flies begin to move on the examination card, pour a little ether onto a cotton or gauze pad taped on the under side of a Petri dish, then invert the dish over the flies long enough to reanesthetize them. When magnification is needed, a 10x hand lens is adequate for the characters studied in this course. In counting flies, it is customary to separate them into piles by phenotypes, then count and record each pile. Camel's hair brushes are convenient for handling the flies, but some will prefer a needle or scalpel.

First, learn to distinguish the sexes. The following criteria are useful for this purpose. *Size*: females are generally larger than males, but this may be misleading, as the size ranges overlap. *Shape*: the abdomen of males is cylindrical, with a blunt end, while that of females is ovoid with a pointed posterior end. With magnification, two points can be made out. The dorsal one is the anus, while the ventral one is the ovipositor. *Color*: the black band at the posterior end of the abdomen of males is continuous, while that of females is confined to the dorsal surface. Viewed ventrally, this appears as a black dot on the abdomen of males which is lacking in females. Viewed dorsally, the abdomen of males is almost solid black, while that of females is transversely striped. These color differences are generally the most easily recognized, however, both sexes emerge with scant pigmentation, and then darken with age. Sex combs: in males, there is a row of tiny bristles on the tarsus of each front leg. These are lacking in females. Sex combs are difficult to observe without magnification.

Observe carefully the size, shape, and color of the following structures: antennae, eyes, thorax, bristles on the thorax (note number and pattern), wings (note size, shape, and the pattern of veins), and abdomen.

Careful sketches of the objects studied in this exercise are a great help to accurate observation, but may be omitted at the discretion of the teacher.

Drosophila EXPERIMENT I A monohybrid cross may be made using flies from the wild type (normal) stock for one parental type, and flies from a stock homozygous for any autosomal recessive gene for the other parental stock. Good examples include *heldout* (*ho*), in which the wings are held out at right angles to the body when at rest; black body (*b*); or sepia eye color (*se*). Some students should use the wild type flies for the female parents and the mutant type for the male parents, while others should make the reciprocal cross.

It is very important that only virgin females be used in these experiments, in order to insure that the progeny obtained actually result from the cross intended. Therefore the stock cultures should be emptied a few hours before class time, and only those females emerging afterwards should be used. As the flies do not mate in the first six to twelve hours after emerging, these can be assumed to be virgins. At each table, a culture of mutant flies and one of wild type flies should be anesthetized. Each student should place several males and females from different cultures in his culture tube. Be sure to keep the tubes on their sides until the flies are thoroughly recovered from the anesthesia. Otherwise, they will get stuck in the medium and die. Be sure that your culture tube has been inoculated with yeast. Label the tube with a description of the cross, your name, and the date. Place culture tubes on their sides in the incubator, and set them upright on the following day.

During the following days, observe the progress of egg laying, larval growth, pupation, and emergence of adults. The F_1 flies should begin emerging in 10 days to two weeks. When a fair number of flies have emerged, anesthetize them, count them out by phenotypes (including sex), and make up a new culture with several pairs of flies to breed the F_2. Label and handle as usual. The F_2 may now be followed and counted in the same way. The entire experiment should require three or four weeks.

Diagram your cross in Mendelian symbols. Calculate the chi-square and determine the P value for your cross. Do the same for the summated results of all similar crosses made by the class.

Drosophila EXPERIMENT II A cross may be made between a wild type stock and a stock homozygous for any of the readily available sex-linked genes, such as white eye color (w), yellow body (y), or bar eyes (B). The procedures are the same as those followed in *Drosophila* I. In this instance, it is especially important that different students make the reciprocal crosses and compare their results.

Was the mutant dominant or recessive? Diagram the cross in Mendelian symbols. Test your results as usual by the chi-square method.

Drosophila EXPERIMENT III Make a dihybrid cross by crossing flies from a normal culture with flies from a curved wing-sepia eye culture. Or use two other independent, autosomal recessives. An interesting variant may be obtained by using one sex-linked and one autosomal gene. The procedure will be the same as in the preceding experiments. After obtaining your results in the F_2, check your results as usual by the chi-square method.

Drosophila EXPERIMENT IV This experiment is concerned with linkage and crossing over. Flies will be supplied from a stock homozygous for black body (b) and vestigial wing (vg) and from a second stock which is wild type. Make a cross between the two stocks. F_1 flies should be heterozygous for both genes. Virgin F_1 females should now be backcrossed to black-vestigial males. The reciprocal cross will not work, as crossing over normally occurs only in females of this species. Obtain the virgin females by the same method described above.

When the backcross generation emerges, count them out by the four phenotypes,

b vg, $++$, b $+$, and $+$ vg. The first two are the parental types, the last two the recombination types. Now calculate the map distance between the two points. Assuming the same number of offspring, what should their distribution among the classes have been, if the genes had been located on different chromosomes?

DROSOPHILA V—PHENOCOPIES Only homozygous vestigial winged flies are needed for this experiment. Each student should obtain a few pairs and start a culture. Half of the students should raise them at room temperature or (preferably) at $25°$ C., while the remaining students should grow them in an incubator at $30-$ C. When the flies emerge, compare the wings of those raised at different temperatures. How could you prove that no new mutation had occurred in those raised at the higher temperature? If time permits, set up the critical experiment and carry it through.

76. CORN EXPERIMENTS

For class studies on the genetics of corn, two types of material may be used. Either whole ears representing the F_2 or backcross generation for seed characters are distributed to the students, or packets of seeds representing smaller samples may be given to each student. The former is more desirable, but, as the ears are expensive and fragile, the latter method is often more feasible.

CORN EXPERIMENT I—MONOHYBRIDISM Any one of many readily available character pairs may be used to illustrate F_2 or backcross segregation. Color differences such as red-white or purple-white are very good. Another good example for class study is the starchy-sugary endosperm alternative. In dried corn, starchy grains are full and opaque, while sugary grains are shriveled and translucent, or sirupy, looking. Obtain an ear (or packet of seed) and count the grains of each class. Start counting a row which is easily identifiable, so that you will know when you have counted all of the rows. It is best to write down the number of grains of each kind in each row, and then add them when the whole ear has been counted. Do not touch the grains with a pencil as you count, because marked grains may become difficult to classify. Now answer the following questions:

1. Does the ear represent an F_2 or a backcross generation?
2. If it is an F_2, which allele is dominant?
3. Calculate the percentage deviation from the expected results.
4. Calculate the chi-square and determine the P value.
5. Class results should be tabulated, and questions 3 and 4 answered for the summated results.

CORN EXPERIMENT II—DIHYBRIDISM Ears (or seed packets) segregating for two different pairs of characters, such as starchy-sugary-purple-white, should be issued. The procedure is then identical with that in the preceding experiment, except that four phenotypic classes must be counted rather than two. Calculate chi-square and P values for both individual and class results.

CORN EXPERIMENT III—LINKAGE The genes c (colorless aleurone) and sh (shrunken seeds) are both located in chromosome 9. Backcross ears from a cross involving both of these loci should be issued. Count the number of grains in each of the four phenotypic classes. Which were the original parental classes? What percentage of the grains fall into the recombination classes? What is the distance between these loci in the chromosome? Diagram the entire series of crosses, beginning with the parental generation.

CORN EXPERIMENT IV—COMPLEX RATIOS Obtain ears or seed packets in which collaboration of factors for aleurone colors leads to modified dihybrid ratios, such as 13 : 3, 12 : 3 : 1, or 15 : 1. In each case, de-

termine the particular ratio represented, then test your results by the chi-square method. As far as possible, determine the parental genotypes.

77. HUMAN GENETICS

PEDIGREE FOR PTC SENSITIVITY Issue to each student several sheets of paper which have been treated with PTC (phenyl-thio-carbamide), a chemical which tastes bitter to most people, but which is tasteless to some. The ability or inability to taste this substance is based upon a single pair of genes. The student should test himself and as many relatives as possible for tasting ability. This is done simply by chewing a fragment of the PTC paper. When all available relatives have reported, a pedigree chart for the family should be drawn. Can you determine from your pedigree which allele is dominant? Does it appear to be sex-linked or autosomal? If your pedigree illustrates any of the major difficulties of the study of human inheritance, discuss it.

BLOOD TYPING Each student should clean the end of a finger with 70% alcohol, then prick the finger with a sterile needle. Now add about two drops of blood to 1 cc. of saline solution (0.9% NaCl). Testing serum from a group A donor will agglutinate group B cells, hence it may be labeled either serum A or anti-B. Similarly, serum derived from a group B donor may be labeled serum B or anti-A. Place a drop of serum A (anti-B) at one end of a slide, and a drop of serum B (anti-A) at the other end. Now add to each drop of anti-serum a small drop of the diluted blood cell suspension. Rock the slide gently to keep the cells agitated. Agglutination will probably be very obvious to the naked eye if it occurs, but it should be checked by microscope to avoid the possibility of confusion with rouleaux formation (this is the formation of stacks of cells, much like stacks of pennies.

Unlike agglutinated cells, rouleaux break up easily). If no reaction occurs within 15 minutes, it may be assumed that none will occur. The possible results may be tabulated as follows:

Cells agglutinated by neither
serum . . . . group O
Cells agglutinated by serum B
but not by serum A . . . . group A
Cells agglutinated by serum A
but not by serum B . . . . group B
Cells agglutinated by both
sera . . . . group AB

The class results should be tabulated, and the distribution of types in the class compared with the distribution in the population of which the class is a small sample. It will not be possible for the students to test their relatives, but whenever a student can obtain information regarding blood types of his relatives, he should make a pedigree chart.

Especially in classes including women, the interest in Rh testing will run very high. Good testing sera are now readily available, and should be used according to the directions on the package.

78. MISCELLANEOUS

MONOHYBRIDISM IN SORGHUM Sorghum is a grass which is widely used as a forage crop and as a source of sirup for human use. The normal green color of the plants is, of course, due to chlorophyll, but a gene for albinism blocks the synthesis of chlorophyll in the seedlings. Packets of 100 seeds from plants heterozygous for this gene should be issued to each student or pair of students. If sufficient flats are available, the seeds may be planted in soil. Otherwise, Petri dishes and wet filter paper will do. Wet several filter papers and put them in a Petri dish. Now arrange the seeds in rows of ten on the wet filter paper and cover with another wet filter paper. Cover the dish, label with name and date, and place it on the window ledge. Check every few days to make sure that the seedlings have water. After ten days to two weeks, the seedlings should be sufficiently large to permit counting of the phenotypes. Faintly green plants should be counted as albinos. Now answer the following questions:

1. Which gene is dominant?
2. Calculate the chi-square and determine the P value for your results.
3. Tabulate the individual experiments on the blackboard. Add them up, then answer question 2 for the summated results.
4. Often, all or most of the individual experiments support the hypothesis, yet the summated results fail to support it. How could this be explained? But when old seed is used, the percentage of germination is lower, but the summated results do support the hypothesis. Try to explain this.

BIOMETRY A very good exercise in biometry may be provided by a sack of commercial dried beans. Although these have been graded for size, they will show considerable variation. Weigh out for each student a sample of 30 to 40 grams of beans. These should then be measured for length in millimeters and a tally kept of the number of beans of each length. The results should be tabulated on the blackboard, and the class results summated. Now make frequency polygons for your own results and for the summated class results. Calculate for each the mean, standard deviation, and coefficient of variability.

Another good experiment can be performed by teaming the students in groups of two to make simultaneous tosses of two coins, recording the number of times that two heads (HH) are obtained, or a head and a tail (HT), or two tails (TT). Let each pair of students toss their coins 100 times.

What result should be expected on the basis of the multiplication theorem? Compare the observed and expected results by the chi-square method. What has this experiment to do with genetics?

79. CYTOLOGY

MITOSIS IN ONION ROOT TIPS OR IN WHITE-FISH BLASTODISC In the *interphase*, note the following: size and shape of the nucleus; the nuclear membrane; number, size, and location of nucleoli; and the chromatin granules on the net-like linin or achromatic network. In the whitefish, note the asters. During the *prophase*, distinct chromosomes are developed from the chromatin, nuclear membrane and nucleoli disappear, and the preparation for division is otherwise completed. As this is a long and complex series of changes, one should look for early, middle, and late prophase stages. Note the gradual formation of the chromosomes, and look for nuclei in which their separation into chromatids can be seen. Note the details of the spindle, the dissolution of the nuclear membrane, and the gradual fading of the nucleoli. In the whitefish, note the asters and centrosomes. Finally, the chromosomes move to the equatorial plate. Once there, the cell is in *metaphase*. Only the centromeres are accurately aligned, and hence the metaphase plate is quite clear in the whitefish, which has many small chromosomes ($2n = 80$), and rather obscure in the onion, which has fewer long chromosomes ($2n = 16$). Note the spindle fibers, the kinetochores or centromeres (at the primary constrictions of the chromosomes), and the doubleness of the chromosomes wherever possible. *Anaphase* is the period of the movement of the chromosomes to the poles of the spindle. Note the separation of the chromatids to form daughter chromosomes, the form of the separating chromosomes, and the central spindle persisting between the separating groups of chromosomes. During the *telophase*, the resting nuclei are reconstituted, and the cytoplasmic division occurs. Note the dense grouping of the chromosomes and their gradual vacuolization and loosening of structure to form the resting nuclei, much like a reversal of prophase. Note the formation of a cell plate across the center of the spindle in the onion, and the constriction of the cytoplasm in the whitefish.

MEIOSIS IN *Ascaris* In this worm, the prophase of the first maturation division occurs in the ovary, and the eggs are passed into the uterus while at the metaphase of the first maturation division. They remain at this stage until fertilized, when the two divisions are quickly completed, and the first cleavage division follows. Obtain a slide with several sections through the upper end of the uterus. This should include all stages of meiosis except the first prophase. Look for primary oocytes showing tetrads (one or two, according to the race of *Ascaris* used) on the spindle ready for the first division. Observe the splitting of the tetrads into dyads and the formation of the first polar body. In the secondary oocytes, the dyads now move onto the spindle for the second division and rotate so that an equational division will separate the halves of the dyads. Observe the division of the dyads and the formation of the second polar body. How many chromosomes now remain in the mature egg? Now observe the formation of the interphase pronuclei from the chromosomes of the egg and from the sperm nucleus (at the center of the egg).

At the discretion of the teacher, detailed drawings of the stages of mitosis and meiosis may or may not be required.

80. SOURCES OF MATERIALS

Drosophila cultures, and the materials necessary for their use in the laboratory, are obtainable from most biological supply houses, such as:

Carolina Biological Supply Co., Elon College, North Carolina.

General Biological Supply House, 8200 South Hoyne Ave., Chicago 20, Illinois.

Dowicide A is obtainable only in large quantities from the manufacturer (Dow Chemical Co., Midland, Michigan), but it can be obtained in small quantities from the Merchants Chemical Co., Chicago.

Corn for genetic studies is available from several sources, including:

George S. Carter, Clinton, Connecticut.

General Biological Supply House.

New York Scientific Supply Co., 111–113 East 22nd St., New York.

Ward's Natural Science Establishment, Inc., 3000 Ridge Road East, Rochester 9, N. Y.

PTC paper is available from the American Genetic Association, 1507 M Street, Washington 5, D. C.

Blood typing anti-sera are available from:

American Hospital Supply Corporation, 2020 Ridge Ave., Evanston, Illinois.

Carolina Biological Supply Co.

Certified Blood Donor Service, 146–16 Hillside Ave., Jamaica 35, N. Y.

General Biological Supply House.

Sorghum seeds for the experiment described above are distributed by the Brooklyn Botanic Garden, Brooklyn, N. Y.

Slides for mitosis and meiosis are available from all biological supply houses.

Index

A

A-B-O blood groups, 91–93
Abraxas grossulariata, 68
Achromatic network, 23
Acquired characters, inheritance of, 273
Addition theorem, 56
Ae, A.S., 81
Age of incidence, 253
Agouti series, 90
Agriculture and genetics, 3, 4, 242–248
Albinism, 7, 254
Albomaculatus plants, 220
Aleurone colors in corn, 102–103
Alkaptonuria, 6, 201
Allele, defined, 14
    multiple, 88–96
Allen, C. E., 192
Allopolyploidy, 172–173
Allotetraploidy, 173
Alloxan, 202, 260
Alternation of generations, 186
    in Coelenterata, 188
Amaurotic idiocy, 86, 259
American Society of Human Genetics, 249
Amino acids, 205–206
Anaphase, 27
Anatomy and genetics, 5–6
Anderson, Edgar, 239
Anencephaly, 269
Angioneurotic edema, 2
Angiostomum, 186–187
Anthocyanin, 201
Anthoxanthin, 201
Antibodies, 90
Antigens, 91
Antirrhinum, 159, 220
Aphids, sex cycle of, 185–186

Architecture of the chromosomes, 144–149
Arey, L. B., 77
Arginine, 205, 206
Ascaris, 26–27
    egg laying, 224
    mitosis in, 24
Asparagus, separation of sexes, 184
Assortive mating, 255
Asters, 23
Attached-X chromosomes, 160–161
Auerbach, Charlotte, 165, 166
Autopolyploidy, 172–173
Autosomes, 64
Autotetraploidy, 172–173
Average man, 44
Aves, 68
Ayrshire cattle, color, 72–73

B

Babcock, E. B., 1, 40, 42, 145, 175, 234, 241, 243, 248
Bacillus cereus, 217
Backcross, 14–15, 37
    defined, 14
    dominant, 254
Bacterial transformation, 207
Barbatula, 229
Barley, 244
Bateson, William, 1, 89, 97, 98, 129, 130, 131, 198, 199, 208, 280, 281
Bauer, H., 282
Beadle, G. W., 104, 105, 203, 209, 214, 282
Beans, pure lines in, 46–48
Bees, sex determination, 185, 273
Bias, 53

Biochemical genetics, 6–7
Biochemical mutants, 200–202
Biochemistry and genetics, 6
Biometrical experiments, 317–318
Biometry, 8
    defined, 43
    evolution and, 44–46
Blakeslee, A. F., 83, 87, 98, 169, 178, 282
Blending theory of inheritance, 10
Blood groups, 50, 201, 252
    inheritance of, 92
    reactions, 91–92
Blood typing, 316–317
Bombyx, gynanders in, 80
Bombyx mori, 79–80
Bonellia, sex determination, 187
Bonner, David, 214
Bottleneck phenomenon, 232
Boveri, Theodore, 20–22, 186, 215
Boycott, 78
Brachydactyly, 86, 252, 254
Bradley, M. V., 178
Brahman cattle, 3
Brassica, 245
Braun, Werner, 223
Breeding, combination, 36–39, 244–245
    objectives, 243
    plant and animal, 243–248
    pre-Mendelian, 242
Bridges, C. B., 143, 151, 152, 153, 156, 180, 181, 182, 192, 193, 281
Bromus, allopolyploidy, 173
Bryonia, sex determination in, 184–185
Bud mutants, 162
Bullfrog, egg laying, 224

C

Cancer, 253
Capsella bursa-pastoris, 106
Carotin, 201
Caspari, Ernst, 111, 218, 223
Castle, William, 281

Cataract, 252
Cattle, Brahman, 3
color, 72–73
Dexter, 85
fat color, 39, 244
freemartins, 77
Hereford, 3
Holstein-Friesian, 242
milk and butterfat production, 246, 247
Santa Gertrudis, 4
Shorthorn, 3
Texas Longhorn, 3
C-D-E and Rh, 95
Central tendency, 50
measurement of, 52
Centriole, 23
Centromere, 26
Chemistry and gene function, 207
Chiasma (-ta), 132
formation, 29
Chicken, chromosome map, 136
comb form, 98–99
creeper, 85
feather patterns, 76–77
feathering rate, 69
plumage colors, 97
Chi-square, 58–61
Chlamydomonas, sex determination, 188–190
Chlorophyll, 201
Chondrodystrophy, 263
Chromagen, 97, 201
Chromatid, 28
Chromatin, 23
Chromocenter, 151
Chromomere, 29
Chromosomes, 8
and linkage, 132–141
and multiple alleles, 89
architecture, 144–149
as basis of heredity, 20–22
attached-X, 160–161
chemistry of, 205–207
duplication of, 25–26
mapping, 132–138
maps, 136–140
movement, 27
mutation, 168–178
and evolution, 229
rearrangements, 175–178
and hybrid sterility, 236
sex determination and, 63–64
WZ, 68

Chromosomes, X, 64–65
Y, 67–68
and sex, 184–185
Chrysanthemum, 239–240
Ciliata, 190
Cirsium, 218
Class interval, 52
Clausen, Jens, 241
Clausen, R. E., 42, 145, 175, 243, 248
CIB method, 163–164
Cleveland, L.R., 191, 192
Clinical diagnosis, 269
Clover, 245
CO$_2$ sensitivity, 221
Coat color in mice, 100–102
Cock feathering, 76–77
Coe, W. R., 188, 192
Coefficient of variability, 55
Coelenterata and sex, 188
Coiling in snails, 78, 79
Coincidence, 135–136
Colchicine, 174, 240
Colias, color in, 74, 75
Colin, E.C., 272
Collaboration of genes, 97–106
Color blindness, 70–71, 90, 261
Comb form in chickens, 98–99
Combination breeding, 36–39, 244 245
Competence, 195
Complementary genes, 97–98
Compounds, 89
Conjugation, 190
Contributions of genetics to breeding, 244
Corn, 221
chromosome map, 136, 138, 139
color, 109
ear length, 117
experiments, 315–316
flinty and floury, 109–110
hybrid, 4, 120–123, 245
production of, 121
vigor, 121–123
importance of, 120
linkage in, 131–132
mutations, 212
rates, 158–159
seed, 102
separation of the sexes, 184
starchy x sugary, 17–18
sun-red series, 89–90
vitamin A content, 244

Corolla, 114
Correns, Carl, 9, 12, 109, 183, 184, 185, 199, 218, 221, 223, 279, 281
Cotyledons, 13
color in peas, 12–14
Coupling, 129–130
Creeper fowl, 85
Crepidula, sex determination, 187
Crepis, 26, 27, 28, 234
Crepis capillaris, mitosis in, 23
Crossing over, 127
cytologically proven, 154–155
double, 134, 135–136
Crossover map and salivary gland chromosomes, 153
Crozier, W. J., 202, 203, 204
Cryptocercus, 191
Cucumbers, 245
Cuénot, L., 82, 87, 281
Currant moth, 68
color inheritance, 69
Cytological exercises, 318
Cytology, 8
Cytoplasm, as basis for differentiation, 194–196
Cytoplasmic inheritance, 215–222
and physiology of genes, 222

D

Daisy, seed cone color, 98
Darlington, C. D., 178
Darwin, Charles, 44, 45, 112, 162, 224, 226, 227, 241, 273
Darwin and Mendel, 280
Darwinism, 44–46
summarized, 226
Datura stramonium, lethal genes in, 83
Datura, trisomics, 169–171
Dauermodification, 216
Deficiency, 145–147
Deletion, 145–147
Demerec, M., 158, 167, 244
DeRobertis, E. D. P., 33
Desoxyribonucleic acid, 206–207
Deviation, average, 53
De Vries, Hugo, 110, 172, 198, 208, 241, 278, 279
Dexter cattle, 85

Diabetes insipidus, 260
Diabetes mellitus, 202, 252, 260, 262
Diagnosis, clinical, 269
Diakinesis, 29
Differential reproductive rates, 263
Dihybridism, 34–39
Dimethyl crocetin and sex determination, 189
Dioecious plants, 183
Diploidy, 27
Diplotene, 29
Diptera, 152
  linkage in, 129
Dispersion, 53–54
  typical, 50
DNA, 206–207
Dobzhansky, Th., 149, 150, 151, 156, 178, 210, 214, 236, 241, 283
Dogs, hemophilia in, 72
Dominance, 14, 110, 198–199
  coefficient of, 198
  incomplete, 124
  modification, 149, 198
  partial, 124
  relative, 109–110, 199
  theories of, 199
    of heterosis, 120, 121, 122
Dominant lethals, 83
Dominant pedigree, typical, 257–258
Double-cross method, 121
Drosera, allotetraploidy, 173
Drosophila, 227, 229, 281
  approximated, 126–128
  aristapedia, 196
  attached-X, 160–161
  bar, 148, 175–177
  blond, 149
  bobbed, 67, 199, 200
  brown, 175
  causes of lethality, 85
  chromosomes, 126
    map, 136, 137
    mapping, 132–137
  CO_2 sensitivity, 221
  crossing over and chiasmata, 132
  crossveinless, 252
  cubitus interruptus, 149, 177
  Curly, 145, 175
  cut, 175
  Dichaete, 138

Drosophila, double crossing over, 135
  ebony, 175
  estimate of gene number, 209
  experiments, 313–315
  eye colors, 65–67, 89
  eyeless, 169, 171, 175
  frequency of mutations, 158
  gynanders in, 79
  hairy, 126–128, 177
  Haplo-IV, 171
  held out, 175
  heterochromatin, 154
  hybrid sterility, 236
  interference, 135
  intersexuality, 179–181
  lethal genes, 82–83, 87
  linkage, 128–129
  metaphase maps, 149–150
  Moiré, 175
  nicked, 250–251
  Notch, 147, 153
  number of genes, 126
  phenocopies, 197
  salivary gland chromosomes, 150–154
  sex determination, 64
  sex-linkage, 65–68
  sex-linked lethals, 84
  somatic mutation, 162
  Star, 138, 175
  Triplo-IV, 168–169
  Truncate, 198
  vestigial wing, 17, 88–89, 100, 175
  white series, 161
  yellow, 175
Drosophila persimilis, heterosis, 120
Dubinin, N. P., 177
Dunn, L. C., 283
Duplicate factors, 106–107
Duplication, 147–148
Duryee, W. R., 136, 143
Dzierzon, 185, 273

E

Ear-to-row selection, 242
East, E. M., 112, 113, 114, 115, 117, 125
Echiuroidea, 187
Ectodermal dysplasia, 2
Education, cost of, 267
Egg, 31

Eichling, C. W., 39, 277, 283
Electric shock therapy, 262
Elephant, reproductive increase, 224
Embryonic differentiation, 193–197
Emerson, R. A., 117, 143
Endosperm, 102, 109
Environmental fluctuations, 48
Enzymatic adaptation, 217
Ephestia, pleiotropy in, 100
Ephrussi, B., 215, 223, 282
Epilepsy, 252
Epilobium, 219–220
Epinephrine, 7
Epistasis, 100, 110
Equatorial plate, 26
Erythroblastosis fetalis, 94–95
Escherichia coli, 217
Euchromatin, 68, 153–154
Eugenics, 265–268, 270
  negative, 265–266
  positive, 266–268
Euplotes, 190
Evening primrose, 172
Evolution, biometrical, 44–46
  defined, 224
  fields of evidence for, 226
  genetics and, 224–240
  polyploidy in, 239–240
Evolutionary statistics, 229–230
Expressivity, 252
Eye color in man, 13, 16,

F

F_2 with linkage, 130–132
Factor interaction, 110–111
Falls, H. F., 262, 272
Family size, 250, 267
Family wage, 267
Fat color in cattle, 39
Fertility, reduction of, 233–238
Fertilization, 9, 32
  double, 21–22
  in plants, 108–109
Filial generations, 9
Fish, chromosomal mutations, 229
Fisher, R. A., 60, 62, 95, 96, 199, 204, 283
Flavone, 201
Flower color in four-o'clocks, 9–12
Flowering plants, sex in, 183–185

Flowers, triploid, 246
Focke, W. O., 281
Ford, E. B., 81
Four-o'clock, 9, 221
    color, 108
Fraser, A.C., 143
Freedom, degrees of, 60
Freemartin, 77
French soldiers, heights of, 44–45
Frequency distribution, 51
Frequency polygon, 51
Friesian cattle, butterfat in milk,
    246, 247
Fusion nucleus, 109

G

Galactose, 217
Galactozymase, 217
Galeopsis, 174, 240,
Galton, Francis, 44, 45, 46, 112,
    265
Gametes, purity, law of, 11, 17
Gametophyte, 28
Gamma globulin, 269
Gammarus, 197
Gastrulation, 194
Gates, R. R., 83, 272
Gay, E. H., 209, 214
Gene(s), 10, 207
    collaboration of, 97–106
    complementary, 97–98
    dosage, 199–200
    frequency, 230
    function and chemistry, 207
    major, 99
    modifying, 99
    number, 209
    physiology, 193–203
    pleiotropic, 99–100
    size, 209
    theory, 205–213
        present status, 212–213
Genetic drift, 232, 264
Genetic symbols, 84, 127
Genetic terminology, 9
Genetics and agriculture, 3–4,
    242–248
    and evolution, 224
    bases of, 8
    biochemical, 607
    defined, 1
    social values of, 268–270
Genic balance, 199–200
Genotype, defined, 14

Geometrical mean, 116–117
Geotropism, 202–203
Gigas habitus, 172
Glaucoma, 250
Glycine, 206
Goldschmidt, R. B., 19, 79, 80,
    81, 181–182, 192, 193, 197,
    198, 204
Goodspeed, T. H., 178
Gordon, M., 234, 241
Gout, 202, 251–252
Gowen, John W., 125, 209, 214
Gray crescent, 194
Growth phase, 30
Grüneberg, Hans, 102, 111
Guinea pig genetics, 36–37
Gynandrism, 78–80, 179
Gynodioecy, 218

H

Habrobracon juglandis, 185
Hadorn, E., 82, 85, 87
Haldane, J. B. S., 204, 261
Haploid, 28
Hardy-Weinberg law, 230
Heart defects, 252
Heitz, 282
Helianthus, 239
Hemizygous defined, 67
Hemolytic icterus, 270
Hemolytic jaundice, 259
Hemophilia, 70, 71, 72, 261, 264
Hen feathering, 76–77
Henking, H., 63
Heredity clinics, 249, 268
Hereford cattle, 3
Hermaphroditism, 179
Hersh, A. H., 198, 204
Heteroantigens, 94
Heterochromatin, 67–68, 153–
    154
Heterogamety, 68
Heterosis, 119–120, 245
    theories of, 119–120, 121–123
Heterozygote, defined, 14
    identification of, 266
Heterozygous, defined, 14
Heterozygous expression, 108–
    110
Hierarchies of genes, 100–106
Himalayan rabbit, physiology
    of, 90
Histogram, 51
Historical review, 273–283

Holandric genes, 261
Hollingshead, 234
Holstein-Friesian cattle, 242
    milk and butterfat, 246, 247
Homeosis, 196
Homogentisic acid, 6, 201
Homology, 5
Homozygosity in beans, 46
Homozygote, defined, 14
Homozygous, defined, 14
Horns of sheep, 73–74
Horowitz, N. H., 111, 204
Housing, cost of, 267
Hr antigens and antibodies, 95
Human genetics, 249–270, 316–
    317
    advantages, 253–254
    American Society of, 249
    difficulties of, 249–253
Human inheritance, norms of,
    254–256
Huntington's chorea, 83, 253, 266
Hutt, F. B., 81, 83, 87, 111
Huxley, Julian 240
Hybrid corn, 4, 120–123
    production of, 121
    productivity of, 121
Hybrid sterility, 233–236
    and chromosomal rear-
        rangements, 236
Hybrid vigor, 119–120
Hybridization, introgressive, 239
Hyman, Libbie, 210
Hymenoptera, sex determina-
    tion in, 185

I

Iltis, Hugo, 283
Immune reactions, 90–91
Immunity, 91
Inbreeding, 245
Independent assortment, 32–33,
    126
    law of, 34, 36, 40–42
Indifferent stage, 77
Inheritance, blending theory of,
    10
    cytoplasmic, 215–222
    maternal, 78–80, 216
    monohybrid, 10
    of acquired characters, 273
    of blood groups, 92–95
    quantitative, 112–124
    sex-related, 63–80

Insulin, 260
  shock therapy, 262
Interference, 135–136
Intermediate inheritance, 110
Interphase, 22–23
Intersexuality, 179–183
  and genic balance, 200
Interspecific lethal, 234
Interspecific sterility, 233–236
Introgressive hybridization, 239
Inversion, 145, 146
Iris, 227
Isogamy, 189
Isolating mechanisms, 233–239
  failure of, 238–239

J

Janssens, F. A., 132, 143
Jaundice, 262
  hemolytic, 259
Jennings, H. S. 190
Johannsen, Wilhelm, 46, 62, 207,
  214, 281
Jollos, V., 216
Jones, Donald F., 121, 125, 184,
  192, 282
Junco, 228

K

Kappa, 222
Karpechenko, G. D., 174, 178
Katsuki, K., 79, 80
Kavanau, J. L., 214
Kerry cattle, 85
Kidney, polycystic, 260
Killer, 221
Kinetochore, 26
King Ranch, 4
Kleberg, Robert J., 4
Koltzoff, N. K., 282, 283
Komai, T., 81
Kuhn, Richard, 192

L

Laboratory manual, 312–319
Lamarck, 273
Lampbrush chromosomes, 212
Landsteiner, Karl, 91, 92, 93,
  94, 96, 249
Lateral loop chromosomes, 212
Lathyrus odoratus, 98
Law of independent assortment,
  34, 36

Law of segregation, 32
Lens induction, 195
Lepidoptera, 68
  linkage in, 129
  polar bodies of, 80
Leptotene, 29
Lethal genes, 82–87
  balanced, 236, 238
  frequency of, 82–83
  gamete lethals, 83
  interspecific, 234
Lethality, causes of, 84–85
Leukemia, 252
Levine, Philip, 93, 94
Lewis, D., 192
Lewis, E. B., 178
Lilium, 209
Lillie, F. R., 77, 81
Limnaea, 78
Linkage and chromosomes, 132–
  141
  defined, 126
  in F₂, 130–132
  in man, 141
Localization of genes, 138–141
Loeb, Jacques, 215
London families, heights of,
  46
Lush, Jay L., 243, 248
Lymantria, 197, 199, 218
  intersexuality in, 181–182
Lysenko, T. D., 282, 283

M

Macrogametes, 190
Macromelanophore, 234
Mainland, Donald, 62
Major genes, 99
Man, albinism, 254
  alcaptonuria, 201
  amaurotic idiocy, 86, 259
  anencephaly, 269
  biochemical mutants, 201–202
  blood groups, 252
  brachydactyly, 86, 252, 254
  cancer, 253
  cataract, 252
  chromosomes, 126
  color blindness, 70–71, 90, 261
  diabetes, 202, 252, 260
  epilepsy, 252
  estimate of gene number, 209
  eye color, 13, 16
  family size, 267

Man, gout, 202, 251–252
  heart defects, 252
  height, 124
  hemolytic jaundice, 259, 270
  hemophilia, 70, 71, 72, 261
  heterozygosity of, 255
  Huntington's chorea, 83, 253,
    266
  lethal genes, 83, 86
  leukemia, 252
  linkage, 141
  manic-depression, 262, 269–
    270
  mental deficiency, 268
  monohybridism, 15–16
  multiple alleles, 90–96
  multiple exostoses, 252
  mutation rate, 262–263
  natural selection, 264
  nearsightedness, 15–16
  number of genes, 126
  pattern baldness, 74, 75
  poliomyelitis, 251, 258–259,
    268–269
  polycystic kidney, 260
  quantitative characters, 123
  red hair, 15
  retinoblastoma, 83, 86, 266
  schizophrenia, 262
  sex chromosomes, 261
  sex determination, 64
  sex-differential chromosomes,
    map of, 261
  sex linkage, 70–72
  sterility, 267–268
  thalassemia, 86, 266
  tuberculosis, 260
  ulcers, 260
  vermiform appendix, 233
  white forelock, 15, 16
  xeroderma   pigmentosum,
    260–261
Mangelsdorf, P. C., 125
Manic-depressive   psychosis,   2,
  262, 269–270
Map unit, defined, 133
Maps, chromosome, 136–140
Marked organisms, 138
Marriage partners, selection of,
  255–256
Marriage prognosis, 268–269
Marriage subsidies, 267
Mass selection, 242
Maternal impressions, 78
Maternal inheritance, 78–80, 216

Maternity clinics, low cost, 267

Mather, Kenneth, 62, 119, 123, 125, 143

Mating, assortive, 255
types, 190

Mayr, E., 241

McClung, C. E., 63, 81

Mean, 52–53
arithmetic, 44
geometric, 53, 116–117

Median, 52

Medicine and genetics, 2–3

Medicolegal problems, 92–93

Megaspores, 108

Meiosis, 22, 27–33
and Mendelism, 32–33
prophase of, 29

Melandrium, sex determination in, 185

Melanin, 7, 201

Mendel, Gregor Johann, 1, 8, 9, 10, 11, 19, 36, 39, 43, 50, 58, 112, 126, 185, 207, 273, 283
and Darwin, 280
and Nägeli, 280
biography, 274–278
crosses, 8–9
original paper, 285–311

Mendelian laws, 10–11, 16–18

Mendelian symbols, 11

Mendelian terminology, 14

Mendelism, and meiosis, 32
rediscovery, 279–280

Mental deficiency, 268

Mermis, sex determination, 188

Merogony, 21

Metaphase, 26–27
maps, 149–150
plate, 26

Mice, agouti, 82
coat color, 90, 100–**102**
short tail, 196–197
tumors, 216
yellow, 82

Michaelis, P., 223

Michurinism, 283

Microgametes, 190

Microspores, 109

Milk factor, 216

Miller, Alden, 228, 241

Mirabilis, 9, 221

Misgurnus, 229

Mitchell, H. K., 204

Mitosis, 22–27
in onion root tips, 318
in whitefish, 318
significance, 27

M-N blood types, 93–94

Mode, 52
defined, 44

Modifying genes, 99, 111
and dominance, 199

Monoecious plants, 183

Monohybridism, 8–18

Monosomics, 140–141, 171–172
and genic balance, 200

Morgan, L. V., 160, 167

Morgan, Thomas Hunt, 65, 81, 126, 132, 143, 176, 186, 189, 208, 214, 281, 282

Morons, reproduction by, 263

Muller, H. J., 63, 162, 164, 165, 167, 210, 214, 266, 281, 282

Multiple alleles, 88–96
and mutation, 161
in relation to chromosomes, 89
summarized, 95–96

Multiple exostoses, 252

Multiple factor hypothesis, 112, 123

Multiple factors, 106–108

Multiple sexuality, 189

Multiplication theorem, 57

Müntzing, A., 174, 178, 247, 248

Muscular dystrophy, 250

Mustard gas, mutagenic effect, 165–166

Mutable loci, 159–160

Mutagenic agents, 165–166

Mutants, bud, 162
detection, 160–161

Mutation, 8, 157–166
and evolution, 227–229
and gene frequency, 262
and multiple alleles, 161
and radiation, 162–165
and selection, 231–232
chromosomal, 168–178
experimental, 162–166
frequency, 158–160
range, 228
rate, measurement of, 160–161, 262–263
reverse, 161
time of, 161–162

Mutator genes, 158

N

Nägeli, 9
and Mendel, 280

Nasturtium, 220

Natural selection, 225, 264

Naudin, 273

Nearsightedness, 15–16

Nectarine, 162

Neel, J. V., 262, 266, 272

Negative eugenics, 265–266

Nervous system, induction of, 194–195

Neurospora, 6, 103–106, 209
biochemical mutants, 104–106, 200
life cycle of, 104
nutrition of, 104

Nicotiana, 240
rustica, 119
sanderae, 184
tabacum, 171–172

Nilsson-Ehle, H., 106, 108, 112, 113, 281

Non-adaptive characters, 233

Norepinephrine, 7

Normal probability curve, 44, 55–56

Nosebleed, spontaneous, 259

Nowinski, W. W., 33

Nucleic acids, 206–207

Nucleolus, 23

Nucleus, transplantation of, 193–194

Number of genes segregating, 116

O

Oenothera, 172
S alleles, 184
translocation complexes, 236–238

One gene–one character theory, 97, 208

One gene–one enzyme theory, 105–106, 209–210

Onions, 245

Oogenesis and spermatogenesis, 29–32

Oogonia, 30

Organizer, genetic control of, 195–196

Organizers, 194–197

Origin of Species, 224

Osborn, Dorothy, 81

Overdominance theory, 120, 122–123
Overpopulation, 44
Ovule, 109
Ovum, 31
Owen, A. R. G., 143
Oxidase, 97
Oxymonas, meiosis in, 191
Oysters, sex determination, 188

P

Pachytene, 29
Painter, T. S., 151, 156
Pangenesis, 273
Panmixis, 255
Papilio, polymorphism, 75, 76
Paramecin, 221
Paramecium, 221
  mating types, 190
Parameter defined, 50
Partial sex-linkage, 261
Particulate gene theory, 208
Paternity tests, 270
Pathological genes, decreasing frequency, 264
  increased frequency, 262–263
Pathology and heredity, 258–262
Pattern baldness in man, 74, 75
Pearl, Raymond, 17
Pearson, Karl, 58
Peas, breeding of, 39
  chromosome number, 126
  cotyledon color in, 12–14
  round x wrinkled, 34–36
  trihybridism, 39
  yellow x green, 34–36
Pedigree method, 249–250
Pedigree notation, 256–258
Pedigree selection, 242
Pedigrees, 70–71
Pelargonium, 220
Penetrance, 250–252
Penicillin, 217, 244
Penicillium, 244
Peptide linkage, 205
Peroxidase, 201
P generation, 9
Phaseolus vulgaris, 46
Phenocopies, 197, 252
Phenotype, defined, 14
Phylloxera, 186
Physiology of gene, 193–203
Pigeons, selection in, 225

Pigments, 200–201
Pigs, breeding, 246–247
Pincus, G., 204
Pistil, 183
Plant breeding, value in Sweden, 247
Plasmagenes, 221–222
Plasmon, 215
Plastids, 220
Pleiotropic genes, 99–100
Pneumococcus, 207
Polar bodies, 31
  of Lepidoptera, 80
Poliomyelitis, 251, 258–259, 264, 268–269
Pollen, 109
  sterility, 219–220
Polycystic kidney, 260
Polygenes, 119
Polyhybrid inheritance, 40
Polymorphism in *Papilio*, 76
Polyploidy, 172–174
  and multiple factors, 107–108
  in evolution, 239–240
  in plant breeding, 245–246
  induced, 173–174
Pooled family data, 250
Populations, constancy of, 225
  defined, 50
  structure, 232–233
Position effect, 175–177, 210–212
Positive eugenics, 266–268
Potential ovary of toads, 188
Potter, Edith L., 96
Presence or absence theory, 89, 199, 208
Prevention of disease, 269–270
Prezent, J. J., 282
Primary oocyte, 30
Primary spermatocyte, 30
Primula, 221
  pleiotropy in, 100–101
Probability, 50
  curve, normal, characteristics, 55
  defined, 56
  laws of, 56–58
Probandus, 257
Prodigality of nature, 44, 224, 225
Progeny test, 13
Progression method, 40–42
Prophase, 23–26
Propositus, 257
Protandry, 187–188

Proteins, 205–206
Pseudodominance, 147
PTC experiment, 316
Punnett, R. C., 12, 36, 89, 97, 98, 111, 129, 130, 131, 143, 199, 208, 281, 283
Punnett square, 12
Pure line concept, 8
Pure lines, 46–50
  variation in, 48–50
Purity of gametes, 32
  law of, 11, 17
Pyrrhocoris, 63

Q

Quantitative inheritance, 112–124
  and breeding, 246–248
  summarized, 123–124
Quantitative traits, and evolution, 228–229
  defined, 112
Quenouille, M. H., 62
Quetelet, L. A. J., 43, 44, 51, 52, 62

R

Rabbit, coat colors, 90
  Himalayan, 198
  physiology of, 90
Race, R. R., 96
Radiation, and mutation, 162–165
  dangers of, 164–165
Railroad analogy to crossing over, 144
Rana esculenta, 195
Random dispersal, restriction of, 233
Random fertilization, 11, 17
Random mating, 255
  restriction of, 233
Range of distribution, 51
Raphanobrassica, 174, 240
Rate control by genes, 197
Rats, geotropism, 202–203
  hooded, 111
Reactions controlled by genes, 200–202
Recessive pedigree, typical, 258
Recessiveness, 13
Red hair, 15
Reduction divisions, 28–29

Reed, S. C., 272
Relative dominance, 109–110
Relative sexuality, 189
Reliability, testing, 50, 58–61
Reproduction, surplus, 224
Reproductive rates, differential, 263
Reptilia, 68
Repulsion, 129–130
Residual heredity, 115
Restriction of random dispersal, 233
Restriction of random mating, 233
Retinoblastoma, 83, 263, 266
    in man, 86
Rh and multiple alleles, 95
    blood types, 94–96
    factor, inheritance, 95
Rhoades, M. M., 223
Ribonucleic acid, 206
RNA, 206
Roe, Anne, 62
Roman square, 12, 36
Roux, Wilhelm, 20
Rudbeckia hirta, 98
Rust resistance, 39
Rye, 245

S

Saccharomyces, 217
Saez, F. A., 33
Salivary gland chromosomes, 150–154, 212
Salk serum, 269
Salmon, spawn, 224
Sample defined, 50
Sanger, Ruth, 96
Santa Gertrudis cattle, 4
Schizophrenia, 262
Schull, W. J., 272
Sea urchin, 20–22
Secondary oocyte, 31
Secondary sex characters, 77
Secondary spermatocyte, 31
Segregation, 9
    law of, 10, 16–17
Selection, and breeding, 242–243
    and mutation, 231–232
    in pure lines, 47
Selfing, 13
Self-sterility genes, 183–184
Semilethal genes, 84

Sex determination, 63–65, 179–191
    environmental, 187–188
    theory of, 182–183
    differential chromosome, 64, 172
    differentiation, 77
    genes, number of, 181
    influence, 72–74
    in microorganisms, 188–191
    limitation, 74–76
        physiology of, 76–78
    linkage, 65–72
        partial, 261
Sex-linked lethals, 84
Sexes, separation of, 184–185
Sexuality, multiple, 189
    relative, 189
Sheep, horns of, 73–74
Shorthorn cattle, 3
Shull, G. H., 106, 121, 125, 281
Silkworm, 79–80
Simplex defined, 67
Simpson, G. G., 6, 62, 241
Singleton, W. R., 123
Smith, H. H., 119, 125
Snails, coiling in, 78, 79
Snakes, limbs, 233
Snapdragon, 220
    mutation rate in, 159
    yellow, 85
Snedecor, G. W., 62
Snyder, L. H., 249, 270, 272
Sonneborn, T. M., 190, 192, 221, 223
Sorghum, monohybridism, 317
Sorsby, Arnold, 272
Sources of variability, 227–229
Spartina, 240
Species synthesis, 174, 240
Spemann, Hans, 194, 204
Spencer, Herbert, 226
Spencer, W. P., 158, 167
Spermatid, 31
Spermatogenesis and oogenesis, 29–32
Spermatogonia, 30
Spermatozoa, 31
Sphaerechinus, 21
Sphyngomyelin, 259
Spindle, 23
Spore, 28
Squash, 245
Stadler, L. J., 158, 167
Stakman, E. C., 248

Stamen, 183
Standard deviation, 53–54
Standard error, 54–55
Star-Dichaete test, 138–141
Statistic, defined, 50
Statistical modification of populations, 229–230
Statistics, 43–62
    defined, 43
Stebbins, G. L., 232, 241
Sterility, 233–239, 267–268
Stern, Curt, 126, 154, 155, 156, 199, 200, 204, 272, 283
Strawberry, sex chromosomes of, 69
Strongylocentrotus, 21
Struggle for existence, 44, 225
Sturtevant, A. H., 78, 132, 143, 144, 175, 176, 178, 281, 282
Sublethal genes, 84
Suctoria, 190
Sugar beets, 245
    triploid, 246
Sundew, 173
Sun-red corn, 89–90
Supply houses, 319
Svalöf, 246–247
Sweet peas, flower color in, 98
    linkage in, 129–130
Symbols, Mendelian, 11
Synapsis, 28, 29
Synthesis of species, 240

T

Taxonomy and genetics, 6
Telangiectasis, 259, 262, 269
Telophase, 27
Tenebrio, color, 198
Teredo, sex determination, 188
Test cross, defined, 14
Tetrad, 28–29, 132
Tetraploidy, 172
Texas Longhorn cattle, 3
Thalassemia, 86, 266
Theognis, 1, 242
Three point cross, 133–134
Threshold concept, 199
Threshold theory of dominance, 199
Thyroxine, 7
Tobacco, 171–172, 239
    allopolyploidy, 173
    flower size in, 113–116
    hybrid vigor, 119

Tomato, chromosome map, 136, 140
Transformation, bacterial, 207
Transgressive variation, 118
Translocation, 148–149
  complexes in *Oenothera*, 236–238
Trihybridism, 39
Triplicate factors, 107
Triploid intersexes, 179–181
Trisomics, 168–171
  and genic balance, 200
Triticum, 245
Triturus, 136
Tryptophan cycle, 105
Tschermak-Seysenegg, Erich von, 279–280, 283
Tuberculosis, 260, 262
Tubularia, 188
Twin studies, 253–254
Twins, 255
Tyrosine, 6–7, 201

U

Ulcer, gastric, 260, 269
Universal donor, 92
Unstable genes, 159–160
Uric acid, 202
Urodela, 68

V

Vanessa, 197
Variability, coefficient of, 55
Variance, 54
Variation among organisms, 44, 225
Variegation, 159
Vavilov, N. I., 282, 283
Vestigial wing 17, 88–89
Villee, C. A., 204
Viola, 229
Virus infection and cytoplasmic heredity, 216–217
Viruses as agents of heredity, 216–217

W

Waddington, C. H., 204
Wagner, R. P. 204
Watermelons, seedless, 245–246
Weismann, August, 20, 27, 65, 193, 194, 215, 274
Whaley, W. G., 125
Wheat, allopolyploidy, 173
  breeding, 245
  color, 106, 107, 113
  polyploidy, 107, 239
  rust resistance, 39, 245
  uses of, 120

Wheat, White Federation, 242
White forelock, 15, 16
Whiting, P. W., 185, 192
Whooping crane, 232
Wiener, A. S., 94, 95, 96
Wilson, E. B., 33, 63
Winge, O., 239, 241
Wright, Sewall, 116, 193, 203, 204, 232, 282, 283
WZ chromosomes, 68

X

X chromosome, 64–65
Xenia, 109
Xeroderma pigmentosum, 260–261
Xiphophorus, 234–236

Y

Y chromosome, 67–68
  and sex, 184–185
Yellow crescent, 194

Z

Zea, 221
Zea mays, 120–123
Zygote, defined, 14
Zygotene, 29